Historical Perspectives
on Climate Change

HISTORICAL PERSPECTIVES

ON CLIMATE CHANGE

James Rodger Fleming

New York   Oxford

Oxford University Press

1998

Oxford University Press

Oxford   New York
Athens   Auckland   Bangkok   Bogotá   Buenos Aires   Calcutta
Cape Town   Chennai   Dar es Salaam   Delhi   Florence   Hong Kong   Istanbul
Karachi   Kuala Lumpur   Madrid   Melbourne   Mexico City   Mumbai
Nairobi   Paris   Singapore   Taipei   Tokyo   Toronto   Warsaw

and associated companies in
Berlin   Ibadan

Copyright © 1998 by Oxford University Press, Inc.

Published by Oxford University Press, Inc.
198 Madison Avenue, New York, New York, 10016

Oxford is a registered trademark of Oxford University Press

Library of Congress Cataloging-in-Publication Data

Fleming, James Rodger.
    Historical perspectives on climate change / James Rodger Fleming.
       p.   cm.
    Includes bibliographical references and index.
    ISBN 0-19-507870-5
       1. Climatic changes—Europe—History.   2. Climatic changes—United
    States—History.   3. Global environmental change—History.
    I. Title.
    QC981.8.C5F45   1998
    306.4'5—DC21   97-22545

9 8 7 6 5 4 3 2 1

Printed in the United States of America
on acid-free paper

To the Rodger, Fleming, and Yamato families

The one constant certainty in the world is change.
—I Ching.

Preface

This book provides historical perspectives on climate and climatic changes from the Enlightenment to the late-twentieth century. What have people understood, experienced, and feared about the climate and its changes? How have privileged and authoritative positions on climate been established? By what paths have we arrived at our current state of knowledge and apprehension? What does a study of the past have to offer to the interdisciplinary investigation of environmental problems?

This project began as a study of climatic change ideas in early America. My research led me to Enlightenment sources in Europe and to the accounts of early explorers and settlers in the New World. The study quickly branched into the development of international networks of observation, the scientific transformation of climate discourse, and early contributions to understanding terrestrial temperature changes, infrared radiation, and the carbon dioxide theory of climate.

Global change views the Earth as an interconnected system of physical, chemical, geological, biological, and human processes. It studies interrelationships in the Earth system and changes and rates of change of environmental variables. It poses new kinds of interdisciplinary questions and proffers new types of answers. At its best it challenges us to change our concepts, our behaviors, and even our values. It is a dynamic research field.

Great uncertainties exist in our scientific knowledge of the Earth system, and there is much to be learned about clouds, the oceans, the biosphere, geochemical cycles, and other processes. Human behavior is also quite varied and represents a real "wild card" in the Earth system. One of the human dimensions, however, the *historical* dimension, has not received adequate attention. Historians can easily demonstrate that over time, *huge* changes in concepts and attitudes have taken place. On time scales ranging from decades to centuries, the rate of change of climate ideas is quite stunning. Ideas and apprehensions may well be changing much faster than the climate itself. Historians of science are trained to examine major conceptual shifts in our understanding of nature. Moreover, newer historiography has established that major paradigm shifts are not solely attributable to changes in science and technology but are due as well to social and cultural factors.

I have not attempted to construct a complete survey of climate change history, grand narratives being out of style and fraught with problems. Instead, I have written a series of interrelated essays on elite and popular understanding of climate change. The book begins with an introductory essay on three basic meanings of the term "apprehension": (1) awareness or understanding, (2) anticipation or dread, and (3) intervention. Subsequent chapters explore the climate apprehensions of scientists, other intellectuals, and the general public from the eighteenth century to the late twentieth century. There are essays on climate and culture in Enlightenment thought, climate debates in early America, the expansion of observing systems, and the development of a scientific mode of climatological discourse. These are followed by chapters on individual scientists and writers: Joseph Fourier, John Tyndall, Svante Arrhenius, T. C. Chamberlin, and the environmental determinist Ellsworth Huntington. A penultimate chapter on global warming before 1957 examines public awareness of climate issues and the work of individuals such as G. S. Callendar, Gilbert Plass, and Roger Revelle. The epilogue argues for a view of global change and its human dimensions rendered more complete by the study of the intellectual, social, and cultural changes that preceded the current environmental crisis.

Waterville, Maine   J. R. F.
March 1998

Acknowledgments

This research was supported by grants from the Interdisciplinary Studies Division and the Natural Science Division at Colby College, an Andrew W. Mellon Fellowship at the American Philosophical Society Library, and a sabbatical year provided by Colby and funded in part by a fellowship from the National Endowment for the Humanities. During this time I was a visiting scholar in the Program in Science, Technology, and Society at the Massachusetts Institute of Technology and a research associate with the Department of History of Science at Harvard University.

I conducted archival research in the libraries and repositories listed in the bibliography, and worked in a number of printed collections including those of the American Philosophical Society Library, Bibliothèque d'Information, British Library, Harvard University, John Crerar Library, Library of Congress, MIT, National Oceanic and Atmospheric Administration Central Library, The Pennsylvania State University, The University of Arizona, University of London, and Yale University. Without exception, the librarians and archivists I worked with were extremely kind, helpful, and knowledgeable. Permission to quote from manuscript sources is gratefully acknowledged from the American Philosophical Society Library, the Bibliothèque nationale, the British Library, the Library of Congress, the Royal Institution of Great Britain, the Royal Society, the Syndics of Cambridge University, the Trustees of the National Library of Scotland, the University of Chicago Library, the U.S. National Academy of Sciences Archives, the U.S. National Archives and Records Administration, and Yale University Library. Permission to reproduce figures was granted by the Controller of Her Britannic Majesty's Stationary Office, the heirs of Virgil Partch, the Library of Congress, the Royal Meteorological Society, *Tellus*, and Yale University Press.

The following individuals went out of their way to make me feel welcome at their institutions: William Deiss and Libby Glenn at the Smithsonian Institution Archives, William Massa at Yale's Sterling Library, Mrs. I. M. McCabe at the Royal Institution of Great Britain, and Steven S. R. B. Smith at the Center of Historical Studies at the University of London. My good friend and colleague Roy Goodman, curator of printed materials at the American Philosophical Society Library, supplied me with references, suggestions, and gentle encouragement.

I presented preliminary ideas and draft chapters in seminars at the following institutions: American Geophysical Union, Boston College, Boston University, Colby College, History of Science Society, MIT, McGill University, Penn State University, Smithsonian Institution, the University of Arizona, and the University of Washington.

I am extremely grateful for the many helpful comments and suggestions given by my friends and colleagues. These include Leo Marx, Jill Ker Conway, Kenneth Keniston, and the many participants in the MIT faculty workshops on "Humanistic Perspectives on Atmospheric Change" and "The Humanities and the Environment" that ran from 1991 to 1995. Eugene Skolnikov, Roz Williams, Charlie Weiner, Merritt Roe Smith, Barbara Rozenkrantz, Larry Buehl, Timothy Weiskel, James Risbey, and Sam Bass Warner, Jr., come immediately to mind. I thank them all for their support, encouragement, and sound advice. John A. Dutton arranged for me to teach a seminar on global change history in the Earth System Science Center at Penn State University. E. Philip Krider was the host of my valuable visits to the University of Arizona where I was a guest of the Institute for the Study of Planet Earth and the Institute of Atmospheric Physics. He offered me encouragement and sound advice as the manuscript neared completion. Many of the ideas in the book were also aired in my seminars on the history of global environmental change at Colby College. My students expanded my horizons and provided me with many new insights.

My very special, hard-working research assistants at Colby filed, abstracted, editorialized, and commiserated with me on innumerable drafts. They are Jodi Adams, Heather Davidson, Michael Gerard, Kristin Girvin, Simone Kaplan, Bethany Knorr, Amy Lyons, Dmitry Mironov, Gretchen Skea, and Dave Thibodeau. Together Amy, Beth, Simone, and

Heather read the final manuscript. Alice Ridky, the department secretary, assisted cheerfully in many stages of the project. Grace von Tobel helped prepare the final manuscript. Special thanks are also due the Colby librarians, especially Susan Cole, the science librarian, and "Sunny" Pomerleau, the interlibrary loan officer. It was my editor, Joyce Berry at Oxford University Press, who suggested that I turn a conference paper into a proposal and then a book. Her confidence in me was unwavering, even when my progress was glacial. Robert Milks and the staff at the press provided superb editorial support.

Through it all, I was sustained by the love of my wife, Miyoko, and our children, Jamitto and Jason.

Contents

Historical Perspectives
on Climate Change

Introduction

Apprehending Climate Change

This most excellent canopy, the air, look you, this brave
o'erhanging firmament, this majestical roof fretted with golden fire,
why, it appears no other thing to me than a foul and pestilent
congregation of vapours. What a piece of work is a man! how noble
in reason! how infinite in faculty! in form and moving how express
and admirable! in action how like an angel! in apprehension how
like a god!

—Shakespeare, *Hamlet*, act 2, scene 2.

Apprehensions have been multiplying rapidly that we are approaching a crisis in our relationship with nature, one that could have potentially catastrophic results for the sustainability of civilization and even the habitability of the planet. Much of the concern is rightfully focused on changes in the atmosphere caused by human activities. Only a century after the discovery of the stratosphere, only five decades after the invention of chlorofluorocarbons (CFCs), and only two decades after atmospheric chemists warned of the destructive nature of chlorine and other compounds, we fear that ozone in the stratosphere is being damaged by human activity. Only a century after the first models of the carbon cycle were developed, only three decades after regular CO_2 measurements began at Mauna Loa Observatory, and only two decades after climate modelers first doubled the CO_2 in a computerized atmosphere, we fear that the Earth may experience a sudden and possibly catastrophic warming caused by industrial pollution. These and other environmental problems were brought to our attention mainly by scientists and engineers, but the problems belong to us all. Recently, policy-oriented social scientists, public officials, and diplomats have turned their attention to the complex human dimensions of these issues. New interdisciplinary and multidisciplinary

3

collaborations have arisen between scientists and policymakers to examine the extremely challenging issues raised by global change.[1] There has been a rising tide of literature—scholarly works, new journals, textbooks, government documents, treaties, popular accounts— some quite innovative, others derivative and somewhat repetitious. This has resulted in growing public awareness of environmental issues, new understanding of global change science and policy, widespread concerns over environmental risks, and recently formulated plans to intervene in the global environment through various forms of social and behavioral engineering, and possibly geoengineering. Global change is now at the center of an international agenda to understand, predict, protect, and possibly control the global environment.

The changing nature of global change—the historical dimension— has not received adequate attention. Most writing addresses current issues in either science or policy; much of it draws on a few authoritative scientific statements such as those by the Intergovernmental Panel on Climate Change (IPCC); almost none of it is informed by historical sensibility. In the "race to save the planet" (to borrow from the PBS film series of the same name), most historians didn't even go to the track. Some scientists work in collaboration with historians, archaeologists, and anthropologists to reconstruct the temperature and rainfall records of the past. Examples of this include the publications of Raymond Bradley and Philip Jones and the work of the Tree-Ring Lab at the University of Arizona. Some historians use the available scientific data to explore the effect of climate variations on past societies. The books of Emmanuel Le Roy Ladurie and H. H. Lamb immediately come to mind.[2] This book is related to but distinct from such works on climate reconstruction and climate history. I am interested in the history of climate change theories and ideas, that is, how global change can be studied as a subset of the history of science and technology.

The history of global environmental change draws in part on the histories of particular sciences such as astronomy, chemistry, computer science, geography, geology, meteorology, paleontology, and physics; and in part from much broader historical currents. All of these fields have been examined before, at least to some extent, by historians with particular disciplinary interests. With global change as the new focus, however, a new interdisciplinary picture begins to emerge that includes both elite and popular apprehensions. What have people experienced, learned, feared about climate change in the past? How have they intervened? By what path have we reached the current state of climate apprehension? Can we possibly claim to have a complete understanding of climate change and other environmental problems if we ignore their intellectual, social, and cultural history?

How then shall we understand the history of climate change and relate it to contemporary concerns? A central metaphor that has helped me organize the massive amount of material on this subject is the term "apprehension." Several senses of the word are intended: (1) awareness or understanding, (2) anticipation or dread, and (3) intervention.[3] I wish to understand how people became aware of climate change, how scientists and the general public understood the issues, how the study of the atmosphere changed over time, and the social and cultural implications of these changes. Throughout the book I will also examine popular awareness of environmental risks and modes of climate intervention, whether proposed or practiced.

Awareness and Understanding

> Fix not too rashly upon your first apprehensions.
> —Richard Baxter (1670),
> *Oxford English Dictionary* (*O.E.D.*)

In pursuing historical research on climate change, I have had to ask several crucial questions. How do people (scientists included) gain awareness and understanding of phenomena that cover the entire globe, and that are constantly changing on time scales ranging from geological eras and centuries to decades, years, and seasons? How was this accomplished by individuals immersed in and surrounded by the phenomena? How were privileged positions created and defined? The answers are varied and worthy of extended reflection. Without the ability to observe the climate system in its entirety (as an astronomer might view a star or planet) or to experiment on it directly (as a chemist might view a reaction), how did scientific understanding of it emerge? What are the historical relationships among the numerous and quite varied theories of and ideas about climatic change? In addition to their scientific bases, how were they related to more general popular perceptions and (mental) apprehensions of the environment?

One approach, popular in the eighteenth century, was through appeals to authority—references to historical literature, first impressions of explorers, or the memory of the elderly. This was the rhetorical strategy of the Enlightenment and early American writers who wanted to support a particular theory of cultural development or decline (see chapters 1 and 2).

Another way of approaching the issue was to collect massive amounts of meteorological data over large areas and extended time periods in the hope of deducing climatic patterns and changes. Individual observers in particular locales dutifully tended to their journals, and networks of cooperative observers gradually extended the meteorological frontiers. Beginning in earnest in the nineteenth century, scientists tabulated, charted, mapped, and analyzed the observations to provide climatic inscriptions. This process profoundly changed climate discourse and established the foundations of the science of climatology (see chapters 3 and 4).

A third approach to privileged knowledge was to establish from first principles what the climate ought to be and how it ought to change. Joseph Fourier, John Tyndall, Svante Arrhenius, T. C. Chamberlin, and many others—all from different eras, and all in their own ways—engaged in such speculative and theoretical practices (see chapters 5, 6, and 7). These approaches, drawn from physical, mathematical, geological, and astronomical evidence and principles, tended to be most satisfying to those scientists working within a particular disciplinary perspective. Most scientists had one favorite causal mechanism and only grudgingly admitted other possible secondary causes of climate change.

A final approach to privileged climate knowledge has been through technology. In part with the invention and standardization of meteorological instruments, the networking of meteorological observers, and the development of statistical analysis, a picture (albeit abstract and imperfect) of the climatic aspects of locations and regions emerged in the second half of the nineteenth century. This fuzzy image of the climate has been rendered three-dimensional in the twentieth century by the development of upper-air observations, extended into the indefinite past by paleoclimatic techniques, and, finally, globalized in the era of satellite remote sensing. Many scientists today are working on links between remote sensing and more sophisticated climate models. They are hoping, through advances in technology, to provide new privileged positions. For most scientists the goal is better understanding of climate; for some it is also prediction and control.

Anticipation and Dread

> The bare fears of such things and apprehensions of their approach.
> —Robert Sanderson (1648), *O.E.D.*

A second meaning of apprehension is related to the question of popular *fears* of climate change, including crop failures, volcano weather, and apocalyptic visions of the return of the deadly glaciers or perhaps global warming. What did the populace fear about the heavens? What did they anticipate might happen? How was their awareness and understanding of climate linked to their anxieties? Terrifying possibilities confronted people whose livelihood, food supply, and health were tied closely to the weather. Everyone feared harsh winters, spring floods, summer drought, and harvest storms that could result in crop failures and famine. Exposure to miasmas, night airs, or getting chilled "to the bone" could mean a sudden downturn in health and even death. As Yi-fu Tuan observed in his book *Landscapes of Fear*, "To apprehend is to risk apprehensiveness. If we did not know so much, we would have less to fear."[4]

For much of history, people feared that the powers of evil were active during inclement weather. Processions, prayer vigils, and the ringing of church bells were used to ward off the "prince of the powers of the air," identified as the devil and his minions. Eighteenth-century divines frequently dwelt on God's providence manifest in specific events such as stormy winds, thunderclaps, drought, and rain. In perhaps the most famous sermon of this genre, "The Voice of God in Stormy Winds," preached on April 9, 1704, Increase Mather outlined the natural origins of storms but argued that secondary causes can be overruled by God. By the end of the century, however, scientific discoveries were supposed to have waylaid such superstitious fears, and Franklin's lightning rods comforted and protected both believers and skeptics.

During the Enlightenment, some philosophes believed that culture was determined, or at least strongly shaped, by climate. They warned of cultural decline attending environmental change, both in the fall of empires and the decline of creative genius in certain nations and periods. According to this theory, Europeans leaving their native lands to establish colonies in the cold and damp New World or in the hot and humid tropics did so at great personal risk, both to themselves and their descendants. Even in more "enlightened" times, fears of a year without a summer, a return to an ice age (even a "little" one), or a secularly cooling globe have generated calls for climate prediction and control. Although today's climate concerns are dominated by the fear of global warming, for most of human history the dominant sentiment has been that "warmer is better."

There are other, perhaps more fundamental fears related to a rift in the social fabric caused by climatic change. Nico Stehr, a contemporary sociologist, fears that climate change may destroy "age-old environmental representations" that are fundamental to social and cultural cohesiveness. As others predicted in connection with the fear of nuclear weapons in the 1960s, Stehr points to the possibility of social breakdowns due to the interruption of natural rhythms. On a more prosaic level, even the United Nations has warned that adverse climatic impacts "may weaken governments at a time when they will need all of their resources to respond to climate change."[5]

Intervention and Control

A warrant for his apprehension was obtained.
—*Chambers' Edinburgh Journal*
(1881), *O.E.D.*

A third task, related to the first two, is to investigate modes of *arresting* (apprehending) or otherwise *intervening* in climate change, whether by big technical fixes or by social engineering of human behavior. In eras other than our own, the climate has been perceived as amenable to human impact or intervention. The ancient Greeks intervened in the natural world on a modest scale by diverting streams and draining marshes. Early modern environmental determinists thought human settlement had caused a gradual warming of the European continent. Settlers in the New World engaged in self-conscious, if ineffective, efforts to modify and "improve" the climate through clearing the forests and cultivating the lands. At the turn of the twentieth century, the climatic effects of industrial emissions—especially the rising use of coal—came under some scrutiny. Most people, however, thought increasing carbon dioxide levels in the atmosphere would have no effect at all. Some believed it could possibly have a long-term beneficial effect on climate by stimulating plant growth and preventing a return of the deadly glaciers. Since the 1950s, new understandings of global change phenomena have led some to conclude that climatic change can be predicted and that climate (or at least human impact on the climate) might even be controlled.

Climate apprehensions—awareness and understanding, fear, and intervention—are all interrelated. In every era, scientists have created climate narratives, theories, and reconstructions in conformity with their personal experiences, experimental techniques, technical capacities, and philosophical preferences. Some theories have been more convincing than others; some have raised public awareness; some have generated serious social concerns; and some have indicated the need for concerted action.

Structure and Purpose

Chapter 1 examines the notion that changes in climate influenced culture, society, and even individuals. Early statements to this effect, found in the work of Jean Bodin and others, had been developed into full-fledged theories of climatic determinism by the mid–eighteenth century by Abbé Jean-Baptiste Du Bos and his famous disciples. Du Bos believed that the climate of Europe had moderated since Roman times due to the gradual clearing of the forests and the spread of cultivation, and that vast cultural displacements had resulted. The American climate was thought by some to be undergoing similar but much more rapid and dramatic changes.

The theory that human efforts might improve the climate of the New World fueled a significant debate in colonial and early America. This debate is examined in chapter 2. Colonists and patriots hoped that by pushing back the wilderness and displacing "primitive" native cultures, a flourishing civilization might take root on American soil. Expectations that the American climate was becoming warmer, less variable, and healthier swelled the national pride and swayed the practical decisions of yeoman farmers. This vision was an integral component of an emerging Republican national ideal. Early Americans, hoping to document climatic changes, faithfully kept weather diaries and compiled observations over large expanses of the country.

Chapter 3 deals with the growth of observing systems and the development of national weather services in many nations. As the systems expanded, they generated massive amounts of data and provided privileged perspectives on the climate for a new generation of theorists. Chapter 4 discusses the resolution of the American debate in favor of climate stability. It illustrates how the evolution of meteorological observing systems contributed to a radical transformation of climate discourse and the emergence of a recognizably modern climatology. These four chapters illustrate the cultural situatedness and historical contingency of our climate knowledge.

Chapter 5 investigates Joseph Fourier's theory of terrestrial temperatures, beginning with a review of recent citations to his climate work. Fourier, who aspired to be the "Newton of heat," was passionately engaged in his theoretical and experimental studies. In his archaic system, the "temperature of space" was more important than the "greenhouse effect" in controlling the Earth's heat budget. The following chapter treats John Tyndall, an accomplished experimenter who made molecules dance in his apparatus, and Svante Arrhenius, a Nobel Prize–winning chemist whose many scientific interests included cosmic physics. Among his many discoveries, Tyndall was able to demonstrate that atmospheric trace gases might have significant radiative effects on weather and climate. Arrhenius's quest for an explanation of the onset of ice ages and interglacial periods led him to construct a crude model in which variations of atmospheric CO_2 concentration had a significant effect on the heat budget and surface temperature of the planet, especially in high latitudes. Later in life, Arrhenius speculated on the potentially beneficial role that industrial carbon emissions might have on the climate. Chapter 7 explores the life and work of T. C. Chamberlin, a glacial geologist who developed an interest in interdisciplinary earth science. His work on the geological agency of the atmosphere informed his understanding of the carbon cycle and led him to propose a new theory of the formation of the Earth and the solar system.

The chapter on Ellsworth Huntington is included to illustrate the pitfalls of environmental determinism. His racially biased work on civilization and climate and his crude efforts to link human performance directly to changes in the weather have been summarily rejected. Yet he was a practitioner of a perennial philosophy of climatic influence, and his errors and excesses serve as an example of how *not* to study the human dimensions of global change.

Chapter 9 traces issues related to global warming in the first six decades of the twentieth century. It begins with the demise of the old carbon dioxide theory of climate, as advocated by Arrhenius and Chamberlin. Other mechanisms of climatic change—especially changes in solar luminosity, atmospheric transparency, and the Earth's orbital elements—received more attention. As temperatures reached an early-twentieth-century maximum and industrial carbon emissions continued to rise, a new carbon dioxide theory emerged that was based on the contributions of scientists such as G. S. Callendar, Gilbert Plass, and Roger Revelle. The book concludes with a chapter that examines recent episodes of global cooling and global warming.

Global change is a pluralistic and dynamic enterprise. Yet its scientific and human dimensions can be further enhanced by the study of history. If these essays expand the horizons of the field in any way—if they raise any new issues, provide any new insights, or provoke any new controversies—I will deem the effort a success.

1

Climate and Culture
in Enlightenment Thought

Genius is not born in every climate.
—Abbé Du Bos

L'empire du climat est le premier de tous les empires.
—Montesquieu

The debate over climate change, both from natural causes and human activity, is not new. Although the Baron C.-L. de Montesquieu is undoubtedly the best known Enlightenment thinker on the topic of climatic determinism, others, notably the Abbé Du Bos, David Hume, and Thomas Jefferson, observed that climatic changes exerted a direct influence on individuals and society and that human agency was directly involved in changing the climate.

Climate—from the Greek term *klima*, meaning slope or inclination—was originally thought to depend only on the height of the Sun above the horizon, a function of the latitude. A second tradition, traceable to Aristotle, linked the quality of the air (and thus the climate) to the vapors and exhalations of a country. The Hippocratic tradition further linked climate to health and national character. As late as 1779, the *Encyclopdédie* of Denis Diderot and Jean le Rond D'Alembert defined "climat" geographically, as a "portion or zone of the surface of the Earth, enclosed within two circles parallel to the equator," in which the longest day of the year differs in length on its northern and southern boundaries by some quantity of time, for example one-half hour. The article goes on to mention Montesquieu's position on "l'influence du climat sur les mœurs, le charactère, et les loix des peuples." The second definition of climate provided by the *Encyclopdédie* was medical, identified primarily as the temperature of a region and explicated through its effects on the health and well-being of the inhabitants.[1]

The idea that climate influenced culture was derived in part from the writings of ancient and medieval philosophers, geographers, and historians, including the works of Hippocrates, Albertus Magnus, and Jean Bodin. With no established science of climatology, Enlightenment thinkers apprehended climate and its changes primarily in a literary way. They compared the ancient writings to recent weather conditions, linked the rise and fall of creative historical eras to changes in climate, and promoted a brand of climatic determinism based on geographic location and the quality of the air.

Abbé Du Bos

Modern European thought linking climate change and culture can be traced to the diplomat, historian, and critic Abbé Jean-Baptiste Du Bos, member of the French Academy (later perpetual secretary), and author of *Réflexions critiques sur la poësie et sur la peinture* (1719), a book Voltaire considered "the most useful book ever written by a European on these matters."[2] The first volume of the book is a wide-ranging review and critique of various artists and their works. Volume 2 begins with brief general observations on "genius in general" and on the "genius which forms painters and poets," after which the author turns his attention to the causes of the rise and fall of the so-called illustrious ages in the arts and sciences. For Du Bos, the emergence of genius was not primarily due to "les causes morales" (education, cultivation, governance) but in large measure to "les causes physiques" (the nature of the air, land, soil, and especially climate). In chapter 13 he offers three "critical reflections" in support of this thesis:

> *First reflection*: There are countries and times in which arts and sciences do not flourish, notwithstanding the vigorous concurrence of moral causes in their favor.
> *Second reflection*: The arts and sciences do not attain their full perfection by a slow advance, but by sudden, spontaneous progress. Moral causes can neither elevate the arts and sciences to the point of perfection nor prevent their decline.
> *Third reflection*: Great painters have always been contemporaries with great poets, and along with other artists and scientists, they have flourished at the same time in their own country.

In his *Critical Reflections*, Du Bos argued that artistic genius flourished only in countries with suitable climates (always between twenty-five and fifty-two degrees north); that changes in climate must have occurred to account for the rise and decline of the creative spirit in particular nations; and that the climate of Europe and the Mediterranean area had changed gradually since antiquity and had caused a decline of creative genius in certain nations. His theory also implied that the deforestation and increased cultivation of North America would result in a rapid change in climate (and culture). He cited four examples of "illustrious ages" that gave rise to extraordinarily creative cultures: Greece under Philip of Macedon and Alexander the Great; Rome under Julius and Augustus Caesar; sixteenth-century Italy at the time of Popes Julius II and Leo X; and his own era, France from Francis I to Louis XIV (1654–1715).[3]

The basic argument may be encapsulated as follows: As the grapes of one particular region or year produce a characteristic vintage, so, according to Du Bos, the inhabitants of a particular nation in a given epoch represent a cultural vintage distilled from the overall quality of the air and soil. Only the most favored nations and epochs produced superior cultural distillations; most produced table wines or vinegars: "'Tis thus that wines have a particular taste in each soil, which they always preserve, tho' they are not always of equal goodness."[4]

In Du Bos's system, the air of different countries and of different eras exercised a direct power over human minds and bodies:

> During the life of a man, and as long as the soul continues united to the body, the character of our minds and inclinations depends very much on the quality of our blood, which nourishes our organs, and furnishes them with matter of accretion during infancy and youth. Now the quality of our blood depends vastly on the air we breathe; as also on the air in which we have been bred, by reason of its having decided the quality of our blood during our infancy. The same air contributes in our younger days to the conformation of our organs, which by a necessary concatenation, contributes afterwards in the state of manhood to the quality of our blood. Hence it comes, that people who dwell in different climates, differ so much in spirit and inclinations.[5]

According to Du Bos, the air was "a mixt body" composed of elementary air and "emanations" released by the earth. "Naturalists prove also that the air is likewise filled with an infinite number of small animals and their seeds."[6] The diversity of the air of different countries (even those of the same latitude) was due to the nature of the "emanations" of the earth that vary from nation to nation. Holland was obviously unique since most of it was covered by water. The soil of Italy contained alum, sulphur, brimstone, and other minerals. In France the gravel consisted of soft, volatile stone, while in England it contained lead, pewter, sea-coal, and other minerals. The salt in Poland's earth caused the soil to be fertile and the people to be large.[7]

Temporal differences within a country were also explained in this manner. All years are not equally salubrious, pluvious, windy, cold, or warm. The number of earthquakes and volcanic eruptions in the same country varies from year to year, as does the number of outbreaks of epidemics, both pestilential and sudden. "There were hardly two claps of thunder heard at Paris in the summer of 1716, but it thundered thirty times and upward in the summer of 1717."[8] Du Bos attributed such differences to the "vast number of vicissitudes and alterations" in the emanations and fermentations of the Earth. If the quality of the emanations varied, so would the temperature and quality of the air. Such climatic changes could impact the spirit and humor of the people of a particular country, making some generations (in France, for example) more sensible and lively than others.[9] Because of this, "the difference we observe in the genius of people of the same country in different ages, must be attributed to the variations of the air."[10] Concerning changes on the Italian peninsula, Du Bos observed, "there has been such a prodigious change in the air of Rome and the adjacent country, since the time of the Caesars, that it is not at all astonishing there should be a difference between the present and ancient inhabitants. Nay, in our system, this is the very thing that ought naturally to have happened, since the alteration of the cause must be always supposed to alter the effect."[11]

According to Du Bos, there are three general avenues through which the air comes in direct contact with the human body: respiration, food, and water. The air we breathe "communicates to the blood in our lungs the qualities with which it is impregnated." The food supply receives aerial influences when the soil is aerated through cultivation. These influences are passed on to humans in everything they consume—fruits, vegetables, even "beasts whose flesh they eventually convert into their own substance." The quality of the air is communicated also to the waters of fountains and rivers by means of snows and rains, "which are impregnated with a part of the corpuscles suspended in the air."[12] For Du Bos, however, the temperature of the air exerted the most direct and immediate influence: "Excess of cold congeals the imagination of some, and absolutely changes the temper and humor of others. From sweet and good humored in other seasons, they become almost savage and insupportable in violent frosts."[13] Du Bos cited as examples of this influence the rise of violent crimes during cold snaps and the tendency of Henry III, king of France to fall into fits of winter melancholy.[14]

Colonization—which usually required settlers to move to new climatic zones—was perceived as a great risk by Europeans. According to Du Bos, air that is wholesome to the inhabitants of one country can be a slow poison to strangers. Blood formed by the air and nourishments of Europe was thought incapable of mixing with the air or with the chyle produced by the food of America. The only medical remedies were bleeding and gradual acclimatization. Other effects of changing climatic zones were more rapid. For example, visitors to the Spanish West Indies were afraid of contracting Tarbardillo, a debilitating fever that attacked almost all Europeans a few weeks after their arrival. "The same disorder attacks the Spaniards born in America upon their coming to Europe; so that the native air of the father proves a kind of poison to the son."[15] Du Bos also believed that climatic influences could be transmitted by commercial exchange. For example, by consuming sugar, spices, coffee, chocolate, and other products of the tropics, people in middle latitudes were incorporating elements of hotter climates into their culture, reducing the effect of latitudinal differences.[16]

Du Bos concluded that differences in the character of nations could be attributed to differences in their airs. Even within a particular country, changes over time in the qualities of the air could lead to changes in the inhabitants. According to this theory, the observable difference between the French and Italians was attributed to differences in their airs; the difference between the manners and genius of the French of two different ages was attributed to the alteration over time of the qualities of the French air. Du Bos concluded, "As the quality of our air varies in some respects, and continues unvaried in others, it ensues that the French in all ages will have a general character which will distinguish them from other nations; tho' this will not prevent a difference between the French of different ages."[17]

Du Bos was undoubtedly influenced by Jean Bodin, who was considered the most important Renaissance thinker on the relationship of society and geography. Clarence Glacken and others saw Bodin as a critical link in a long chain of environmental determinists stretching from Hippocrates to Montesquieu:

> We would not err greatly, in fact, if we wrote the history of environmental theories around the names of Hippocrates, Aristotle, Ptolemy, Albert the Great, and St. Thomas, summarizing the results of over two thousand years of speculation in the syntheses of Bodin. From Bodin one can easily see the way to Montesquieu.[18]

Du Bos was also influenced by the *Travels in Persia* of Sir John Chardin, first published in London in 1680. Chardin's narrative emphasized the great diversity of climates and soils he had experienced within the borders of the empire and pointed to their profound influence on the health and the culture of the inhabitants. Most of Persia was under the "happy" influence of very dry, hot air, free of tempests, earthquakes, and violent meteors:

> And in those countries, the goodness and virtue of the air spreads and diffuses itself over all the face of nature, that it ennobles all its productions, and all the works of art with unparallel'd lustre, solidity and duration; not to speak how much this serenity of air enlivens and invigorates the constitution of the body, and how happily it influences the disposition of the mind.[19]

Along the Caspian Sea, however, the air was damp and unwholesome, "the worst air that could be." Chardin thought that because of this the people were "more yellow, more defective in their make, [and] more weakly and sickly" than elsewhere. Due to the poor air quality, communities of Christians transplanted there by the emperor Abas the Great failed to flourish. Chardin may have heard about these climatic influences from the Arab cultural historian Ibn Khaldûn.[20] Like generations of environmental determinists who would follow, Chardin thought that "from a right observation of the different climates, one may form a better judgment of the food, clothes and lodging of the several people of the world, as also of customs, sciences, and their industry; and if one have a mind to it, of the false religions which they follow."[21]

Du Bos cited Chardin frequently and enthusiastically in his work and probably gave others (notably Montesquieu) the idea of citing the *Travels in Persia*.

Montesquieu

The most famous and influential environmental determinist of the Enlightenment was Charles Louis de Secondat Baron de Montesquieu. Many authors have mentioned his influence on others, up to and including the twentieth century.[22] What is less well known are some of the direct influences on Montesquieu himself, including the Abbé Du Bos. As Robert Shackleton noted, "Shortly before departing on his travels [to Italy], Montesquieu had had his attention drawn to . . . the *Réflexions critiques sur la poësie et sur la peinture*."[23] The cordial personal relationship between the two men was perhaps of greater significance—Du Bos was a sponsor of Montesquieu's candidacy for a position in the French Academy. Undoubtedly, there are echoes of Du Bos and other determinists in Montesquieu's notion, set forth in *L'Esprit des lois* (1748), that climate shaped the character of both individuals and nations:

> We have already observed that great heat enervates the strength and courage of men, and that in cold climates they have a certain vigor of body and mind which renders them capable of long, painful, great, and intrepid actions. . . .
>
> This has also been found true in America; the despotic empires of Mexico and Peru were near the Line, and almost all the little free nations were, and are still, near the Poles.[24]

Montesquieu also agreed with Du Bos that Europeans were at great risk when they *changed climates*, for example, in moving to colonies in Africa, Asia, or the New World. According to Montesquieu, the good life was one lived from cradle to grave within the same country, preferably the same region; individuals should stay where they are. Traveling to new lands was risky enough, but settling in new climes would most probably be fatal.[25]

The intellectual affinity between the two was not deep, however. First, Montesquieu wrote on climatic influences and did not write explicitly on the topic of climate change. Second, moral causes meant much more to Montesquieu than physical causes, while for Du Bos their importance was reversed. Third, as articulated by Johann Gottfried von Herder, "Montesquieu built his climatic theory on latitudes [die Himmelsstriche] while Du Bos reckoned according to evaporations of the earth."[26] In other words, Montesquieu emphasized geographic location, while Du Bos's argument was based on changes in atmospheric humors, vapors, and exhalations.

Others influenced Montesquieu, including the English physician and writer John Arbuthnot, who suggested that climate operates on the minds, emotions, and language of human beings.[27] Another was the all-but-forgotten determinist François-Ignace Espiard, who stressed the "paramountcy" of climate about five years before Montesquieu. For Espiard, "le climat est pour une nation la cause fondamentale"; "le climat est cette principale qui préside au génie des peuples"; and "le climat est de toutes les causes la plus universelle, la plus puissante."[28]

While for Montesquieu climate was the first of all the empires, it was not the only one. Human ingenuity and effort in areas such as education, government, medicine, and agriculture could overcome the negative influences of climate. "Man is not simply subject to the necessity of nature; he can and should shape his own destiny as a free agent, and bring about his destined and proper future."[29]

Hume

David Hume followed the Abbé Du Bos explicitly on the issue of climate change and in turn influenced Montesquieu.[30] In his essay "Of the Populousness of Ancient Nations" (ca. 1750), Hume argued that the climate of Europe and the Mediterranean area had been colder in ancient times and that the Tiber River, which never freezes now, froze then. "The annals of Rome tell us," says Du Bos, "that in the year 480 . . . the winter was so severe that it destroyed the trees. The Tyber froze in Rome, and the ground was covered with snow for forty days. . . . At present the Tyber no more freezes at Rome than the Nile at Cairo."[31] Hume's essay also contrasted the current mild climate of France and Spain with accounts drawn from ancient writers, among them Diodorus Siculus, who described Gaul as "infested with cold to an extreme degree"; Aristotle, who said that Gaul was so cold a climate that an ass could not live in it; and the geographer Strabo, who claimed the northern parts of Spain were ill inhabited because of the great cold.

Hume believed that the moderation of the climate had been caused by the gradual advance of cultivation in the nations of Europe.

Allowing, therefore, this remark [of Du Bos] to be just, that Europe is become warmer than formerly; how can we account for it? Plainly, by no other method, than by supposing that the land is at present much better cultivated, and that the woods are cleared, which formerly threw a shade upon the earth, and kept the rays of the sun from penetrating to it.

Hume also thought that similar but much more rapid changes were occurring in the Americas as the forests were cleared. "Our northern colonies in America become more temperate, in proportion as the woods are felled; but in general, every one may remark that cold is still much more severely felt, both in North and South America, than in places under the same latitude in Europe."[32]

Conclusion

The ideas of Du Bos, Montesquieu, and Hume dominated the discussion of climate in the second half of the eighteenth century. Du Bos developed an environmental theory of the rise and fall of creative eras. Montequieu was more interested in the ability of men to govern, even in inhospitable climates, while Hume speculated directly on climatic changes in the Americas. They appealed directly to cultural sensibilities and prejudices; the authority of their positions resided in their considerable literary skills and the lack of other evidence to prove them wrong. Collectively, they generated a powerful vision of the climates of Europe and America shaping the course of empire and the arts; the concerted efforts of innumerable individuals in turn shaping the climate itself. By the end of the eighteenth century, Enlightenment thinkers had come to the following conclusions regarding climate change, culture, and cultivation:

1. Cultures are determined or at least strongly shaped by climate.
2. The climate of Europe had moderated since ancient times.
3. The change was caused by the gradual clearing of the forests and by cultivation.
4. The American climate was undergoing rapid and dramatic changes caused by settlement.
5. The amelioration of the American climate would make it more fit for European-type civilization and less suitable for the primitive native cultures.

Such ideas crossed the Atlantic in two directions. Initially, travel accounts from the New World influenced some of the climate ideas of European thinkers. Their works, in turn, influenced generations of colonials and early American nationals.[33] While colonists were initially surprised by the rigor of the climate, many European intellectuals held the climate in disdain and thought the colonists were foolhardy to be risking their lives and health. New World promoters and patriots thought their concerted efforts would improve the climate, making it even better than that of Europe. In response to these ideas, Thomas Jefferson advocated a practical policy: "Measurements of the American climate should begin immediately, before the climate has changed too drastically. These measurements should be repeated at regular intervals."[34] Subsequent chapters will explore in more detail the importation of these ideas to America, their transformation, and their ultimate rejection.

The Great Climate Debate in Colonial and Early America

[When the colonists arrived in America] the whole continent was one continued dismal wilderness, the haunt of wolves and bears and more savage men. Now the forests are removed, the land covered with fields of corn, orchards bending with fruit, and the magnificent habitations of rational and civilized people.

—John Adams

Enlightenment ideas of climate and culture, developed in an era of European expansion, were stimulated by the writings of explorers, colonists, and travelers. Initially, colonists were confused and confounded by the cold winters and harsh storms. The New World was the object of considerable disdain for many European elites. Convincing them that the North American continent was not a frozen, primitive, or degenerate wasteland became a crucial element in American apologetics. The notion that a harsh climate could be improved by human activity—draining the marshes, clearing the forests, and cultivating the soil—was a major issue in colonial and early America and remained so until the middle of the nineteenth century. If the climate could truly be transformed, the implications were enormous, involving the health, wellbeing, and prosperity of all. There were contrarians, however, who called these ideas just so much wishful thinking.

Dissonance

Early settlers in North America found the climate harsher, the atmosphere more variable, and the storms both more frequent and more violent than in similar latitudes in the Old World.[1] In 1644–45, the Reverend John Campanius of Swedes' Fort (Delaware) described mighty winds, unknown in Europe, which "came suddenly with a dark-blue cloud and tore up oaks that had a girt of three fathoms."[2] Another colonist in New Sweden, Thomas Campanius Holm, noted that when it rains "the whole sky seems to be on fire, and nothing can be seen but smoke and flames."[3] James MacSparran, a missionary to Rhode Island for thirty-six years until his death in 1757, spent considerable energy warning colonists against emigrating to America. He found the American climate "intemperate," with excessive heat and cold, sudden violent changes of weather, terrible and mischievous thunder and lightning, and unwholesome air—all "destructive to human bodies."[4]

While new settlers in all countries and climates are subject to many hardships, Dr. Alexander Hewatt observed that the hardships experienced by the first settlers of Carolina "must have equalled, if not surpassed, everything of the kind to which men in any age have been exposed. . . . During the summer months the climate is so sultry, that no European, without hazard, can endure the fatigues of labouring in the open air." Hewatt found the winds in Carolina changeable, erratic, and commonly boisterous, especially around the vernal and autumnal equinoxes. "The first settlers could scarcely have been cast ashore in any quarter of the globe where they could be exposed to greater hazards from the climate."[5]

Today meteorologists agree that the United States experiences more severe local storms and flooding than any other nation in the world, including India and China.[6] It also has some extreme climates, especially in comparison to Europe. In colonial times, explaining this was a major problem both for natural philosophy and for the practical affairs of settlement and governance of the new colonies.

Because of its seemingly favorable location in latitudes farther south than most European nations, the New World was expected to have a warm, exotic climate. Initially, colonists and their sponsors envisioned a rich harvest of wine, silk, olive oil, sugar, and spices from their investment. In 1588, colonial promoter Thomas Hariot, attempting to put the best possible spin on the situation, pointed out that the latitude of Virginia was the same as many exotic places, including Persia, China, and the island of Japan in the East, and southern Greece, Italy, and Spain in the West. He assured his readers that the air of Virginia had an "excellent temperature" in all seasons and was neither as cold as England nor as violently hot as the tropics. To prove the "wholesomeness" of the environment, he pointed out that he and the first settlers lived quite well in Virginia after the ship's provisions had run out—drinking the water, eating the victuals of the country, and taking winter lodging, often in the open air upon the ground; and yet only four (who were already feeble) of 108 colonists died in the first year.[7] But in 1607–8, a year with an "extremely cold" winter, the Jamestown colonists suffered deprivation, disease, and death; 73 of the 105 in the company perished before the arrival of the first supply ship the following summer.[8] The Virginia Company's *Declaration of the State of Virginia* claimed that, with hard work and dedication, the region could become a cornucopia: "Wee rest in great assurance, that this Countrey, as it is seated neere the midst of the world, betweene the extreamities of heate and cold; So it also participateth of the benefits of bothe, and is capable (being assisted with skill and industry) of the richest commodities of most parts of the Earth."[9] Nor was this just an early colonial promotion. In a letter to the American Philosophical Society written in 1769, Edward Antill expressed similar sentiments:

> Whoever considers the general climate of North America, the soil, the seasons, the serenity and dryness of the air, the length and intenseness of the heat, the fair and moderate weather, that generally prevails in the fall, when Grapes are coming to maturity, and arrive at their great perfection; whoever compares the present state of the air, with what i[t] was formerly, before the country was opened, cleared and drained, will find that, we are every year fast advancing to that pure and perfect temperament of air, fit for making the best and richest Wines of every kind.[10]

An anonymous author in *Gentleman's Magazine* in 1750 argued that if weather registers were kept faithfully and methodically in North America, the effects and extent of climatic changes due to settlement and cultivation would become obvious. The article suggested that new draft animals such as camels and new crops such as dates or figs might be profitably introduced as the climate warmed.[11]

Disdain

Many Europeans held considerable disdain for the New World and for its climate, soil, animals, and indigenous peoples. One possible, but very speculative, explanation for the North American anomaly was that the continent was quite new and had recently emerged from the sea or perhaps from under a massive ice cap. Such theories, linked to a universal deluge, were quite common. In 1694, Edmund Halley, Britain's astronomer royal, proposed that the harsh climates of the New World and their gradual amelioration might be due to the impact of a comet that had shifted the position of the Earth's axis:

> and 'tis not unlikely, but that extream Cold felt in the North-West of *America*, about *Hudson's Bay*, may be occasioned by those Parts of the World having once been much more Northerly, or nearer the Pole than now they are; whereby there are immense Quantities of Ice yet unthaw'd in those Parts, which chill the Air to that degree, that the Sun's warmth seems hardly to be felt there.

In a similar vein, the noted Parisian naturalist Georges Louis Leclerc, Comte de Buffon, considered the flora and fauna of the New World degenerate, basing his opinion on the notion that the climate was cooler and more humid than Europe, because the Americas had "remained longer than the rest of the globe under the waters of the sea." The traveler Peter Kalm observed, rightly or not, that every life-form had less stamina in the New World. People died younger, women reached menopause earlier, and soldiers lacked the vitality of their English counterparts—even the imported cattle were smaller. He pointed to climatic influences as the probable cause.[12] Cornelius de Pauw's *Recherches philosophiques sur les Américains* (1771) advanced the thesis, buttressed by borrowings from Buffon, Kalm, and others, that the American climate produced degeneracy among the aborigines. De Pauw extended his thesis to cover European settlers and their descendants as well.[13] Abbé Raynal, a prolific writer and well-known philosophe, largely agreed with De Pauw's ideas but seemed to be of two minds in formulating his own position. On one hand, European settlers "appeared, and immediately changed the face of North-America," turning the chaos of primitive nature into the order of pastoral settlements.[14] On the other hand, settlement was not without its risks. "Under alien skies" both the minds and bodies of colonists were enervated. Raynal was amazed that "America has not yet produced a good poet, a capable mathematician, or a man of genius in a single art or a single science."[15]

Patriotism

Colonials were quite defensive about these opinions and argued that the climate was improving as the forests were cleared. In 1721, Cotton Mather believed it was getting warmer: "Our cold is much moderated since the opening and clearing of our woods, and the winds do not blow roughly as in the days of our fathers, when water, cast up into the air, would commonly be turned into ice before it came to the ground."[16] Benjamin Franklin agreed, writing to Ezra Stiles in 1763 that "cleared land absorbs more heat and melts snow quicker." He thought that many years of observations, however, would be necessary to settle the issue of climatic change.[17]

Hugh Williamson of Harvard College wrote in 1771 that the winters were becoming less severe and the summers more moderate: "[I]t is generally remarked by people who have resided long in Pennsylvania and neighboring colonies, that within the last forty or fifty years there has been a very great observable change of climate, that our winters are not so intensely cold, nor our summers so disagreeably warm as they have been." According to Williamson, this was because open fields were better able to absorb and retain heat as forests were cut down, thus ameliorating the northwest winds. In his vision of the future, when generations have "cultivated the interior part of the country, we shall seldom be visited by frosts or snows."[18] Williamson maintained this position over the years. In 1811, he observed that recent accumulations of snow in New England were less than half of what they had been fifty years earlier. "It is well known, that in the Atlantic States, the cold of our winters is greatly moderated. As the surface of the country is cleared, a greater quantity of heat is reflected; the air becomes warmer, and the north-west winds are checked in their progress."[19] He went on to note that the Delaware River used to freeze earlier than at present, and that westerly winds were decreasing and easterly winds increasing in frequency. Williamson explained these changes in part as follows:

> The cold of the winter is chiefly moderated by the heat of the earth; and much evaporation, in summer or autumn, cools the earth to a considerable depth. It appears, from experiments, that land covered by trees, emits one third more vapour, than a surface of the same extent, covered with water. The vapours that arise from the forests, are soon converted into rain, and that rain becomes the subject of future evaporation, by which the earth is further cooled. Hence it follows, that a country, in a state of nature, covered with trees, must be much colder than the same country when cleared.[20]

For Williamson, as for generations of Enlightenment philosophes, these changes added up to a continent better suited to white settlers and less suited for natives:

> While America remained a great forest, inhabited by savages, under the constant dominion of westerly winds, there was not any climate on the eastern coast, in which we could expect a fair skin. By the progress of cultivation, the general course of the winds is materially affected, in the middle and northern States; and in the process of time, we may expect such a prevalence of easterly winds, near the coast, in those States, as shall prevent the tendency of complexion to the clear brunet, which prevails in temperate climates, in other parts of the world.[21]

The total effect of all these anthropogenic environmental changes would be a temperate climate and clear atmosphere that would serve as "a proper nursery of genius, learning, industry and the liberal arts." These circumstances, combined with "a high degree of civil liberty," would enable the civilization of the American states to compare favorably "with the Grecian republics, or any other people recorded in history."[22]

According to Samuel Williams, author of the *Natural and Civil History of Vermont*, the recent change in the climate of America was "so rapid and constant, that it is the subject of common observation and experience." He linked the long-term warming of the climate of

Europe to deforestation and cited a number of classical and historical sources as evidence for this. According to Williams, the temperature of Italy had risen seventeen degrees since ancient times while Vermont had warmed ten to twelve degrees in only a century and a half. Williams experimented with thermometers buried in the soil and noted a substantial rise in soil temperature after land had been cleared. Recent changes in the weather of New England, he concluded, "extend exactly in proportion as the land is divested of wood." He believed that this process would cause the cold to decrease, the earth and air to become warmer, and the overall climate to become more equal, uniform, and moderate.[23]

Thomas Jefferson's *Notes on Virginia*, which is well known for its patriotic defense of the fauna of the New World, also presented an apology for the harsh American climate and an optimistic prognosis for its improvement by settlement. Jefferson summarized the positions of those who believed the climate was milder than before:

> A change in our climate . . . is taking place very sensibly. Both heats and colds are become much more moderate within the memory even of the middle-aged. Snows are less frequent and less deep. They do not often lie, below the mountains, more than one, two, or three days, and very rarely a week. They are remembered to have been formerly frequent, deep, and of long continuance. The elderly inform me, the earth used to be covered with snow about three months in every year. The rivers, which then seldom failed to freeze over in the course of the winter, scarcely ever do so now.[24]

Jefferson's "Weather memorandum book" echoes this sentiment and adds the following, probably derived from Samuel Williams:

> The same opinion prevails as to Europe; and the facts gleaned from history give reason to believe that, since the time of Augustus Ceasar, the climate of Italy, for example, has changed regularly, at the rate of 1° of Fahrenheit's thermometer for every century. May we not hope that the methods invented in later times for measuring with accuracy the degrees of heat and cold, and the observations which have been and will be made and preserved, will at length ascertain this curious fact in physical history?[25]

Perceptions of climatic change followed settlers westward into the frontier. According to the famous traveler and diarist Count Constantin-François Volney:

> On the Ohio, at Gallipolis, at Washington in Kentucky, in Frankfort, at Lexington, at Cincinnati, at Louisville, at Niagara, Albany, everywhere the same changes have been mentioned and insisted on: Longer summers, later autumns, shorter winters, lighter and less lasting snows and colds less violent were talked of by everybody; and these changes have always been described in the newly settled districts, not as gradual and slow, but as quick and sudden, in proportion to the extent of cultivation."[26]

What does modern climate reconstruction say about the temperature trends of the eighteenth century? From 1730 to the mid-1780s, the temperature of New England was "extremely variable" with several years in which the weather was "very cold" in all seasons. There was a short-lived warming trend beginning with the extremely cold winter of 1758 and extending to about 1784, just when Williamson was writing and when Jefferson was composing his *Notes on Virginia*.[27] There is no evidence, however, for climatic change in the upper Mississippi Valley.

Moisture and Phlogiston

Explorers and colonists believed that rainfall patterns could possibly be changing as the forests were cleared. For example, Christopher Columbus supposedly knew "from experience" that afternoon rains in the West Indies were produced by the luxuriant forests of the islands, and that removal of these forests would reduce their mist and rain, as had already happened elsewhere.[28] William Wood, a Massachusetts colonist, observed in 1634:

> In former times the rain came seldom but very violently, continuing his drops (which were great and many) sometimes four and twenty hours together, sometimes eight and forty, which watered the ground for a long time after. But of late the seasons be much altered, the rain coming oftener but more moderately, with lesser thunders and lightnings and sudden gusts of wind.[29]

John Evelyn, a councilor of the Royal Society of London, thought that by clearing large tracts of forest, both the climate and the healthfulness of a region could be improved. In his book *Sylva, or, a discourse of forest-trees, and the propagation of timber in His Majesties dominions* (1664), prepared for the Royal Navy, Evelyn argued that the excessive humidity of Ireland and North America was due to excessive rain and mists attracted by their dense forests. He attributed the poor health of the inhabitants of these regions to diseases caused by increased humidity. The air should be "neither too keen or sharp, too hot or cold, not infected with fogs or poisonous vapours, or exposed to sulpherous exhalations, or frigiverous winds." Evelyn maintained that cutting the forests would result in a better climate and better health for the settlers. He further claimed that the process of climatic change was already underway in New England after only a few decades of European settlement. According to Evelyn, by felling and clearing the forests, letting in the air and the sunshine, and making the soil fit for tillage and pasture, the weather in New England was "much improved" and "those gloomy tracts are now become healthy."[30] Echoing these sentiments, John Woodward, an English naturalist, observed that the great Moisture in the Air was a mighty inconvenience and annoyance to those who first settled in *America*; which at that time was much overgrown with Woods and Groves. But as these were burnt and destroy'd, to make way for Habitation and Culture of the Earth, the Air mended and cleared up changing into a Tempest much more dry and serene than before."[31]

Edward Holyoke, a Massachusetts physician, used the meteorological data being collected by the Societas Meteorologica Palatina in Mannheim (see chapter 3) to compare the climates of Europe and America and their progressive changes. He thought that deforestation over several centuries had moderated the American climate—a process that had occurred over several millennia in Europe. Holyoke explained lower temperatures in America by the theory that plants, especially evergreens, absorb phlogiston and produce pure air that can become intensely cold. Holyoke thought "our pine woods are a source of cold" because they produce an abundance of "pure dephlogisticated" air, even in the winter.[32] Noah Webster cited the severe frost of May 19, 1794, in upstate New York as a possible confirmation of Holyoke's theory:

The effects of the frost were more visible on wheat, oats and flax that were surrounded by pines, than on the same vegetables surrounded by other kinds of trees, and in situations otherwise similar. . . . I am strongly inclined to believe, that the theory is just, and that tender plants surrounded with forests of evergreens, are more likely to be injured by untimely frosts, than in the neighborhood of other species of trees.

Parker Cleaveland in Maine thought the issue was worthy of further examination:

If [Holyoke's theory] be true with regard to the continent at large, some particular sections of the country, in which evergreens abound, may have an excess of cold above those parts of the same country, which have fewer evergreens. Surrounded as I am by trees of the aforementioned description, I design to pay further attention to this subject by observation and experiment.[33]

Intervention

Jefferson believed he had witnessed a change in the climate in his lifetime due to the greater incursion of sea breezes inland. He proposed the following mechanism by way of explanation: As the settlements of Virginia progressed inland from the seacoast, an increasing area of cleared and cultivated land was being heated strongly by the Sun. Cool air from the mountains to the west and from the ocean to the east rushed in to replace hot rising air over the cultivated land. The western flow, however, was slowed by the greater roughness of the terrain, allowing sea breezes to penetrate farther inland than ever before:

> The eastern and south-eastern breezes . . . have advanced into the country very sensibly within the memory of people now living. They formerly did not penetrate far above Williamsburg. They are now frequent at Richmond, and every now and then reach the mountains. . . . As the lands become more cleared, it is probable they will extend still further westward.[34]

Jefferson wondered when and if the incursion of the sea breezes would ultimately be stopped. He thought that when cultivation extended from Virginia to the Mississippi River, winds would be drawn into the region from the east and west.[35] The result, which Jefferson illustrated with two diagrams (fig. 2-1), would be zones of air rising over the cultivated areas east and west of the Appalachian Mountains and a general shift in wind patterns.

Jefferson also speculated on the possibility of purposeful environmental modification. He suggested that the Spanish should open a narrow passage through the Isthmus of Panama ("a work much less difficult than some even of the inferior canals of France"), and let the

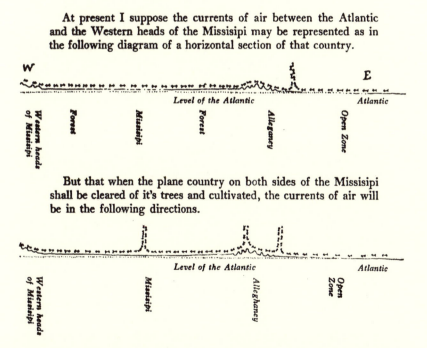

Fig. 2-1. Jefferson's depiction of the sea breeze. *Source:* Thomas Jefferson to Jean Baptiste Le Roy, November 13, 1786, in *The Papers of Thomas Jefferson*, ed. Julian Boyd (Princeton: Princeton University Press, 1950–95), 10:528.

force of the tropical current widen the passage. Then Spain could circumnavigate the globe without encountering the Dutch at the Cape of Good Hope or the stormy seas of Cape Horn. Such a canal would also render the dangerous currents and sandbars of the Gulf of Mexico "stagnant and safe," stop the flow of the Gulf Stream (then considered an impediment to navigation and thus an endangerment to shipping along the coast), and eliminate the fogs on the banks of Newfoundland. Vessels from Europe would be able to perform "with speed and safety the tour of the whole globe, to within about 24° of longitude." The sole negative impact might be on the fisheries of the area.[36]

Health

Climatic change had a medical dimension as well. In the tradition of Arbuthnot, the effects of air on human bodies could be very great indeed. Many physicians warned of the dangers of sleeping in night air, of lying out in the open on the grass, and of drinking or bathing in excessively cold water. Benjamin Franklin knew an instance of four young men, who, "having worked at harvest in the heat of the day, with a view of refreshing themselves plunged into a spring of cold water; two died on the spot, a third the next morning, and the fourth recovered with great difficulty."[37]

Thomas Wright and William Curry argued that draining the marshes would make the country healthier. Wright suggested a pattern of deforestation to purify the countryside:

> Let it be supposed that the N.W. and S.E. are the asseclae or prevailing winds of North America; let the surveyor general mark out a tract of say 100 or 200 miles in a right line to be cleared of trees; then every blast from these two opposite points will ventilate 200 miles of country, bearing along the fumes of all the marshes, while the great *visto* or avenue skirted with wood at both sides would furnish the most salubrious and consequently valuable situation for settlers.[38]

The physician Benjamin Rush did not hesitate to speculate on the effects of climatic change on disease, although, due to lack of measurements, he was not sure the climate was changing. In 1785, Rush suggested that "while clearing a country makes it sickly, . . . cultivating a country, that is, draining swamps, destroying weeds, and exhaling the unwholesome and superfluous moisture of the earth by means of frequent crops of grain, grasses, and vegetables of all kinds, renders it healthy." He argued that in several areas of the United States, there had been a three-stage evolution. The original climate was healthy; however, "fevers soon followed their improvements," and they did not ease until cleared land was brought into production. The way to avoid these problems was to "let cultivation always keep pace with the clearing of our lands. Nature has in this instance connected our duty, interest, and health, together."[39]

In 1800, Thomas Jefferson, on behalf of the American Philosophical Society, petitioned the U.S. Congress to include within the upcoming census considerations of the effect of the soil and climate on the population. He suggested that from such a study "truths will result very satisfactory to our citizens that under the joint influence of soil, climate, and occupation the duration of human life in this portion of the earth will be found at least equal to what it is in any other and that its population increases with a rapidity unequaled in all others."[40]

Contrarians

There was no consensus of opinion about climatic change, and many believed the climate might be getting colder. Dr. Job Wilson of Salisbury, Massachusetts, offered his opinion, based on sixteen years of meteorological records, that the "extensive clearing and cultivation" of the country had increased the extremes of heat and cold—causing added stress to his patients.[41] William Dunbar, one of Jefferson's correspondents, thought that clearing and cultivation might just as likely result in colder winters. He supported these assertions in the *Transactions* of the American Philosophical Society:

> It is with us a general remark, that of late years the summers have become hotter and the winters colder than formerly. . . . Doctor Williamson and others have endeavored to show that clearing, draining and cultivation, extended over the face of a continent, must produce the double effect of a relaxation of the rigours of winter, and an abatement of the heats of summer; the former is probably more evident than the latter, but admitting the demonstration to be conclusive, I would enquire whether a partial clearing extending 30 or 40 miles square, may not be expected to produce a contrary effect by admitting with full liberty, the sunbeams upon the discovered surface of the earth in summer, and promoting during winter a free circulation of cold northern air.[42]

David Ramsay, a legislator and historian in South Carolina, concurred. He found it "remarkable" that oranges, which had been plentiful forty or fifty years earlier, were "now raised with difficulty."[43]

Dr. Johann David Schoepf of Anspach, physician to the Hessian troops in the 1780s, critiqued the theories of improving climate in his book *The Climate and Diseases of America during the Revolution.* Schoepf believed that colonial promotions and patriotic fervor had influenced the views of many Americans: "[T]he credulous Americans have long flattered themselves that by the great progress of cultivation and by the destruction of the forests of the country, their climate has been rendered much milder and the severity of the winters have been moderated." He cited the harsh winter of 1780 as a counterexample for the adherents of the "moderating winters" theory to ponder.[44] Noah Webster added the harsh winters of 1784, 1796, 1797, 1798, and 1804 as examples that "will leave very little room to believe in a change of climate."[45]

Conclusion

The defense of the American climate was spearheaded by colonial promoters and early patriots who agreed that their new world experiment was being strongly shaped if not determined by climatic conditions. Responding to early disillusionment and the contempt of European naturalists, they firmly believed that improvements wrought by settlement—clearing the forests, draining the marshes, cultivating the fields —were causing rapid and dramatic changes in the climate. A warmer, less variable, and healthier climate soon became an integral component of a Republican national ideal. Documenting such progress became the avocation of numerous individuals who thought they could see the manifest destiny of climatic change occurring in their lifetimes. On the other hand, the editors of the *New Edinburgh Encyclopedia* thought the prevailing theory of climate change caused by cultivation was "to be regarded rather as the birth of a lively fancy, than the offspring of accurate science."[46]

Is climate change caused by clearing and cultivation? A sample of authors *accepting* the proposition

Date	Author	Short Title
1634	William Wood	*New England's Prospect*
1664	John Evelyn	*Silva*
1695	John Woodward	*Natural History of the Earth*
1719	Abbé Du Bos	*Réflexions critiques sur la poësie et sur la peinture*
1721	Cotton Mather	*Christian Philosopher*
1750	David Hume	"Populousness of Ancient Nations"
1771	Hugh Williamson	"Attempt to Account for the Change of Climate"
1785	Thomas Jefferson	*Notes on the State of Virginia*
1786	Benjamin Rush	"Cause of the Increase of Fevers"
1793	Edward Holyoke	"Heat and Cold of the American Atmosphere"
1794	Samuel Williams	*Natural and Civil History of Vermont*
1804	Constantine-François Volney	*Soil and Climate of the United States*
1809	David Ramsay	*History of South Carolina*
1812	Baron Cuvier	*Discours préliminaire [sur les révolutions de la surface du globe]*
1830	Charles Lyell	*Principles of Geology*
1837	Heinrich Wilhelm Dove	*Meteorologische Untersuchungen*

For a sample of authors *rejecting* the proposition, see the table at the end of chapter 4.

3

Privileged Positions

The Expansion of Observing Systems

The astronomer is, in some measure, independent of his fellow
astronomer; he can wait in his observatory till the star he wishes to
observe comes to his meridian; but the meteorologist has his
observations bounded by a very limited horizon, and can do little
without the aid of numerous observers furnishing him
contemporaneous observations over a wide-extended area.

—James P. Espy (1851)

Earlier, I posed the question of how privileged perspectives are established on the ubiquitous and changeable climate. Enlightenment
philosophes based their arguments on the impressions of travelers and
colonists. Their perspectives were framed by memory, history, and
folklore; their reasoning colored by environmental determinism. Early
American writers followed this pattern, adding patriotic hopes to the
rhetorical mix. A new approach to the climate issue was developing,
however, based on projects that set out to collect large amounts of
meteorological data. Thomas Jefferson, who participated vigorously
in the great climate debate, was a staunch advocate of widespread,
comparative, and long-term meteorological measurements. Inspired
by Benjamin Franklin's suggestion that extensive measurements of the
climate would be necessary to resolve the issue, Jefferson advised his
correspondents to keep weather diaries and send them to the American Philosophical Society.[1] Throughout his life, Jefferson maintained
the belief that human-induced climate change due to settlement would
be proved by extensive measurements. He wrote the following to Lewis
Beck in 1824: "We want . . . [an index of climate] for all the States,
and the work should be repeated once or twice in a century, to show
the effect of clearing and culture towards the changes of climate."[2]

In the closing decades of the eighteenth century in Europe, and slightly later in Russia and the United States, serious attempts were made to broaden the geographic coverage of observations, standardize their collection, and publish the results. Individual observers in particular locales dutifully tended to their journals, and networks of cooperative observers gradually extended the meteorological frontiers. Much of the work was state funded and motivated primarily by desires to improve agriculture, answer health-related questions, and provide public storm warnings. Military issues and national pride were also at stake. Most of the projects were motivated, at least in part, by the hope that climatic patterns and their temporal changes would be revealed directly.

National Systems

The development of sytematic data collection networks occurred over several centuries. Its history can be traced to many roots, some more significant than others. Descriptive records of phenomena related to the climate, such as the opening and closing of rivers, the first and last frosts, and the blossoming and harvesting of fruit trees, existed from early times. In the mid-seventeenth century, savants began to develop new instruments to monitor the weather, and the new scientific societies of Europe promoted the collection of meteorological observations over widespread areas.[3] Systematic observations in Germany, Russia, and the United States date to the eighteenth century. By the 1870s, most nations had established official weather services, and international cooperation in meteorology was well underway. A simple list of the dates of the founding of various national weather services, however, would not reveal the complexity of events in this predisciplinary era of the science. Here, we will consider the varied origins of a number of state meteorological observing systems, most of which began as ad hoc efforts staffed by volunteers.

Italy

The first documented system of uniform meteorological observations was that of the Accademia del Cimento in Florence, founded by Grand Duke Ferdinand II of Tuscany. Instructions were issued by the Jesuit court priest and secretary Luigi Antinori in 1654, and observations were taken by members of the order with barometers, thermometers ("ampolla"), and hygrometers at seven locations in Italy (Florence, Pisa, Vallombrosa, Curtigliano, Bologna, Parma, Milan) and four abroad (Osnabrück, Innsbruck, Warsaw, Paris). An illustrated account of the instruments used at the Accademia was published at the time.[4]

The Italian observations continued from 1654 to 1670, and were published along with Antinori's correspondence.[5]

England

In 1667, Robert Hooke and Robert Moray, following an earlier request of Christopher Wren, proposed that the Royal Society of London collect meteorological observations for "making a history of the weather." No significant collection of observations resulted from this plan, although Robert Boyle and John Locke followed Hooke's suggestions.[6] In 1732, James Jurin, secretary of the Royal Society, tried again, issuing a plea for comparable observations.[7] Correspondents were to keep their journals in a standard format and submit a copy each year to the Royal Society for comparison with one another and with the society's own weather book. Observations were received from Britain and parts of Europe, India, and North America. William Derham attempted to discuss the results, but because the correspondents did not specify the exact nature of their instruments, location, or altitude, the observations were not comparable.[8] A third appeal was issued in 1744, which failed to attract participants.[9] The Royal Society did not begin its own register until 1774, and continued it only until 1781 when it declined an invitation to join the Societas Meteorologica Palatina (see p. 37).

Until 1823, there was no meteorological organization of any kind in England. Individuals kept long series of records, but there was no uniformity or combined effort in observation. The Meteorological Society of London, founded in 1823, set no higher standards and produced no lasting results. Members needed no qualification other than "a desire to promote the science of Meteorology."[10]

After more than a decade of inactivity, the Meteorological Society of London produced the first English rainfall map in 1840 with results from fifty-two stations.[11] In the first volume of its *Transactions* (1839), John Ruskin of Oxford laid out the society's ambitious goals: "The Meteorological Society . . . has been formed, not for a city, nor for a kingdom, but for the world. It wishes to be the central point, the moving power, of a vast machine, and it feels that unless it can be this, it must be powerless; if it cannot do all, it can do nothing."[12] The society held meetings for only three more years, however, and ceased its publications soon thereafter, leaving its goals unrealized.[13] Results from this group of enthusiasts were far from trustworthy. As George Symons noted in his history of English meteorological societies, "I have seen results published as air temperatures obtained from thermometers inside a hen house, I have seen a rain gauge under the eaves of a cottage, and another under a tree."[14]

In 1850, the British Meteorological Society was founded to establish a "general system of observation, uniformity of registry, systematic communication, and other measures for insuring precision to the advancement of the aerostatical branch of physics."[15] James Glaisher was elected secretary and organized the first current daily weather reports from observations sent by train along lines running to London.[16] A royal charter was granted to the society in 1866.

In 1854, the British Board of Trade established a Meteorological Department. Robert Fitzroy, former captain of the *Beagle*, served as director. He coordinated observations and compiled data, but initially he issued no forecasts. It was not until 1859, following the wreck of the luxury ship *Royal Charter* during a storm off the coast of Wales, that Fitzroy set up a coastal warning system in Britain. The network included fifteen stations in Britain with additional reports from Paris. Fitzroy's budget was 218 pounds in 1860 and increased to 2,989 pounds in only three years. In 1867 the Meteorological Office was reorganized under the Royal Society, but did not produce a daily weather map until 1872.[17]

France

In the 1670s, Edme Mariotte in France attempted to delineate the weather over the region covered by his numerous correspondents. His data allowed him to estimate the average annual rainfall in France and to develop a theory for the wind systems of Europe and the globe.[18] Over a century later, the Société Royale de Médicine sponsored a system in which thirty-nine observers, many of them physicians, followed a standard format in reporting their observations. Père Louis Cotte compiled and published the data in the society's *Histoire* (1776–86).[19] By 1778, the system had fifty observers and included several calibrated barometers set up by Antoine-Laurent Lavoisier, who planned to extend this system throughout Europe.[20] In two related visionary proposals, J. H. Lambert suggested covering the Earth with observations at points defined by the vertices of twenty equilateral triangles, while the Marquis de Condorcet advocated an international meteorological *plan général* which included observations at sea and with balloons.[21] None of these ambitious plans were ever realized.

Since 1798, the meteorological records of the Paris Observatory have been published *in extenso*. Observations appeared in the *Journal de Physique* (1798–1816), in the *Annales de Chimie et de Physique* (1816–35), and, after 1835, in the *Comptes rendus de l'Académie des Sciences*. Rain measurements at Baye, Corbigny, Decize, and Laroche were taken by the Service des Ponts et Chaussées beginning in 1835.[22] The *Annuaire météorologique de la France* began publication in 1849 and the Société Météorologique de France, which continued this publication and issued other reports and monographs, was founded in 1852.

In 1854, Urbain Le Verrier replaced François Arago as director of the Paris Observatory. The same year a destructive gale in the Crimean Sea near the port of Balaclava wrecked Anglo-French transport ships during the Crimean War. In response, the observatory began an experiment in telegraphing weather facts. It did not, however, issue warnings.

It was not until 1863 that Le Verrier telegraphed forecasts of impending weather. That delay was caused by the Paris Observatory being limited to its own observations. Although there were many observers in France, there was no central organization. The first notable government organization began in 1864, when Le Verrier, with the approval of the minister of public instruction, invited public schools in France to establish observing stations. Fifty-eight schools responded. In addition, various departmental commissions collected observations made under their control and forwarded them to the Paris Observatory. Other volunteers—clergy, physicians, and teachers—also maintained meteorological correspondence. Most, however, observed without instruments. One of the products of this joint venture was the *Atlas météorologique de la France* (1865–76). Another series, *Nouvelles météorologiques* (1868–76), contained detailed observations from approximately sixty stations, but the stations were not inspected or standardized until 1873. It was not until after the death of Le Verrier in 1877 that the Bureau Central Météorologique de France was founded under the directorship of Eleuthère Mascart.[23]

Germany

In 1717, a Breslau *mediciner*, Johann Kanold, and his colleagues, naturalists Johann Christian Kundmann and J. G. Brunschweig, began to collect information on weather history, weather-related diseases, and other geophysical and natural phenomena. Observations were received first from individuals in Schlesien, then throughout Germany, and finally from several stations in other countries, including Copenhagen, Stockholm, London, Paris, Turin, and Rome. For thirteen years, Kanold compiled and published the data in the *Breslauer Sammlung*.[24]

The most famous and best documented project of the eighteenth century was the Societas Meteorologica Palatina (1781–95), founded by Elector Karl Theodore of the German state of Palatinate-Bavaria in 1780 and managed by the court priest Johann Jakob Hemmer.[25] Hemmer's stated motive was a "precise understanding" of the weather's influence on agriculture and health.[26] To address the concerns of their patron, the society recorded nonmeteorological cameralist data such as the growth of crops and statistics on mortality, fertility, and disease. In addition, observations on the progression of the Sun through the zodiac, the Moon's phase, and the migration of birds were requested. Fifty-seven locations, extending from Siberia to North America and southward to the Mediterranean, received instruments, forms, and instructions free of charge. The observers sent their results to Mannheim, where they were published *in extenso* in the society's *Ephemerides*.[27]

Until the 1870s, systems of meteorological observation in the German states suffered from the political fragmentation of the region. Nevertheless, inspired by the early example of Mannheim, numerous Germanic data-collection unions were attempted, including the Anstalten für Witterungskunde in Sachsen-Weimar-Eisenach, begun in 1821, and the Süddeutsche Meteorologische Verein, begun in 1841, which included Baden, Württemberg, Norddeutschland, Austro-Hungary, and parts of France, Italy, Belgium, and Holland.[28]

The Prussian Meteorological Institute was established in October 1847 in Berlin with Carl H. W. Mahlman as director. In 1848, its scope was roughly comparable to that of the early Smithsonian meteorological project (see 41): there were thirty-five stations, a staff of only two persons, and a budget of nine thousand marks (approximately three thousand dollars). Mahlman's *Manual for Observers* was used throughout Heinrich Wilhelm Dove's long tenure as director (1849–79). Bavaria organized a meteorological network centered in Munich in 1878. Small networks were also established in Baden, Württemberg, and Saxony.[29]

The Norddeutsche Seewarte (1868), although primarily a maritime institution, was also the central bureau that issued telegraphic weather announcements from data provided by the diverse state land services. It became the Deutsche Seewarte in 1872 and began issuing storm warnings in 1875.[30]

Russia

In Russia, an attempt was made to describe the climate of Siberia during the "Great Northern Expedition" of 1734–49, founded by Vitus Bering, a Danish navigator in the Russian service. Instructions for observers were written by Daniel Bernoulli, who was working in St. Petersburg. Approximately twelve stations, from Kazan to Yakutsk, took measurements in 1734. Summaries of the observations appear in Louis Cotte's *Traité de métérologie* (1774).[31]

Before 1835, Russia had only a few widely scattered private meteorological observers.[32] Because of the Magnetische Verein, eight magnetic observatories were set up in Russia. By 1837, Adolf Theodore von Kupffer had established meteorological stations at seven locations run by the Institute of Mining Engineers and at four other observatories. The results were published in the *Annuaire magnetique et météorologique* (St. Petersburg, 1837–48).

Between 1849 and 1864, the Central Physical Observatory sponsored a meteorological project roughly comparable to that of the Smithsonian Institution. The staff of six received hourly obversations from eight principal stations and monthly journals from up to forty-eight private observers. The observatory published its observations separately in the *Annales de l'observatoire physique central* (1849–64).

The number of private observers had declined to twenty-four by 1864; moreover, they had no standard instruments, methods, or times of observation. Results were published quarterly in *Correspondence Météorologique* (1850–64). In 1857, Konstantin Stepanovich Veselovskii, the permanent secretary of the Russian Academy of Sciences, published *O Klimate Rossii* in two volumes with data taken from his collection of old journals. The work is similar to Lorin Blodget's *Climatology of the United States*, published in the same year.

The director of the observatory, Kupffer, who was also in charge of the department of standard weights and measures for the Russian Empire, established the first Russian telegraphic weather reports in 1864, but his network was limited to nine domestic and two foreign stations.[33]

Heinrich Wild, who served a long term as director from 1868 to 1895, brought a new standard of observation to the Russian Empire.[34] He was trained in Switzerland, where he had been in charge of the Swiss meteorological stations and had established standardized instruments and procedures. When he came to Russia, he found numerous errors in the observations and was surprised that none of the meteorological stations had been inspected for the past twenty years. Perhaps Alexsandr Khrgian in his "History of Meteorology in Russia" can be excused for his patriotism when he said that Kupffer's systems "were models for that time and were adopted since, with minor modifications, as an international standard."[35]

In 1872, with the cooperation of the Hydrographic Department, Wild began a lithographed meteorological bulletin that contained telegraphic reports from fifty-five stations (thirty-six in Russia and nineteen in Europe and Asia) and provided synoptic charts for Russia and parts of Asia. Telegraphic storm warnings commenced in 1874.

United States

On the western side of the Atlantic, isolated diarists, without reliable instruments, sponsoring institutions, or proper instruction, contributed to meteorological science by keeping records of the local weather and climate in the seventeenth and eighteenth centuries.[36] Thomas Jefferson and the Reverend James Madison, president of the College of William and Mary, are credited with making the first simultaneous meteorological measurements in 1778. Jefferson also exchanged observations with many others, including individuals in Pennsylvania, Quebec, Mississippi, and England. Jefferson hoped to supply observers in each county of each state with accurate instruments. The entire system, to be funded by the federal government, was to be supervised by the American Philosophical Society. Such a national meteorological system, however, did not materialize in Jefferson's lifetime.

Exploring expeditions also provided occasions for meteorological and phenological observations of new territories. The American Philosophi-

cal Society enthusiastically endorsed such opportunities. In 1819, thirteen years after the return of the Lewis and Clark expedition, the society asked Major Stephen Long to take meteorological observations during his expedition to the Rockies. The society provided forms for daily
observations and instructed him to pay particular attention to the following phenomena: the temperature of springs, the dates of the freezing and
thawing of rivers, the known plants that flourish in any situation, and
other related phenological observations.[37] The society also prepared a
list of questions pertaining to climatic changes since the travels of Lewis
and Clark. The list, covering the complexion and health of the natives,
weather, and fauna, reveals many of the underlying assumptions on
environmental change of the time:

> Is the darkness of the skin in direct proportion to hardship, ex-
> posure, etc.? Which are the darkest in complexion, tribes inhabit-
> ing mountains or valleys? What peculiarities of soil, climate, or
> habits of life are we to attribute the uncommon stature of the Osage
> tribe?
>
> What are the natural signs remarked by Indians which usually
> precede or accompany those constitutions of the atmosphere most
> unfavorable to human health? Is the vision of savages who are al-
> most continually exposed to strong light in the plains of the Mis-
> souri, subject to a more early decay than that of civilized man, who
> spends so much of his time in the shade? Are the Indians who hunt
> or the white inhabitants who have settled on the vast plains of the
> Missouri, as subject to remittant and intermittant fevers as those
> who inhabit a country shaded by forest trees? At what distance from
> rivers, ponds, or marshes, does miasma (the supposed cause of these
> fevers) cease to be noxious? Are the dews, in any season, supposed
> to be prejudicial to health?
>
> Is the cold on any parts of the Missouri as intense as reported by
> [Lewis and Clark]? From what quarter do the long continued rain
> and deep snows of the Missouri country come? What winds, in
> particular districts of country, are considered salubrious and what
> the contrary? What are the prevailing winds and what are the ef-
> fects they produce on animal and vegetable life?
>
> What animals, whether quadrupeds or bipeds become torpid or
> change their color in the cold regions north of the Missouri? Whether
> the buffalo is diminished in number, or has changed its haunts, since
> the expedition of Lewis and Clark? Whether the furred animals are
> undergoing a sensible decrease?[38]

Other expeditions and surveys—local, state, national, and international—paid considerable attention to similar issues. Perhaps the most
notable was the United States Exploring Expedition—the Wilkes Expedition—of 1838–42, which investigated, among other things, the
geography, hydrography, geology, and meteorology of the Pacific region, taking observations "designed to give the lie to all disparagements
of American culture."[39]

In the first quarter of the nineteenth century, groups of college professors in New England, the United States Army Medical Department, the General Land Office, and academies in the state of New York began the systematic collection of climatic and phenological statistics over large areas of the country.[40] These early projects attempted to broaden the geographic coverage of observations, standardize their collection, and publish the results. Of particular relevance to the question of climate change was the "geometric exemplification" of the weather, developed in 1820 by Josiah Meigs, head of the General Land Office and sponsor of a system of widespread climate measurements. Each month of the year, Meigs plotted winds, temperatures, and other weather elements on a compass rose. The resulting traces provided an indication of spatial and temporal variations of climate.[41]

In the 1830s and 1840s, inspired by the "storm controversy" between James Espy and William Redfield, the Joint Committee on Meteorology of the American Philosophical Society and Franklin Institute, the United States Navy, and the Albany Institute collected data on the behavior of storms and winds. Many private diarists also observed the weather.

Between 1849 and 1861, the Smithsonian meteorological project, directed by Joseph Henry, served as the national center for meteorological research, focusing on storm movement and climate statistics. Organizations cooperating with the Smithsonian included the states of New York and Massachusetts, the Canadian government, and several United States government agencies—the Navy, the Army Topographical Engineers, the Patent Office, the Coast Survey, and the Department of Agriculture. Experiments with weather telegraphy began at the Smithsonian in 1849. In 1870, Chief Signal Officer Albert J. Myer of the United States Army became the first director of a well-funded national storm warning system employing the nation's telegraph lines "for the benefit of commerce and agriculture." The Signal Office provided daily reports of current conditions and "probabilities" for the next day's weather.[42]

International Cooperation

The establishment of national weather services and applied climate networks was fundamental to the emergence of effective international cooperation in meteorology and climatology. Two cases will serve to illustrate this point. In 1851, Matthew F. Maury, director of the United States Naval Observatory, proposed a plan for a "universal system" of meteorological observations for sea and land.[43] This visionary (but premature) idea was sparked by a request from the British Royal Engineers for cooperative meteorological observations at foreign stations. Maury responded that indeed cooperation at the observatory and at United States navy yards was possible and that the system of observation should be extended throughout the world.[44] Maury sent letters announcing his plan to the foreign ministers of numerous countries, to scientific societies, and to private meteorologists:

> The object is to enlist in this great work, the public and private meteorological observatories, the good will of the friends of science, the labors of amateur meteorologists, and the cooperation of the Navigators, both of the naval and commercial marine of all countries; and by consultation and conference with them, to devise plans and methods of observing and recording, which by being common, effective, and of easy execution, may be followed by Meteorologists and Navigators generally. For this undertaking the Government of the U.S. desires to secure the friendly cooperation of the government and people of all countries; and for the purpose of giving effect to this wish, I have been authorized to confer with the proper authorities on the subject.[45]

Maury's universal plan was soon reduced in scope to a "conference upon the subject of a uniform system of observations on board of vessels of war at sea." The conference was held in 1853, in Brussels.[46] The United States Navy subsequently kept its logs according to the plan suggested at the conference, but the British and French failed to cooperate. Johann von Lamont, the Bavarian representative, noted, "[T]he members of the conference returned home, every one followed his own plan and did what he pleased."[47]

Maury may have had one shining moment as a scientific diplomat, but his plans for international cooperation ultimately came to naught. This was because in the 1850s, state systems of meteorological observation had not yet been established. Maury had tried to organize an international meteorological system from the top down with little or no support at the grassroots level. Even in his own country, he was deeply embroiled in a dispute with the Smithsonian Institution and the United States Army Medical Department over the taking of meteorological observations.[48]

Twenty years later, after the United States and most nations of Europe had established national weather services, international cooperation in meteorology was more easily attained. The International Meteorological Organization (now the World Meteorological Organization) traces its roots to an international conference held in Leipzig in 1872 and to the First International Congress of Directors of Weather Services held in Vienna in 1873.[49]

Because of its well-funded weather service (over four hundred thousand dollars in 1874) and its aggressive director, the United States played a leading role, at least initially, in international cooperation. In 1873, Chief Signal Officer Myer, representing the United States at the Vienna congress, proposed that the nations of the world prepare an international series of simultaneous observations to aid the study of world climatology and weather patterns. Myer's suggestion led to the *Bulletin of International Simultaneous Observations*, published by the Signal Office beginning in 1875. The *Bulletin* contained world-wide synoptic charts and summaries of observations recorded simultaneously at numerous locations around the world.[50] The "metrological" standards established by the work of these international congresses initiated a new era of worldwide observation and more rapid and homogeneous data inscription as a practical result.

Conclusion

Observational systems and national weather services in Europe, Russia, and the United States followed complex, yet somewhat similar, paths of development. Before 1800, nations with older and more developed scientific communities took the lead in organizing international projects that attempted to collect and compile observations. Later in the nineteenth century, state meteorological observing systems emerged (see table 3-1).

Table 3-1. Comparisons of observational systems in England, France, Germany, Russia, and the United States in the nineteenth century

Country	System
England	
1823	Meteorological Society of London
1850	British Meteorological Society
1854	Meteorological Department of the Board of Trade
1867	British Meteorological Office reorganized under the Royal Society
France	
1849	*Annuaire météorologique de la France*
1852	Société Météorologique de France
1864	Paris Observatory as a central station, observations at public schools
1878	Bureau Central Météorologique de France
Germany	
1821	Anstalten für Witterungskunde in Sachsen-Weimar-Eisenach
1841	Süddeutsche meteorologische Verein
1847	Prussian Meteorological Institute
1868	Norddeutsche Seewarte
1872	Deutsche Seewarte
Russia	
1832–41	Institute of Mining Engineers
1849	Central Physical Observatory (CPO)
1872	Cooperation between the CPO and the Hydrographic Department
United States	
1819	Army Medical Department
1825	New York State Board of Regents
1836–39	Joint Committee on Meteorology, Philadelphia
1849–74	Smithsonian meteorological project
1870s	Army Signal Office

Climatic surveys of various nations were initiated in the first half of the century, telegraphic experiments began in the 1850s, and storm warning services were established after 1860. International cooperation and an international bulletin of observations began in the 1870s. However tortuous and halting the path of development, it is clear that the establishment of national weather services was an important antecedent to effective international cooperation.

The expansion of observational systems provided scientists with new views of weather and climate. Beginning in earnest in the nineteenth century, the observations were tabulated, charted, mapped, and analyzed to provide mobile inscriptions of climate (albeit abstract and imperfect ones). The large amounts of data transformed meteorological practice and provided theorists with new privileged perspectives on climate.[51] This process irrevocably changed climate discourse and established the foundations of the science of climatology.

4

Climate Discourse Transformed

The true problem for the climatologist to settle during the present century is not whether the climate has lately changed, but what our present climate is, what its well-defined features are, and how they can be most clearly expressed in numbers.

—Cleveland Abbe (1889)

The impressionistic Enlightenment view of the American climate and its changes was rebutted in two distinct ways—literary and scientific. The literary critique was spearheaded by Noah Webster in 1799 and finally put to rest four decades later by Samuel Forry, a surgeon and climatologist in the United States Army. The scientific response came from pioneer climatologists who subjected the growing amounts of meteorological data to statistical analysis. Both approaches contributed to the radical transformation of climate discourse and, along with the expansion of meteorological networks, led to the emergence of a recognizably modern climatology.

Noah Webster

In his essay "On the Supposed Change in the Temperature of Winter," Noah Webster criticized the "popular opinion" advanced by "many writers of reputation . . . the Abbé Du Bos, Buffon, Hume, Gibbon, Jefferson, Holyoke, Williams" that the climate of Europe and America, especially the temperature of winter, had become warmer in modern times. His critique emphasized their loose citation of sources, both ancient and contemporary, and the improper deductions they drew from these citations:

> Men are led into numberless errors by drawing *general* conclusions from *particular* facts. "Lady Montague sat with her window open in January, 1718, and therefore there is little or no winter in Constantinople," is very bad logic. The farmers on Connecticut River plowed their lands, as I saw in February, 1779; and the peaches blossomed in Pennsylvania. What then? Are the winters all mild in America? Not at all; in the very next year, not only our rivers, but our bays, and the ocean itself, on our coast, were fast bound with ice.[1]

Webster was particularly critical of Samuel Williams, whose contention that Italy had warmed seventeen degrees in eighteen centuries was based on selective citations from ancient Roman writers. Williams erred in his assumption that reports of extreme weather were representative of ordinary conditions. Webster used historical accounts of the range of frost-sensitive plants—olive, fig, and date trees—to argue that Italy's climate had not changed since antiquity and "could never have been colder than the Carolinas" and that its winters "were not severe, but mild." Regarding Williams's practice of selectively citing icing conditions on American rivers, Webster commented, "It is thus men are misled by founding general opinions on particular facts."[2]

Webster disagreed with Jefferson's contention that there had been a sensible alteration in the climate of recent decades that could be remembered by the elderly. He considered it "extremely unphilosophical" to suppose such changes when astronomical controls of *klimata* were unchanging:

> We have no reason to suppose that the inclination of the earth's axis to the plane of its orbit has ever been varied; but strong evidence to the contrary. If this inclination has always been the same, it follows that the quantity of the solar rays, falling annually on the particular country, must have always been the same. Should these data be admitted, we are led to conclude that the general temperature of every climate, from the creation to this day, has been the same, subject only to small annual variations, from the positions of the planets in regard to the earth, or the operations of the element of fire in the globe and its atmosphere.[3]

People tend to remember severe or unusual weather events. They cannot accurately recall the climate of their youth or even accurately gauge the weather of an entire year or season. Memories, however, are influenced and stimulated by reports and stories of severe weather, which is always more likely to be recorded. Such shortcomings of memory were not restricted to America. Luke Howard wrote the following in *The Climate of London*:

> The result of my experience is, on the whole, unfavorable to the opinion of a permanent change having taken place of latter times,

either for the better or the worse, in the climate of this country; our recollection of the weather, even at the distance of a few years, being very imperfect, we are apt to suppose that the seasons are not what they formerly were; while, in fact, they are only going through a series of changes such as we may have heretofore already witnessed and forgotten.[4]

Webster's critique of earlier authors was blunted, however, by his own indecision on the question of climate change and cultivation. After a careful rereading of the sources, Webster convinced himself that the climate, if it had not changed outright, had become more variable and had in fact rearranged itself in response to cultivation: "It appears that all the alterations in a country, in consequence of clearing and cultivation, result only in making a different distribution of heat and cold, moisture and dry weather, among the several seasons."[5] He argued that clearing the forests did not change the climate of the land but merely redistributed it. Trees protected the land from severe weather conditions. They moderated the heat of summer, prevented the ground from being scorched by the Sun, protected the land from severe winds, and regulated the temperature of the air. Clearing the land caused it to be hotter in summer and colder in winter, making the seasons more irregular. Spring was colder, and vegetation was more susceptible to frost.[6]

Based on his review of ancient and modern writers, Webster could see no reason to conclude that the heat of the Earth was increasing. Although he found the climate more variable, he could find no evidence for a major climatic change either in Europe or in America. His critique of improper deductions and loose citations set the tone for the scientific studies that followed.

Samuel Forry and the Army Medical Department

In 1826, the United States Army Medical Department issued its first *Meteorological Register*, a compilation of meteorological observations for the previous four years.[7] The volume used the perennial issue of human agency in climatic change to justify the effort and inspire further observations, through the question "whether in a series of years there be any material change in the climate of a given district of country" and, if so, how much it depended on cultivation, population density, or other factors. The chief objective of the observations was to record climatic facts in the face of a rapidly receding wilderness and aboriginal population. Directly echoing Enlightenment thought, the register explained:

The United States . . . appear to offer an opportunity of bringing the question to the test of experiment and observation. . . . For here within the memory of many now living the face of whole districts

of country has been entirely changed; and in several of the States
two centuries have effected as much as two thousand years in many
parts of Europe. In this respect, the "Landing of the Pilgrims" in
1620, is as remote a period as that of the invasion of Gaul or of Great
Britain by Julius Caesar.[8]

In other words, a climatic change that took two millennia in Europe
was thought to be taking place in only two centuries in America.

In 1827, the *American Journal of Science* published surgeon Joseph
Lovell's table of temperature, winds, and "weather" for eighteen stations covering nearly twenty degrees of latitude and thirty degrees of
longitude. A second table compared temperatures of seventeen places
of approximately the same latitude in Europe, Russia, Africa, and
China. Temperatures in Europe tended to be higher than those in comparable latitudes elsewhere. The editors praised the collection as "the
best base for general conclusions respecting the climate of the U.S.
hitherto published."[9] The *Meteorological Register,* distributed free to
the scientific institutions of Europe, immediately received a very favorable notice from Alexander von Humboldt, who cited the American
system as a model for the Russians to emulate:

> If only, following this fine example, there could be similar calibrated
> thermometer observations at the behest and expense of a mighty
> monarch in the eastern part of our old continent—in the widespread
> space, equal to half the lunar surface, between the Vistula and the
> Lena . . . ; then all of climatology would gain a new and improved
> stature in a few years.

Humboldt reiterated this opinion two years later at the Imperial Academy of Science in St. Petersburg.[10] Notwithstanding this high praise,
fourteen years elapsed until the next publication of meteorological
statistics by the Army Medical Department.

The republication of Noah Webster's essay on climate change in
1843 stimulated the investigations of Samuel Forry, army surgeon and
author of *The Climate of the United States and Its Endemic Influences*
(1842). Forry reviewed existing literature on climate change, criticized
it, and introduced new evidence based on data recently gathered at
over sixty locations by the Army Medical Department. He reexamined
the much-debated question of whether, in a series of years, the temperature of the Earth or the atmosphere had undergone any percep-
tible changes since the earliest records, either from human efforts in
clearing away the forests, draining marshes, and cultivating the ground
or from other causes. He found the opinion that the average temperature of the winter season in northern latitudes was higher than in
ancient times was a widespread but erroneous fact based on little
evidence. The Abbé Du Bos, Buffon, Hume, Gibbon, Volney, Jefferson,
Williams, and Holyoke all believed that in the time of the first Roman
emperors the winters of Europe were much more severe. Each suc-

ceeding author cited the other, and all had based their opinions on passages from ancient authors—Juvenal, Virgil, Ovid, Cæsar, and Diodorus Siculus—who had based *their* opinions not on firsthand information but on "loose notices scattered through the old chronicles" relative to the state of the harvest, the quantity of the vintage, or the endurance of frost and snow in the winter. Forry warned that great allowance must be made for "the spirit of exaggeration" in the old records and pointed out that the thermometer, invented in the late sixteenth century, had not been standardized until after Gabriel Daniel Fahrenheit's work in the 1720s.[11]

Turning his attention to the climate of North America, Forry found no evidence for the popular belief that the climate west of the Alleghenies was milder by three degrees of latitude than that to the east. Selective evidence from plant geography could in fact be used to prove the inverse. Some erroneously believed that the climate of the northwestern frontier territories resembled that of the eastern states on their first settlement. Forry also found no evidence for the popular aphorism of Conrad Malte-Brun that "vanquished nature yields its empire to man, who thus creates a country for himself." According to Malte-Brun, when Canada and the United States become thickly popu-lated, their climates would be similar to the same parallels of Europe at present: "Snow and ice will become rare phenomena, and the or-ange, the olive, and other vegetables of the same class, now strangers to the soil, will become objects of the labor and solicitude of the agri-culturist."[12] Forry also did not hesitate to criticize Charles Lyell for parroting the opinion, "unsustained by any well observed facts," that "in the United States of North America, it is *unquestionable* that the rapid clearing of the country has rendered the winters less severe, and the summers *less* hot. . . . there is no doubt that the climate has be-come, as Buffon would have said, 'less excessive'."[13]

Forry drew three main conclusions from his study: (1) climates are stable, and no accurate thermometric observations indicate system-atic climatic change; (2) climates *are* susceptible to melioration by the changes wrought by the labors of man; but (3) these effects are much less influential than those of latitude, elevation, and proximity to bodies of water.[14] These results were in basic agreement with those expressed in Humboldt's popular *Views of Nature*:

> The statements so frequently advanced, although unsupported by measurements, that since the first European settlements in New England, Pennsylvania, and Virginia, the destruction of many for-ests on both side of the Alleghanys has rendered the climate more equable,—making the winters milder and the summers cooler,—are now generally discredited. No series of thermometric observations worthy of confidence extend further back in the United States than seventy-eight years. We find from the Philadelphia observations that from 1771 to 1824, the mean annual heat has hardly risen 2°.7

Fahr.;—an increase that may fairly be ascribed to the extension of the town, its greater population, and to the numerous steam-engines. . . . Thirty-three years' observations at Salem in Massachusetts show scarcely any difference, the mean of each one oscillating within 1° Fahrenheit, about the mean of the whole number; and the winters of Salem, instead of having been rendered more mild, as conjectured, from the eradication of the forests, have become colder by 4° Fahr. during the last thirty-three years.[15]

Humboldt formed his opinions after examining a large number of thermometric observations collected at different military posts from Florida to Council Bluffs. He believed the records collected by the United States Army Medical Department and interpreted by Samuel Forry contained "far more exact ideas on the climate of North America than existed in the times of Jefferson, Barton and Volney."[16]

Pioneer Climatologists

The trend established by Forry and supported by Humboldt—to cite meteorological records rather than ancient authorities or the memories of the elderly—was continued by Lorin Blodget, who used thermometric and precipitation data from both the Army Medical Department and the Smithsonian Institution in his *Climatology of the United States* (1857). In a chapter entitled "Permanence of the Principal Conditions of Climate," he argued that climates must be assumed permanent until proven changeable. He held that the Sun was the only climatological source of heat, and since its heat was a constant quantity, the average temperature always returns to a line of the "most absolute permanence." For Blodget, vegetation was an effect, not a cause, of climate. Rather than changing the climate, cleared and cultivated lands, unless maintained constantly, will inevitably revert to a state of nature dictated by the climate. According to Blodget, the only reliable way to judge climatic change was in the thermometric record. The eight decades of available thermometric records in the United States showed no trends that could not be explained by the expansion of cities, observer error, and other causes.[17]

At Yale, the noted meteorologist Elias Loomis and his assistant H. A. Newton studied climate change using the instrumental temperature records of New Haven from 1779 to 1865. The available records had been compiled by more than twenty different observers working independently of one another. The observations included thermometers of various makers and various exposures, journal entries for earliest and latest frosts and snows, and records of the flowering of six varieties of fruit trees. After accounting for anomalies in the data, Loomis and Newton concluded that the climate of New Haven was remarkably stable and that during the past 86 years there has been no permanent change at New Haven either in the mean temperature of the year, or in that of any of the separate months; and . . . there has been no permanent change in the average occurrence of the last frost of spring, or the first frost of autumn—of the first snow of winter, or the last snow of winter—or in the average date of flowering of fruit trees, such as the peach [and the] cherry.[18]

Charles A. Schott, an employee of the United States Coast Survey, arrived at a similar conclusion using a much larger data base. With the support of the Smithsonian Institution, Schott prepared two innovative monographs on the rainfall (1868) and temperature (1874) of the United States using records gathered by the Smithsonian, the Army Medical Department, the Lake Survey of the Army Topographic Engineers, the Coast Survey, the states of New York and Pennsylvania, and private journals extending back to the eighteenth century.[19] Schott published extensive tables, maps, and charts showing the average distribution of rain and temperature across the continent and its secular variation since 1780. To examine the question of climatic changes since the beginning of instrumental meteorological observations, he prepared a harmonic analysis of all the available temperature data using the latest statistical techniques. His conclusion, which put to rest uninformed speculation about temperature changes caused by settlement of the continent, argued *against* the notion of a changing climate: "There is nothing in these curves to countenance the idea of any permanent change in the climate having taken place, or being about to take place; in the last 90 years of thermometric records, the mean temperatures showing no indication whatever of a sustained rise or fall." Admitting that more extensive and comprehensive rainfall observations were desirable, Shott further concluded from existing records that precipitation had "remained permanent in amount as well as in annual distribution."[20]

William Ferrel, the most mathematically astute geophysicist in America and a theorist of the general circulation of the Earth's oceans and atmosphere, argued that increased (or reduced) rainfall could not be directly attributed to the presence (or absence) of forests and cultivated fields. Basing his arguments on continental and planetary scale factors rather than local conditions, Ferrel reasoned that abundant rainfall depended on evaporation at a distance, and that any increased water vapor due to local influences "would be carried so far and spread over so great a territory, that the increased rainfall at any given place would perhaps be entirely insensitive to observation." He had a dim view of the opinion, popularized by Charles Wilbur, that "rain follows the plow":

I saw a man recently from southwestern Kansas, who, apparently entirely sane in other respects, gave it as his opinion, that it would be only a few years after the settlement and cultivation of Oklahoma until there would be an abundance of rainfall there. The cultivation of a given amount of the soil would perhaps increase the evaporation as much or more than an equal area of forests, but the effect upon rainfall, if sensible anywhere, would not be in Oklahoma, but somewhere to the east or northeast.[21]

It is interesting to note that Ferrel understood the greenhouse effect in a general, but quantifiable way (see chapters 5 and 6). In 1884 he published a mathematical investigation of the factors controlling the temperature of the atmosphere and the earth's suface. After developing equations for the distribution of sunlight over the globe and over the year, he turned his attention to laws governing the escape of heat from a diathermanous ("diaphanous for heat") envelope. In such cases, according to Ferrel, "the conditions determining the rate of losing or gaining heat and the temperature of the body, do not depend merely on the radiating and absorbing powers of the body, but likewise upon those of the diathermanous envelope." He made it clear that one-half of the radiation absorbed in the envelope would be again radiated back toward the body. "The effect, therefore, of the envelope is to hinder the escape of heat radiated by the body and to retard the rate of cooling." Ferrel calculated a "diathermancy constant" for the atmosphere of 0.213, a value that produced the observed mean temperature of 15.4 degrees Celsius. He pointed out, however, that without this effect, the Earth's temperature would fall to approximately –96 degrees Celsius. According to Ferrel:

> It is seen, therefore, of what great advantage the atmosphere is in raising the mean temperature of the earth's surface. *This effect is similar to that of the glass covering of a conservatory of plants*, which is a diathermanous medium which permits the heat of the sun to pass through with facility, but is almost completely impenetrable by the heat radiated from the air and all bodies within.[22]

Cleveland Abbe, chief scientist in the weather service of the Army Signal Office, agreed with Loomis, Schott, and Ferrel that the old debates about climate change had finally been settled. In an article entitled "Is Our Climate Changing?" Abbe defined the climate as "the average about which the temporary conditions permanently oscillate; it assumes and implies permanence."[23] After discussing the variations introduced into a series of measurements by instrument breakage, changes of thermometers, changes in exposure due to vegetation or buildings, observer error, and so on, Abbe presented a series of records from three German cities for a period of twenty-four years. These records exhibited a "probable variability of the average," of about four tenths of a degree, an amount Abbe deemed statistically insignificant:

> [E]ven if the mean temperature for 25 years should differ from that for the succeeding 25 years, or even should the differences for four such successive periods move steadily in one direction, this would

not imply any change, permanent or otherwise, in the climate of a place, unless the four successive means should differ by quantities that appreciably exceed their indices of variability.[24]

Abbe concluded that the indices of variability for all the temperature records known to meteorology were so large and the constant errors so insidious that "there is scarcely a single station with respect to which we have data competent to decide the question as to whether the mean temperature of any month may have changed 0°.2 centigrade or 0°.5 Fahrenheit during the past century."

Alluding to the recent discovery of the ice ages, Abbe conceded that "great changes have taken place during geological ages perhaps 50,000 years distant." Abbe was a leading practitioner and proponent of "rational climatology," an emerging nexus of empirical data collection, analysis, and theoretical reasoning. He held that "no important climatic change has yet been demonstrated since human history began" and that climatology would be better served by the introduction of greater scientific and mathematical rigor:

> It will be seen that rational climatology gives no basis for the much-talked-of influence upon the climate of a country produced by the growth or destruction of forests, the building of railroads or telegraphs, and the cultivation of crops over a wide extent of prairie. Any opinion as to the meteorological effects of man's activity must be based either upon the records of observations or on *à priori* theoretical reasoning. . . . The true problem for the climatologist to settle during the present century is not whether the climate has lately changed, but what our present climate is, what its well-defined features are, and how they can be most clearly expressed in numbers.[25]

Conclusion

In 1799 Noah Webster launched an offensive against poorly reasoned and unscientific modes of climate discourse. Samuel Forry continued the attack on the older popular literature and brought statistics gathered by army physicians to bear on the issue of climate change. In the second half of the nineteenth century, the work of pioneer meteorologists, including Lorin Blodget, Elias Loomis, Charles Schott, William Ferrel, and Cleveland Abbe, completed the shift from literary to empirical studies of climate, from impressionistic evidence to statements of fact, from dim apprehensions to a recognizably modern climatology.

Is climate change caused by clearing and cultivation? A sample of authors *rejecting* the proposition

Date	Author	Short Title
1780	J. D. Schoepf	*Climate and Diseases of America*
1799	Noah Webster	"Change in the Temperature of Winter"
1808	David Brewster	*New Edinburgh Encyclopedia*
1820	Luke Howard	*Climate of London*
1844	Samuel Forry	"Distribution of Heat over the Globe"
1850	Alexander von Humboldt	*Views of Nature*
1857	Lorin Blodget	*Climatology of the United States*
1866	Elias Loomis	"Mean Temperature at New Haven"
1876	Charles Schott	"Variations of the Atmospheric Temperature"
1889	Cleveland Abbe	"Is Our Climate Changing?"

For a sample of authors *accepting* the proposition, see the table at the end of chapter 2.

5

Joseph Fourier's Theory
of Terrestrial Temperatures

The earth receives the rays of the sun, which penetrate its mass, and
are converted into non-luminous heat; it likewise possessed an
internal heat with which it was created, and which is continually
dissipated at the surface; and lastly, the earth receives rays of light
and heat from innumerable stars, in the midst of which is placed
the solar system. These are the three general causes which
determine the temperature of the earth.

—Joseph Fourier (1824)

The concept of the greenhouse effect has yet to receive adequate historical attention. Although most writing about the subject is concerned
with current scientific or policy issues, a small but growing fraction
of the literature contains at least some historical material, which, as
this chapter shows for the case of Joseph Fourier, is largely unreliable.

Jean Baptiste Joseph Fourier is best known today for his Fourier
series, a widely used mathematical technique in which complex func-
tions can be represented by a series of sines and cosines. He is known
among physicists and historians of physics for his book *Théorie
analytique de la chaleur* (1822), an elegant but not very precise work
that Lord Kelvin described as "a great mathematical poem." Most of
his contemporaries knew him as an administrator, Egyptologist, and
scientist. Fourier's fortunes rose and fell with the political tides. He
was a mathematics teacher, a secret policeman, a political prisoner
(twice), governor of Egypt, prefect of Isère and Rhône, friend of Napo-
leon, baron, outcast, and perpetual member and secretary of the French
Academy of Sciences.[1]

Most people writing on the history of the greenhouse effect merely
cite in passing Fourier's descriptive memoir of 1827 as the "first" to
compare the heating of the Earth's atmosphere to the action of glass

in a greenhouse. There is usually no evidence that they have read
Fourier's original papers or manuscripts (in French) or have searched
beyond the obvious secondary sources. Nor are most authors aware
that Fourier's paper, usually cited as 1827, was actually read to the
Académie Royale des Sciences in 1824, published that same year in
the *Annales de Chimie et de Physique*, and translated into English in
the *American Journal of Science* in 1837![2] No one cites Fourier's earlier references to greenhouses in his magnum opus of 1822 and in his
earlier papers. Nor do they identify the subject of terrestrial temperatures as a key motivating factor in all of Fourier's theoretical and experimental work on heat. Moreover, existing accounts assume far too
much continuity in scientific understanding of the greenhouse effect
from Fourier to today.

Beginning with recent articles and proceeding in reverse chronological order, I will trace the practice of citing Fourier's article of 1827
as the first reference to the greenhouse effect. This strategy allows me
to begin with the problems in the recent literature before attempting
to clarify what Fourier actually said in 1824. I will then locate the
subject of terrestrial temperatures within the context of Fourier's analytical theory of heat, provide authoritative references to a greenhouse
analogy in Fourier's earlier writings, and point out still earlier work
by others.

Contemporary Fourier Citations: Patterns and Problems

Many scientific review articles and textbooks contain brief historical
allusions, typically drawn from secondary rather than original sources.
This trend can be identified in recent citations of Fourier's work on
terrestrial temperatures. In a 1988 review essay, V. Ramanathan, an
authority on atmospheric radiation, cited Fourier's 1827 article, claiming, "The greenhouse effect of the atmosphere was pointed out, perhaps for the first time, by Fourier, who also suggested that human
activity can modify climate."[3] Again in 1988, Ramanathan repeated
the claim that perhaps Fourier's 1827 article was a famous first:

> The mathematician Baron Jean-Baptiste Fourier suggested in early
> 1827, albeit ambiguously, tha[t] human activity can modify surface
> climate. Fourier's (1827) paper is basically a discourse on the pro-
> cesses governing the heat balance of the atmosphere, the surface,
> and the interior of the Earth. Fourier pointed out that the atmosphere
> behaves like the transparent glass cover of a box (exposed to the
> sun) by allowing sunlight to penetrate to the Earth's surface and
> retaining the longwave radiation (or "obscure radiation" according
> to Fourier) from the Earth's surface. This inference is perhaps one
> of the earliest suggestions of the now well-known greenhouse ef-
> fect of the atmosphere.[4]

M. D. H. Jones and A. Henderson-Sellers cited Ramanathan rather than Fourier in their 1990 article "History of the Greenhouse Effect," asserting the following:

> The French physicist, Fourier, was probably the first person, in 1827, to allude to the greenhouse effect when he compared the influence of the atmosphere to the heating of a closed space beneath a pane of glass. Fourier may also be credited with the suggestion that human activities could influence the climate.[5]

In *Dead Heat*, Michael Oppenheimer and Robert Boyle also cited Fourier's 1827 article but severely garbled the citation.[6] In their notes the authors quoted an English translation of a section of Fourier's article that, although relevant, does not mention the greenhouse effect directly and that stops just short of Fourier's important statement that "the effect of solar heat upon air confined within transparent covers has long since been observed."[7] Ian Rowlands repeated this error in his otherwise excellent book, *The Politics of Global Atmospheric Change* (1995); he briefly cited the 1827 article and cited it wrongly in his notes in a way very similar to Oppenheimer and Boyle. History was not his focus, however; he covered the 130 years from Fourier to Roger Revelle in one page.[8]

Revelle himself alluded broadly to Fourier's pioneering work on the greenhouse effect but did not give references; William Kellogg cited Revelle. Wilfrid Bach said Fourier (1827) "[w]as probably the first to discuss the CO_2 [*sic*]/greenhouse effect and compare it with the warming of air isolated under a glass plate." Never mind that the radiative properties of CO_2 would not be investigated until the mid–nineteenth century.[9]

Spencer Weart, a historian of physics, cited Fourier (1827) and claimed that the greenhouse effect was "discovered" in 1896 by Arrhenius. His article, a stimulating comparison of nuclear issues and global warming, followed the established pattern of citing Fourier: "In 1827 [*sic*], French physicist Jean-Baptiste Fourier had suggested that the Earth is kept warm because air traps heat, as if under a pane of glass." Weart did not distinguish between the natural greenhouse effect and the possibility of global warming. He also overestimated the state of spectroscopic knowledge circa 1900 (see chapters 6, 7, and 9).[10]

Mark Handel and James Risbey have improved the situation somewhat by noting that Fourier's essay was in fact published in 1824 and reprinted in 1827. The following annotation appears in their very helpful bibliography:

> This was the first paper to qualitatively describe the greenhouse effect. Compares the effect of the atmosphere of the earth to that of a pane of glass covering a bowl. (It is easier to find the 1827 version than the nearly identical 1824 version. In French. No known published translation, though unpublished ones exist.)[11]

Several corrections are in order here. Both the *Annales de Chimie et de Physique* and the *Mémoires de l'Académie Royale des Sciences de l'Institut de France* are easy to find in most major libraries. The 1827 article also appeared in the *Oeuvres de Fourier*, a readily available source.[12] As mentioned earlier, an English translation of Fourier's 1824 essay, by Ebeneser Burgess, was published in the *American Journal of Science* for 1837. Moreover, as I will demonstrate, these articles are not the first in which Fourier mentioned the behavior of greenhouses. Nor is Fourier's article in essence *about* the greenhouse effect.

As mentioned earlier, recent writers have given Fourier credit for being the first to suggest that human activities could influence the climate. But the idea of human agency in climatic change goes back at least to Theophrastus, a student of Aristotle, who wrote of local changes of climate caused by human agency, specifically agricultural activities. He observed that draining wetlands removed the moderating effects of water and led to greater extremes of cold, while clearing woodlands for agriculture exposed the land to the Sun and resulted in a warmer climate.[13] As noted in chapter 2, in the 1750s, David Hume, speculating on a larger scale, believed the advance of cultivation had caused a gradual change in the climate of Europe and could cause similar but much more rapid changes in the Americas.[14] Thomas Jefferson believed that the harsh climate of the New World was gradually being improved by settlement.[15]

According to Jones and Henderson-Sellers, "the history of the greenhouse effect is not well known outside the atmospheric sciences."[16] We may also safely say that it is not well known *inside* the atmospheric sciences.

Nineteenth-century Citation Patterns

If writers in the late twentieth century have misquoted Fourier, how did earlier authors fare? In his famous essay on the influence of carbon dioxide on climate, Svante Arrhenius had this to say about Fourier's 1827 article: "Fourier maintained that the atmosphere acts like the glass of a hot-house, because it lets through the light rays of the Sun but retains the dark rays from the ground."[17] (Arrhenius's hothouse analogy will be examined further in chapter 6). John Tyndall also referred to Fourier's work in his classic essay of 1861, "On the Absorption and Radiation of Heat by Gases and Vapours," in which he credited Fourier and others with the notion that "the interception of terrestrial rays [by the atmosphere exercises] the most important influence on climate." Tyndall's experiments showed that water vapor, although transparent to light rays, was the best absorber of "calorific rays" and that "every variation of this constituent must produce a change of climate." He thought similar effects could be caused by carbon dioxide and by "an almost inappreciable admixture of any of the hydrocarbon vapours." Without venturing quantitative estimates, he suggested that changes in the amount of radiatively active gases in the atmosphere could have produced "all the mutations of climate which the researches of geologists reveal."[18] Tyndall's work will be examined further in chapter 6.

In 1836, the physicist C. S. M. Pouillet wrote a memoir on solar heat, the radiative effects of the atmosphere, and the temperature of space. Tenth on his list of sixteen related objectives was to determine the "general conditions of equilibrium of temperature of a body protected by a diathermanous covering analogous to the atmosphere."[19] Three years earlier the exiled Italian physicist Macedonio Melloni had defined the term "diathermic" as "diaphanous for heat," from "dia" (across) and "thermo" (to warm). The term was meant to replace John Herschel's term "trans-calescence."[20]

Pouillet argued that the equilibrium temperature of the atmosphere must be lower than the temperature of outer space and higher than the temperature of the Earth's surface. This was mainly because the atmosphere exerts "unequal absorbing actions" on "rays of heat derived from space" as well as those emitted from the Earth's surface. He credited Fourier with this insight, which was itself based on earlier experimental work by the noted mountaineer Horace Benedict de Saussure:

> M. Fourier is, I think, the first who has had the idea of regarding the unequal absorption of the atmosphere as exercising an influence on the temperatures of the soil. He had been led to this by the beautiful experiments made by De Saussure, in 1774, on some elevated summits of the Alps and in the adjacent plains, with a view to compare the relative intensities of solar heat. On that occasion [1824] M. Fourier states in a precise manner one of the principles which have served me to establish the equations of equilibrium.[21]

Pouillet compared the atmosphere to experiments he had done on solid and liquid diathermanous screens, for example, panes of glass and layers of water, concluding that "the atmospheric stratum acts in the manner of screens of this kind, and . . . exercises a greater absorption upon the terrestrial than on the solar rays." He called this the "effect of diathermanous envelopes." Neither Pouillet nor Fourier, however, had come to a final theory of terrestrial temperatures. Pouillet was also quite interested in what was called "the temperature of space" and the quantities of heat the Earth received from the Sun, from space, and from other "celestial bodies." As I will show, these factors were more central to Fourier's theory of terrestrial temperatures than was the greenhouse effect.

What Fourier Actually Wrote in 1824

From the title of Fourier's 1824 essay, we learn that it consists of "general remarks" on the temperatures of the Earth and interplanetary space. Fourier provided no equations, and he told his readers that "the analytic details which are omitted here are found in the works which I have already published";[22] he called this work a "résumé" that included results from several earlier memoirs. According to John Herivel, Fourier's biographer, the essay was "largely expository in character and added nothing essentially new" on the subject of terrestrial temperatures.[23]

In the article, Fourier described the heating of the Earth by three distinct sources: (1) solar radiation, which is unequally distributed over the year and which produces the diversity of climates; (2) the temperature communicated by interplanetary space irradiated by the light from innumerable stars; and (3) heat from the interior of the Earth remaining from its formation. Fourier examined in turn each of these three sources and the phenomena they produce (fig. 5-1).

Fourier's article included a nine-page discussion of the unequal distribution of solar heating over the globe; the argument was based

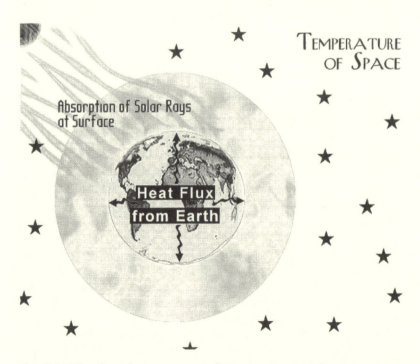

Fig. 5-1. The three heat sources influencing terrestrial temperatures (Fourier).

on his memoir of 1807 on the heating of the globe and his note of 1809 on the periodic movement of solar heat.[24] In the next section, he examined the temperature of space and its effect on the temperature of the Earth. Here are most of his comments on the heating of the atmosphere (to which I will return). Finally, he discussed the internal heat of the globe and its secular cooling, which he determined to be no more than three-hundredths of a degree during the course of recorded history.

In his discussion of the temperature of space, Fourier pointed out that the thickness of the atmosphere and the nature of the surface "determine" the mean value of the temperature each planet acquires. He also observed that, in very general terms, "the motion of the air and waters, the extent of the seas, the elevation and form of the surface, the effects of human industry and all the accidental changes of the earth's surface, modify the temperatures of each climate." He admitted, however, that it is "difficult to know how far the atmosphere influences the mean temperature of the globe; and in this examination we are no longer guided by a regular mathematical theory."[25] The statement most suggestive of the greenhouse effect was the following:

> the temperature [of the Earth] can be augmented by the interposition of the atmosphere, because heat in the state of light finds less resistance in penetrating the air, than in repassing into the air when converted into non-luminous heat.[26]

Fourier compared the heating of the atmosphere to the action of a solar thermometer, or heliothermometer, an instrument designed and used in the 1760s by Saussure. It consisted of a thermometer inside a small wooden box lined with a layer of black cork. Sunlight entered the box through a window covered with three panes of glass that were separated by air spaces. This arrangement served to magnify the heating effect of the Sun's rays while eliminating the cooling effect of wind currents. In 1774, simultaneous heliothermometric observations taken at different locations by Saussure and an assistant demonstrated an appreciable increase in solar heat with altitude.[27] Fourier described the theory of the heliothermometer and concluded that the results of his calculations were "in exact accordance with those of observation."[28]

The analogy to the heliothermometer and the conclusion of the essay demonstrate that in Fourier's mind, the three main factors controlling terrestrial temperatures were the heat of the Sun, the Earth's internal heat, and the heat of innumerable stars—the "temperature of space"—not the greenhouse effect (see epigraph to this chapter). "The third, that is, the influence of the stars, is equivalent to the presence of an immense hollow sphere, with the earth in the center, the constant temperature of which should be a little below what would be observed in polar regions."[29] For Fourier, the atmosphere was like a giant heliothermometer, sandwiched between the surface of the Earth and the imaginary cap provided by the finite temperature of interstellar space. The interior of this heliothermometer, especially the fluid and aerial components, possessed radiative properties of its own: "The transparency of the waters appears to concur with that of the air in augmenting the degree of heat already acquired, because luminous heat flowing in, penetrates, with little difficulty, the interior of the mass, and non-luminous heat has more difficulty in finding its way out in a contrary direction."[30] For Fourier both the oceans *and* the atmosphere resisted the free exchange of luminous and nonluminous heat.

Fourier concluded by claiming that he had "united in this article all the principal elements of the analysis of terrestrial temperature" and had summarized the results of his earlier researches, "long since given to the public." While raising the possibility that new properties of radiating heat or causes modifying the temperature of the globe might yet be discovered, he was positive that "all the principal laws of the motion of heat are known." In his mind, his analytical theory of heat was rendered more complete by this essay on terrestrial temperatures. Still, his analytical theory of heat, which he claimed rested on "immutable foundations" and constituted "a new branch of mathematical science," presented the equations of motion of heat in solids and liquids only. When it came to the equilibrium conditions of radiant heat in the atmosphere, it was just a hypothesis, not an analytical theory.[31]

Earlier Comments by Fourier on Greenhouses

Fourier did not actually use the term "serre" (greenhouse) in his often wrongly cited essay of 1824. The final footnote of that memoir was a reference to his *Théorie analytique de la chaleur,* which appeared in 1822 and in English translation in 1878. In this book, Fourier introduces the elements of a comprehensive mathematical theory of heat: the differential equations describing the movement of heat in solids and fluids, the variations introduced by external periodic heat sources, and the transmission of heat by diaphanous substances. While these topics were all contributions to basic physical theory and have been read as such by generations of physicists and historians of physics, they were also the elements of Fourier's theory of terrestrial temperatures, with the Earth as the cooling body, the Sun as the periodic heat source, and the atmosphere as the diaphanous intermediary.[32]

Fourier compared results of experiments done on a series of glass plates enclosing a vacuum to those done on glass plates separated by layers of atmospheric air; he explained that the latter retained heat more efficiently but all were sensitive to the distances between the surfaces. He also analyzed the case in which heat from an external source crossed successive diaphanous envelopes, and he discussed the heating of enclosed spaces, specifically the heliothermometer and the temperature of buildings such as greenhouses.

> In general the theorems concerning the heating of air in closed spaces extend to a great variety of problems. It would be useful to revert to them when we wish to foresee and regulate temperature with precision, as in the case of green-houses, drying-houses, sheep-folds, work-shops, or in many civil establishments, such as hospitals, barracks, places of assembly.[33]

Nearly the same language appears in his paper "Sur la température des habitations," presented to the French Academy in 1817.[34]

The question of terrestrial temperatures was on Fourier's mind as early as 1807, when he wrote on the unequal heating of the globe. In subsequent years, he made observations on the heating power of the Sun and on nighttime refrigeration. He conducted experiments on the heating and cooling of objects of different composition and shape, and on the transmission, absorption, and reflection of radiant heat. He employed basic physical principles and formulated mathematical laws to explain and predict universal phenomena, such as "the progressive extinction of heat rays in the atmosphere."[35]

It is clear that Fourier considered himself the Newton of heat: "The principle of heat penetrates, like gravity, all objects and all of space, and it is subject to simple and constant laws."[36] As an example of these laws, he cited the distribution of solar heat over the globe—the daily, yearly, and longer periodic variations that heat both the surface and the interior of the Earth, which cause variations beneath the surface and affect the grand movements of the oceans and the atmosphere. Fourier also cited the principle of radiative equilibrium:

> the heat that is dissipated by the radiation at the surface of the earth is compensated at each instant by that which is received by the sun. The rays of that star in which the earth is continually bathed penetrate the entire mass. The elements divide and change their direction, but the rays conserve a constant quantity of heat; they maintain the terrestrial temperature as they follow their route toward the heavens.[37]

For Fourier, the analytical theory of heat constituted a "rational law of atmospheric motion, ocean motion, change of seasons, and so on— a grand geophysical law confirmed in the laboratory and expressed by calculus."[38]

Conclusion

Fourier's article of 1827, cited by Arrhenius and by many others since as containing the first allusion to the greenhouse effect, was merely a reprint of a descriptive memoir published in 1824. Fourier presented his first analytic and experimental investigations on heat in 1807. By 1816, he had composed a manuscript of 650 pages on the subject. Two of his earlier publications, including his magnum opus of 1822, discuss the problem of terrestrial temperatures and the principles governing the temperature of a greenhouse ("serre").[39]

Fourier acknowledged earlier works on heat by John Leslie, Count Rumford, and others. He was especially influenced by the experiments done by Saussure some fifty years earlier using heliothermometers.[40] In 1681, Edme Mariotte wrote that although the Sun's light and heat easily passed through glass and other transparent materials, heat from other sources ("chaleur de feu") did not.[41] Obviously, those seeking to understand the history of terrestrial temperature research must look well beyond the secondary literature and well before 1827. They must also remember that for Fourier, the "temperature of space" was much more important than the greenhouse effect in controlling terrestrial temperatures.

John Tyndall, Svante Arrhenius, and Early Research on Carbon Dioxide and Climate

In the second half of the nineteenth century two prominent scientists, working in two distinct specialties, identified the importance of atmospheric trace constituents as efficient absorbers of long-wave radiation and as factors in climatic control. John Tyndall conducted the first convincing experiments on the radiative properties of gases, demonstrating that "perfectly colorless and invisible gases and vapours" were able to absorb and emit radiant heat. Svante Arrhenius, in pursuing his interests in meteorology and cosmic physics, demonstrated that variations of atmospheric CO_2 concentration could have a very great effect on the overall heat budget and surface temperature of the planet. It would be a mistake, however, to consider either of these individuals as direct forerunners or prophets of contemporary climate concerns. Each of them had extremely broad scientific interests and pursued climate-related research as one interest among many. Tyndall worked on absorption in the near infrared at temperatures far above those of the terrestrial environment. Arrhenius, who has recently gained renewed attention as the "father" of the theory of the greenhouse effect, held assumptions and produced results that are not continuous with present-day climate research.

Tyndall

> The solar heat possesses, in a far higher degree than that of lime light, the power of crossing an atmosphere; but, when the heat is absorbed by the planet, it is so changed in quality that the rays emanating from the planet cannot get with the same freedom back into space. Thus the atmosphere admits of the entrance of the solar heat, but checks its exit; and the result is a tendency to accumulate heat at the surface of the planet.
>
> —John Tyndall (1859)

John Tyndall was born in Leighlin Bridge, County Carlow, Ireland, on August 2, 1820, the son of a part-time shoemaker and constable.[1] He attended the national school in Carlow and, at the age of eighteen, joined the Irish Ordnance Survey as a draftsman and surveyor. In 1842, as the Irish survey neared completion, Tyndall was transferred to the English Survey at Preston, Lancashire, but due to his protests against the survey's oppressive policies and incompetent management, he was dismissed. Following a brief visit in Ireland, Tyndall found work in Lancashire and Yorkshire as a surveyor and engineer during the railway mania of 1844–45.

In 1847, Tyndall took a job teaching mathematics and drafting at Queenwood College in Hampshire, a new school and one of the first such institutions in England to have a laboratory for the teaching of science. However, as he confided to Michael Faraday, his teaching duties left him no time for research:

> To settle myself down at Queenwood, even granting it permanent, would be to sacrifice an object for which I have battled harder than anybody knows, and that is to approve myself a worker in science. Seven hours plus meal times and other contingencies, plus the time required to depolarize the intellect after having been engaged with other matters is a heavy subtraction from the day. I ask for your counsel in this state of things. . . . I have already written to Magnus and Poggendorff for testimonials so that if you advise the step I shall be ready to take it promptly.[2]

Tyndall went on to study at the University of Marburg, where he completed a doctoral dissertation in mathematics under Friedrich Stegmann. He conducted research on diamagnetism in the laboratory of Karl Herrman Knoblauch, and his first article, on the behavior of crystalline bodies between the poles of a magnet, appeared in the *Philosophical Magazine* in 1851.

In 1852, Tyndall was elected a fellow of the Royal Society. A year later, with the support of Michael Faraday, he became a professor of natural philosophy at the Royal Institution of Great Britain, where he continued his investigations into the magnetic properties of crystals, the transmission of heat through organic structures, the physical properties of ice, and the radiative properties of gases. Through-out his career at the Royal Institution he demonstrated his talents in laboratory research and public lecturing. To supplement his meager salary, Tyndall also served as examiner for the Royal Military College (1855–57), lecturer at Eton (1856) and the London Institution (1856–59), and professor of physics at the Royal School of Mines (1859–68).

Starting in 1854, Tyndall turned his attention to problems of geology, including the effects of pressure on slate and the movement of alpine glaciers. He also developed an interest in meteorology, enhanced by his scientific mountaineering excursions. He popularized the sport of mountaineering and pioneered solo attempts. He climbed Mont Blanc several times and was the first to climb the Weisshorn. After ascending the Galenstock in the Swiss Alps, Tyndall was inspired to write to Faraday of his experience:

> We did not hope to see any thing from the summit, nevertheless we attained it and were rewarded: not only by the clearness of the prospect, but by the changes of the atmosphere, which were quite marvelous, sometimes shrouding all, sometimes melting as if by magic and revealing the mountains. The atmosphere is a wondrous factory; the grand origin of all its power being overhead, lifting the snows and driving the clouds by its individual might.[3]

In 1859, Tyndall began a notable series of experiments on the radiative properties of various gases. He established that the absorption of thermal radiation by water vapor and carbon dioxide was of importance in explaining meteorological phenomena such as nighttime cooling, the formation of dew and frost, and possibly the variation of climates in the distant past. He also experimented on the polarization of light and its scattering by molecules and dust. Of course, in Victorian London, smoke and dust were readily available. In 1864, Tyndall confided to Sir John Herschel that "sunshine is a luxury beyond my means—all the experiments which I have hitherto made have been executed with the electric light."[4] He demonstrated light scattering by aerosols, what has come to be known as the Tyndall effect, and ventured an early explanation of the blue color of the sky, a phenomenon later explained by Lord Rayleigh.

> Assuming that the action of aqueous vapour upon radiant heat is established beyond doubt—(which it is) we have in the vapour a body which absorbs the same rays as the water which produces it—in other words it shares the colour of water. Through the operation of this cause our atmosphere is certainly *a blue medium*. The quantity of vapour might not be sufficient to produce a sensible blue, if the rays went straight through it; but the reflections within the body of the atmosphere must be innumerable, and thus its *virtual depth* increased. I wonder is this likely to throw any light on the blue of the sky![5]

Herschel liked Tyndall's idea "of accounting for the blue colour of the air as due to the vapour of a blue liquid (water) *if you intend it to be regarded as an absorptive colour.* Analogies are not wanting—Liquid chlorine and gas yellow; iodine liq[uid] and gas purple; bromine liq[uid] and gas deep ruddy brown; sulphur above melting point and vapour both brown."[6]

Tyndall received the Royal Medal of the Royal Society of London in 1863 and, in 1867, at the height of his scientific reputation, succeeded Michael Faraday as superintendent of the Royal Institution.[7] In his later career Tyndall developed a technique for destroying airborne organic matter by discontinuous heating and disproved the notion of spontaneous generation by demonstrating that generation (spontaneous or otherwise) was impossible in a sterile environment. He also devoted considerable time and effort to the popularization of science. He was one of the leading lecturers in Great Britain and, in 1872 and 1873, delivered a series of well-attended scientific lectures in the United States. During his lifetime, he published more than 180 articles on experimental topics and a large number of popular essays on science, literature, religion, mountaineering, and travel. He received five honorary doctorates and was an honorary member of thirty-five scientific societies.

Tyndall fell seriously ill in 1886. The following year he retired from the Royal Institution and withdrew to his house at Hindhead, Surrey. Bedridden by insomnia and indigestion, he died on December 4, 1893, from an overdose of chloral, accidentally administered by his wife.

Experiments on Radiant Heat

> The great Goethe affirmed that by experiment nothing could be proved; that experiments might be accurately executed, but that deductions must be drawn from every man for himself. This is not quite so, for individual willfulness or caprice is evanescent when opposed to natural truth. There is one advantage possessed by the scientific man, that his errors cannot indefinitely extend themselves. Outside of him, and entirely independent of his desires and will, is a standard that never changes, a logic that never errs—ever tending to correct his errors and vindicate his truth.
>
> —John Tyndall (1881)

As noted earlier, in January 1859, Tyndall turned his attention to radiant heat and the absorption of radiation by gases and vapors, which he saw as "a perfectly unexplored field of inquiry," in order to bring molecules "under the dominion of experiment."[8] He experimented on the radiative properties of various gases, including aqueous vapor, carbonic acid, ozone, and hydrocarbons. By May 18 of that year he was able to exclaim in his journal, "Experimented all day; the subject is completely in my hands!"[9]

Tyndall's experimental apparatus, the first ratio spectrophotometer, consisted of a long tube that he filled with various gases (fig. 6-1). He capped the ends of the tube with slabs of rock salt crystal, a substance known to be highly transparent to heat radiation. A standard Leslie cube emitted radiation that traversed the tube and interacted with the gas before entering one cone of a differential thermopile. Radiation from a second Leslie cube passed through a screen and entered the other cone. The apex of the cones contained the differential thermopile with its junctions facing opposite directions. This was connected in series to a galvanometer that measured small voltage differences. Zero voltage (or deflection) indicated equal temperatures and equal radiant fluxes. The intensity of the two sources of radiation entering the two cones could be compared by measuring the deflection of the galvanometer, which is proportional to the temperature difference across the thermopile. Different gases in the tube would cause varying amounts of deflection of the galvanometer needle. If the intensity of the reference source of radiation was known, the intensity of the other source (and thus the absorptive power of the gas in the tube) could be calculated.

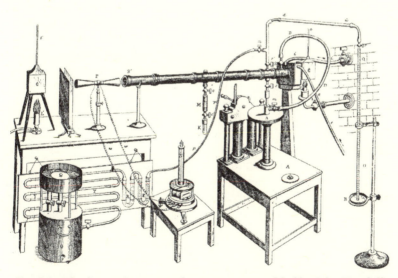

Fig. 6-1. The first ratio spectrophotometer, assembled by John Tyndall. **C** Leslie cube source. **S–S'** Tube with gas. **P** Differential thermopile. **C'** Reference Leslie cube source. **H** Attenuating filter. **N** Galvonometer where current from one thermopile balances the other. **G** Source of gas. **O** Pressure gauge. *Source:* John Tyndall, *Contributions to Molecular Physics in the Domain of Radiant Heat* (London, 1872), frontispiece.

The differential thermopile, the central experimental apparatus employed by Tyndall, was based on the thermoelectric effect, which had been discovered in 1821 by the German-born physicist Thomas Seebeck. In 1829, the Italian scientists Macedonio Melloni and Leopoldo Nobili published a joint article on a thermoelectric device they called a thermoscope. Although the device measured heat electrically, it required contact with the hot body and it tended to follow the fluctuations in temperature of the medium in which it was immersed. Two years later Melloni developed a much more sensitive device by adding a galvanometer to a thermopile; this device he called a thermo-multiplicateur. It was forty times more sensitive than a thermometer and could detect radiation and measure temperature differences between objects thirty feet apart.[10]

Melloni believed that solar and thermal radiation resulted from the same fundamental physical phenomenon. He experimented with the transmission of radiant heat through solids and liquids, but he only speculated on the radiative properties of variable atmospheric gases such as water vapor. For example, in 1839, Melloni observed that the relative magnitude of the radiation incident on his thermo-multiplicateur changed from day to day, but he merely hypothesized that the variation might be due to changes in water vapor content that had altered the ability of the atmosphere to absorb radiation. According to Tyndall, "Melloni left untouched by his experiments the gaseous forms of matter" and had merely demonstrated that the action of air upon radiant heat was totally inappreciable over distances of about twenty feet. This "negative" result of Melloni was the only one known to Tyndall.[11]

After he began experiments with gases, Tyndall announced some of his early results to the Royal Society on May 26, 1859. Two weeks later, he demonstrated his experiments to a distinguished audience at the Royal Institution. Tyndall's most striking discoveries were the vast differences in the abilities of "perfectly colorless and invisible gases and vapours" to absorb and transmit radiant heat. The "elementary gases," oxygen, nitrogen, and hydrogen, were almost transparent to radiant heat, while others were quite opaque.[12] Tyndall experimented with many gases, and he determined that complex molecules such as water vapor, carbon dioxide, ozone, and even perfumes were the best absorbers and radiators of heat radiation. His experiments showed that some of the transparent compound gases, even in very small quantities, absorb much more strongly than the atmosphere itself.[13] Tyndall demonstrated that the amount of thermal radiation absorbed by water vapor was eighty times greater than that of pure air. He estimated that for every two hundred "atoms" of oxygen and nitrogen there is about one of aqueous vapor.

> This one, then, is eighty times more powerful than the 200; and hence, comparing a single atom of oxygen or nitrogen with a single atom of aqueous vapour, we may infer that the action of the latter

is 16,000 times that of the former. This was a very astonishing result, and it naturally excited opposition, based on the philosophic reluctance to accept a result so grave in consequences before testing it to the uttermost.[14]

Concerning perfumes, Tyndall wrote, "the substances to which odours are due exercise a very energetic action on radiant heat. . . . Thus, the perfume of a flower-bed may exert a greater action upon radiant heat than the entire oxygen and nitrogen of the atmosphere above the bed."[15]

Tyndall was an accomplished lecturer and writer, and he employed numerous metaphors to describe his experiments with radiant heat. His desire in 1859 was to apply to gases and vapors "a coercion far more powerful than any to which they had previously been subjected."[16] He wanted to "question the vapour itself as to its absorbent power and to receive from it an answer which did not admit of doubt."[17] The answer he received was that water vapor, among the constituents of the atmosphere, was the strongest absorber of radiant heat and was the most important gas controlling the Earth's surface temperature.

> The aqueous vapour constitutes a local dam, by which the temperature at the earth's surface is deepened; the dam, however, finally overflows, and we give to space all that we receive from the sun.[18]

According to Tyndall, water vapor "acts more energetically upon the terrestrial rays than upon the solar rays; hence, its tendency is to preserve to the earth a portion of heat which would otherwise be radiated into space."[19] There could be no doubt about the "extraordinary opacity of this substance to the rays of obscure heat," particularly to the rays emitted by the Earth after it has been warmed by the Sun. He painted a verbal picture of an England devoid of the blanketing effect of water vapor and devastated by frost.

> It is perfectly certain that more than ten percent of the terrestrial radiation from the soil of England is stopped within ten feet of the surface of the soil. This one fact is sufficient to show the immense influence which this newly-discovered property of aqueous vapours must exert on the phenomena of meteorology. This aqueous vapour is a blanket more necessary to the vegetable life of England than clothing is to man. Remove for a single summer-night the aqueous vapour from the air which overspreads this country, and you would assuredly destroy every plant capable of being destroyed by a freezing temperature. The warmth of our fields and gardens would pour itself unrequited into space, and the sun would rise upon an island held fast in the iron grip of frost.[20]

Meteorological and Climatological Implications

Tyndall linked his laboratory results to meteorological experiments in the free air. Citing earlier work by William Wells and others on minimum nighttime temperatures and the formation of dew, Tyndall pointed out that dew and hoarfrost were caused by a loss of heat through radiation, "the radiating body being so chilled as to precipitate and freeze the atmospheric vapour," and that radiative cooling was greatest when the dew was least.[21] One of his experiments led him to consider London as a "heat island" and to speculate on the influence of the moon's light on water vapor in the atmosphere. On the roof of the Royal Institution, Tyndall had a platform erected that allowed him to sweep the heavens with his thermoelectric pile, "without impediment from the chimney pots of London." Wires connected the pile to a differential galvanometer in the laboratory below. When pointed at the moon, the instrument indicated a lower temperature than when pointed elsewhere in the sky. As he explained in a letter to John Herschel, "In other words, less heat was lost by the instrument when directed off the moon, than when directed towards it. This, as I have stated, is equivalent to a radiation of cold from our satellite." Tyndall ventured an explanation of this effect based on his newly gained understanding of the immense absorptive power of water vapor.

> I pictured the matter thus: Supposing the earth to be surrounded by an atmospheric veil of precipitated vapour, the depth to which the moon's heat could clear away the veil would be greatest along the line drawn from the earth's centre to the moon, and would diminish from this normal all round, thinning off to nothing where the incidence became sufficiently oblique. The escape of terrestrial heat as far as the atmosphere is concerned would be less impeded along the normal than in any other direction. Theoretically speaking, when I turned my pile off the moon I turned it toward a portion of the atmosphere, where the moon's heat was less effective in rendering the sky clear, but whether the difference could be measured is another question.

Tyndall worried about the disturbing influences of the city of London on his experiment and noted, "On referring to a map I find that in turning my pile off the moon I turned it more *over the mass of London*, and the diminution of the cold may have been due to the temperature of the air suspended over this vast focus of artificial heat."[22]

Herschel rejected Tyndall's hypothesis that the moon could influence the water vapor of the atmosphere directly beneath it and advised Tyndall to seek an observing station far from the smoke, hot air, and vapors of London.[23] He was astonished by Tyndall's ability to measure the radiative effects of a small amount of water vapor, writing that "you are opening up a highly interesting chapter in the book of Thermotics."[24] He encouraged Tyndall to continue his research program and sent him a large crystal of rock salt for his experiments on thermal radiation. "You have made a *grand* step in meteorology in showing that the *dry* air is perfectly transcalescent and that the invisible moisture is what stops the sun's heat."[25] Only four years after

Tyndall had begun his experiments on the transmission of thermal radiation through gases, his results were considered reliable and, according to Sir George Gabriel Stokes, "quite beyond doubt."[26]

Reminding his audience that each molecule of water vapor absorbs and radiates sixteen thousand times more heat than a molecule of air, Tyndall composed the following poetic image of cumulus convection.

> The sun raises the vapours of the equatorial ocean; they rise, but for a time a vapour screen spreads above and around them. But the higher they rise, the more they come into the presence of pure space, and when, by their levity, they have penetrated the vapour screen, which lies close to the earth's surface, what must occur? . . . Into space [the vapour] pours its heat, chills itself, condenses, and the tropical torrents are the consequence. . . . In the presence of space, the head of each [convective] pillar wastes its heat by radiation [and] condenses to a cumulus, which constitutes the visible capital of an invisible column of saturated air.[27]

From these and other results, Tyndall correctly pointed out that the role of water vapor "must form one of the chief foundation-stones of the science of meteorology."[28]

Tyndall's work was important in understanding the "ultra-red rays" missing from the solar spectrum. He wondered why the "obscure radiation" of the Sun was only two times larger than its luminous radiation, while in an electric light the ratio was eight to one. "In 1865 I worked on this subject and I thought that this was due to the enormous absorption of the solar rays by the aqueous vapour of the air."[29] He believed that measurements made at high altitudes, above most of the atmosphere's water vapor, would reveal a spectrum quite different from that observed at sea level. By 1881, this conclusion had been established by Samuel P. Langley, who, while conducting the first experiments with his new bolometer, wrote to Tyndall from the summit of Mount Whitney, California, that there "the air is perhaps drier than at any other equal altitude ever used for scientific investigation."[30]

Tyndall thought that changes in the amount of any of the radiatively active constituents of the atmosphere—water vapor, carbon dioxide, ozone, or hydrocarbons—could have produced "*all the mutations of climate which the researches of geologists reveal* . . . they constitute true causes, the *extent* alone of the operation remaining doubtful."[31] He gave credit to his predecessors Saussure, Fourier, and Pouillet, among others, for the *intuition* that "the rays from the sun and fixed stars could reach the earth through the atmosphere more easily than the rays emanating from the earth could get back into space."[32] The experimental verification of this phenomenon, however, belonged to Tyndall.

In 1865, Charles Lyell asked Tyndall if changes in the eccentricity of the Earth's orbit could possibly induce an ice age in one hemisphere because of excessive cooling of the hemisphere with the longer winter. At the time, Lyell was trying to decide whether or not to accept James Croll's theory of the climatic significance of secular changes in the Earth's orbital elements.[33] Tyndall's reply demonstrated his grasp of both meteorological and geological principles.

> I hardly think that geologists *are* entitled to assume "a refrigeration of the hemisphere" which is exposed to the extremes of heat and cold, solely on account of the existence of such extremes. . . . the existence of our atmosphere and the transport of water in the shape of snow from the equatorial regions to the polar ones, render the actual problem a complicated one.[34]

It was Tyndall's position that the greater the quantity of snow, the greater must have been the quantity of heat required to produce so much vapor. Lyell, whose fundamental theory of climate change was based on changes in the distribution of land and water, especially in polar and equatorial regions, wondered if such changes would make a difference in the amount of heat lost to space. Tyndall responded that the difference in radiative power between water and land, whether barren or covered with ice or snow, was unlikely to furnish the solution of the glacial epoch.[35] Three decades later, scientists were still looking for the "solution."

Arrhenius

> By the influence of the increasing percentage of carbonic acid in the atmosphere, we may hope to enjoy ages with more equable and better climates, especially as regards the colder regions of the earth, ages when the earth will bring forth much more abundant crops than at present, for the benefit of rapidly propagating mankind.
>
> —Svante Arrhenius (1906)

Svante August Arrhenius is best known as an electrochemist who, along with Wilhelm Ostwald and Jacobus Henricus van't Hoff, pioneered the theory of electrolytic dissociation.[36] He was born near Uppsala, Sweden, on February 19, 1859, the second son of Carolina Christina Thunberg and Svante Gustav Arrhenius, an *akademifogde*, or rent collector, for Uppsala University and an agent for a noble family. The year of his birth was the year John Tyndall first turned his attention to experiments on the absorption of radiation by gases. Arrhenius was tutored at home until he was eight and attended Cathedral School in Uppsala. In 1876 he entered Uppsala University, where he followed a broad curriculum, including mathematics, physics, chemistry, Latin, history, geology, and botany. He finished his first degree in physics in four semesters without laboratory work (*approbateur*) and began preparing for the *filosofie licentiat*, or lower doctorate. In 1881, Arrhenius left Uppsala because of widely publicized problems in the Physics Department. He went to Stockholm to work at the Institute of Physics of the Swedish Academy of Sciences with Erik Edlund, a professor of physics who was interested in meteorology and who had ties to the Central Meteorological Office. He also studied chemistry with Otto Pettersson at the Stockholm Högskola. Arrhenius applied his knowledge of physics to problems in electrochemistry and wrote a dissertation on the chemical theory of electrolytes, which he published in 1884. His examination committee, ignoring the theoretical aspect of his dissertation, did not award him the highest distinction. This constituted a severe blow both to Arrhenius's psyche and to his academic career. He spent the next two years at home with his parents.

Although his chemistry professors at Stockholm did not appreciate his work, Wilhelm Ostwald, a professor of chemistry at the Riga Polytechnicum, thought Arrhenius's dissertation was "the most important to have been published regarding the theory of affinity."[37] Arrhenius collaborated with Ostwald and, with the help of a valuable travel stipend from the Academy of Sciences, worked in a number of Continental laboratories to complete his theory of electrolytic dissociation.

After a long postdoctoral period of six years and several unsuccessful candidacies, Arrhenius, with the support of Ostwald, accepted a lectureship in physics at the Stockholm Högskola in 1891. This position kept him close to home and provided him with stable employment and a laboratory, but it also kept him out of the mainstream of German electrochemistry. He was a founder and first secretary of the Stockholm Physical Society, whose members included geologists, meteorologists, and astronomers. In 1894 he married Sophia Rudbeck, his student and assistant. The union produced a son, but the marriage dissolved after only two years.

Arrhenius was promoted to professor of physics in 1895 and served as rector of the Högskola from 1896 to 1902. He was elected to the Swedish Academy in 1901, and his work on the electrolytic theory of dissociation earned him the Nobel Prize for Chemistry in 1903. His second marriage, to Maria Johansson in 1905, produced three more children, a son and two daughters. Arrhenius rejected an offer of a chair in physics from the Prussian Academy but accepted the invitation of King Oscar II of Sweden to serve as first director of the Nobel Institute for Physical Chemistry. His interests in later life included theoretical immunochemistry and the popularization of science. He was elected a foreign member of the Royal Society of London in 1911, and he presented both the Faraday Lecture to the Royal Chemical Society and the Tyndall Lectures to the Royal Institution of Great Britain in 1914. Even after suffering a stroke late in 1925, he continued to work until declining health forced him to retire from the Nobel Institute in February 1927. He died in Stockholm after a brief illness on October 2, 1927, and was buried in Uppsala.

Cosmic Physics and Carbon Dioxide

The Stockholm Physical Society, founded in 1891, helped to stimulate Arrhenius's interest in "cosmic physics"—the physics of the Earth, sea, and atmosphere. He published numerous articles and several books on earth science and cosmology, including works on ball lightning, the influence of the rays of the Sun on the electric phenomena of the Earth's atmosphere, the influence of the Moon on the electrical state of the atmosphere, and the action of cosmic influences on physiological processes.[38]

Arrhenius did little experimental or observational work in geophysics. His basic approach was to apply physical and chemical principles to make sense of existing observations. He developed a theory of the formation of the solar system based on the condensation of a rotating nebula. He also proposed an indefinite age for the universe and a new solar heat source that contradicted Lord Kelvin's estimate of fifteen million years for the age of the Sun. As his grandson and biographer, Gustav O. S. Arrhenius, pointed out, "theoretical explanations of poorly known natural systems display a high mortality rate when confronted with accumulating evidence." Such was the fate of Arrhenius's geophysical work, which served primarily as a catalyst for the more empirically based investigations of others.[39]

In 1895, Arrhenius presented a very significant geophysical paper to the Stockholm Physical Society in which he suggested that a reduction or augmentation of about forty percent in the concentration of a minor atmospheric constituent, carbon dioxide, might trigger feedback phenomena that could account for the glacial advances and retreats. His important memoir on the subject, "On the Influence of Carbonic Acid in the Air upon the Temperature of the Ground," was published the following year.[40] In this article he developed an energy budget model that considered the radiative effects of carbon dioxide and water vapor at ambient temperatures and studied the response of his model to changes in the CO_2 concentration. He relied heavily on the experimental and observational work of others, including Josef Stefan's new law that radiant emission was proportional to the fourth power of temperature, Samuel P. Langley's measurements of the transmission of heat radiation through the atmosphere, Léon Teisserenc de Bort's estimates of cloudiness for different latitudes, Knut Ånsgström's values for the absorption coefficients of water vapor and CO_2, and Alexander Buchan's charts of mean monthly temperatures over the globe. Arrhenius made very rough estimates of surface and cloud albedo and included simple radiative feedback effects in the presence of snow cover. He ignored the effects of changes in horizontal heat transport and cloud cover:

> we suppose that the heat that is conducted to a given place on the earth's surface or in the atmosphere in consequence of atmospheric

or oceanic currents, horizontal or vertical, remains the same in the course of the time considered, and we will also suppose that the clouded part of the sky remains unchanged. It is only the variation of the temperature with the transparency of the air that we shall examine.[41]

Arrhenius argued that variations in trace components of the atmosphere could have a very great influence on the overall heat budget. Using the best data available to him, but neccessarily making many estimates and simplifying assumptions, he calculated the mean alteration of temperature that would follow if the quantity of carbonic acid (K) varied from its present mean value (K = 1) to a value of K = 0.67, 1.5, 2.0, 2.5, and 3.0, respectively. He made these calculations for every tenth parallel and for every season. His calculations, presented in the form of a table, yielded the general principle that "if the quantity of carbonic acid increases in geometric progression, the augmentation of the temperature will increase nearly in arithmetic progression." The effects were slightly greater in higher latitudes, and the latitude of maximum effect moved poleward with higher values of K. In general, the effect was greater in the *winter* than in the summer. Of considerable importance, given the many approximations that had already gone into his model, was Arrhenius's note that "the above calculations are found by interpolation from Langley's numbers for the values K = 0.67 and K = 1.5, and that *the other numbers must be regarded as interpolated.*"[42]

Högbom and the Geological Consequences of CO_2

It is important to remember that Arrhenius was addressing the issue of the probable cause of the "Ice Age" and would probably not have undertaken such a series of tedious hand calculations without the interest and support of members of the Physical Society of Stockholm. He wanted to determine the likelihood of great variations in carbon dioxide in relatively short geological times. To do this, he devoted five entire pages of his article to the translation of a memoir by his friend and colleague, the geologist Arvid Gustaf Högbom, who had worked on the geochemistry of carbon.[43]

From Högbom's perspective, neither the combustion of fossil fuels nor the removal of organic carbon (deforestation) influenced atmospheric CO_2 levels nearly as much as crustal processes—the formation of limestone and other carbonates, which removed carbon dioxide from the atmosphere, and the decomposition of silicates, which added to it. Högbom estimated that the current atmospheric concentration of carbon dioxide was of the same order of magnitude as the amount of carbon "fixed in the living organic world." He further estimated that if the world's production of coal, approximately five hundred million tons per year, were converted into carbon dioxide, it would equal only one-thousandth of the total atmospheric concentration. The sedimentary rocks, however, contained an enormous amount of carbon dioxide: "[W]e find that about 25,000 times as much carbonic acid is fixed to lime in the sedimentary formations as exists free in the air. Every molecule of carbonic acid in this mass of limestone has . . . existed in and passed through the atmosphere in the course of time." Högbom thought that in different geological eras, this could result in enormous variations of the CO_2 content of the atmosphere. In his opinion, there was probably a balance between industrial output of carbon dioxide—which, as a geologist, he considered to be of a "temporary nature"—and the carbon consumed in the formation of limestone and other carbonates. A secular rise in CO_2 concentration due to industrial emissions was of no concern to him.[44]

Högbom rejected the widespread opinion of the time that the CO_2 content of the atmosphere was diminishing and had been much greater in earlier eras. Proponents of this viewpoint argued that it fit well with a secularly cooling Earth and the advance of glacial ice sheets. Högbom argued that over geological time, enormous variations in carbon sources and sinks must have occurred, resulting in the rise and fall of atmospheric CO_2 concentrations. He did not believe that coal and limestone deposits were formed simply from the CO_2 of the archaic atmosphere. His carbon cycle contained many more components—notably the combustion of carbonaceous meteorites in the atmosphere, which was wholly incalculable; the regulative role of the oceans, which was unknown; and volcanic "exhalations," which he considered to be the "chief source of carbonic acid for the atmosphere." Because these processes were largely independent of each other, Högbom concluded that there was little probability "for the permanence of an equilibrium of the carbonic acid in the atmosphere. . . . [and] there is no conceivable hindrance to imagining that [the quantity of carbonic acid in the air] might in a certain geological period have been several times greater, or on the other hand considerably less, than now."[45]

Having the assurance of Högbom that large variations in atmospheric CO_2 content were quite likely in different geological eras, Arrhenius turned his attention to other theories of climatic change. The publication a year earlier of a book on this subject, *Le cause dell' era glaciale*, by the Italian scientist Luigi De Marchi, provided a convenient critique of the major geological theories of the time. De Marchi's list of current theories of ice ages and interglacials, which Arrhenius reproduced, included changes in the following factors:

1. The temperature of the Earth's place in space.
2. The Sun's radiation to the Earth (solar constant).
3. The obliquity of the Earth's axis to the ecliptic.
4. The position of the poles on the Earth's surface.

5. The form of the Earth's orbit, especially its eccentricity ([James] Croll).
6. The shape and extension of continents and oceans.
7. The covering of the Earth's surface (vegetation).
8. The direction of the oceanic and aerial currents.
9. The position of the equinoxes.

De Marchi rejected all these hypotheses and personally supported the notion (for reasons other than those of Arrhenius) that a "change in the transparency of the atmosphere would possibly give the desired effect."[46] Arrhenius was happy to rely on the authority of De Marchi and agreed with his conclusions because they supported his model. What is not clear is why Arrhenius, like other scientists of his time, was so intent on promoting a single causal mechanism of climatic change.

Arrhenius concluded his 1896 article with the following words: "I trust that after what has been said the theory proposed in the foregoing pages will prove useful in explaining some points in geological climatology which have hitherto proved most difficult to interpret." His model could account for the onset of interglacials and ice ages. His calculations showed that "the temperature of the Arctic regions would rise about 8° to 9° C, if the carbonic acid increased to 2.5 to 3 times its present value. In order to get the temperature of the ice age between the 40th and 50th parallels, the carbonic acid in the air should sink to 0.62–0.55 of present value (lowering the temperature 4°–5° C.)"[47]

Arrhenius's contemporary, the American geologist T. C. Chamberlin, had mixed opinions of the work. He believed that "Dr. Arrhenius has taken a great step in advance of his predecessors in reducing his conclusions to definite quantitative terms, deduced from observational data."[48] Chamberlin, however, found the assumption of Högbom and Arrhenius, that volcanic eruptions were the chief source of carbonic acid for the atmosphere, overly simplistic and not "clearly and inevitably connected with the known current of geological events."[49] Chamberlin later regretted his overeager acceptance of Arrhenius's results (see chapter 7).

More recently, Arrhenius has been lauded as the father of the theory of the greenhouse effect, even of global warming. One author claimed that "Arrhenius had *enough spectroscopic information* to estimate that doubling the amount of carbon dioxide in the air could warm the world by four to six degrees," that "the industrial output of carbon dioxide had already reached a level comparable to the amount that circulated naturally," and that Arrhenius had "discovered" the greenhouse effect in 1896.[50] All three statements are misleading and incorrect. The spectroscopic information available to Arrhenius was quite primitive. Langley's bolometer, an instrument composed of two thin strips of metal, a Wheatstone bridge, a battery, and a galvanometer, routinely measured a spectral region between 0.3 and 3 microns and could be extended further only with great difficulty. This is in accord with Arrhenius's statement that for wavelengths greater than 9.5 microns, "we possess no direct observations of the emission or absorption of the two gases."[51] Thus, the infrared atmospheric window between eight and twelve microns and the strong carbon dioxide and water vapor absorption bands beyond twelve microns were unknown at the time. Moreover, we have already seen that in Högbom's view, the industrial output of carbon dioxide was much smaller than geophysical variations in the carbon cycle due to volcanism and other processes. Given the work of Mariotte, Saussure, Fourier, Pouillet, Tyndall, Chamberlin, and many others (see chapters 5 to 7), simple claims about the "discovery" of the greenhouse effect are impossible to sustain.

Worlds in the Making

During the next decade, Arrhenius continued working on his carbon dioxide theory of climate. His two-volume encyclopedic *Lehrbuch der kosmischen Physik* (1903) included a discussion of the carbon cycle and a review of shortwave and long-wave radiation, including new measurements at wavelengths greater than sixteen microns. The *Lehrbuch*, however, was not widely read; it was a textbook for a discipline that did not exist. Several years later, Arrhenius published *Worlds in the Making*, a nontechnical book that reached a much larger audience.[52] Here he provided a short overview of historical work by Fourier, Pouillet, and Tyndall on what he called the "hot-house theory" of the atmosphere.

> That the atmospheric envelopes limit the heat losses from the planets had been suggested about 1800 by the great French physicist Fourier. His ideas were further developed afterwards by Pouillet and Tyndall. Their theory has been styled the hot-house theory, because they thought that the atmosphere acted after the manner of the glass panes of hot-houses.

As Arrhenius explained, glass is transparent to "heat rays of small wavelengths" in the visible spectrum, but not to "dark heat rays" such as those generated by a heated furnace. Solar radiation readily passes through the glass of the hothouse and heats the enclosure, while the "dark" radiation emitted within the enclosure cannot freely escape. Mixing his metaphors, Arrhenius ventured that the glass stops the loss of heat, "just as an overcoat protects the body against too strong a loss of heat by radiation." Of course, the heating of greenhouses is explained only in part by the opacity of glass (and possibly condensed moisture on the glass) to infrared radiation. In fact, it is largely the suppression of mixing by the shelter that generates the higher temperatures in greenhouses. The atmospheric greenhouse effect is even more complex than this, and a simple "hot-house theory" of planetary atmospheres is not accepted today by atmospheric scientists.[53] Arrhenius also discussed an experiment done by Samuel Langley in 1881 on Pike's Peak, Colorado, at an altitude of forty-two hundred meters: "Langley made an experiment with a box, which he packed with cotton-wool to reduce loss by radiation, and which he provided, on the side turned towards the sun, with a double glass pane. He observed that the temperature rose to 113°, while the thermometer only marked 14° or 15° in the shade."[54] Whether or not Langley was aware of it, his experiment replicated the heliothermometer experiments of Saussure a century earlier (see chapter 5).

Based on the results of his model, Arrhenius pointed out that the observed temperature of the Earth is about thirty degrees higher than that calculated from simple geometrical considerations. He explained this discrepancy "by the heat-protecting action of the gases contained in the atmosphere"—water vapor, carbon dioxide, ozone and hydrocarbons, as Tyndall had known in the 1860s.[55] His calculations showed that if the atmosphere had no carbon dioxide, the temperature of the Earth would fall by about twenty-one degrees. A cooler atmosphere would contain less water vapor, resulting in an additional temperature decrease of about ten degrees.

> If the quantity of carbonic acid in the air should sink to one-half its present percentage, the temperature would fall by about 4°; a diminution to one-quarter would reduce the temperature by 8°. On the other hand, any doubling of the percentage of carbon dioxide in the air would raise the temperature of the earth's surface by 4°; and if the carbon dioxide were increased fourfold, the temperature would rise by 8°.[56]

The agreement between these numbers and the results of recent computer simulations, although merely fortuitous, has been widely noted. One writer called his results "not too different from recent estimates." However, as John Kutzbach, a paleoclimate modeler, has recently pointed out, "[t]hese values *happen to be* very close to modern-day estimates . . . even though Arrhenius ignored the possible effects of changes of horizontal advection and cloud cover and used a radiative transfer model that was much less detailed than present-day models."[57]

By 1904, Arrhenius had become concerned by the rapid increase in anthropogenic carbon emissions. In his article of 1896, he had cited Högbom's figure of five hundred million tons for the annual combustion of coal. Since then the amount had risen rapidly, and by 1904 it had reached almost nine hundred million tons. Arrhenius found it significant that "the slight percentage of carbonic acid in the atmosphere may by the advances of industry be changed to a noticeable degree in the course of a few centuries." After reviewing new research on the carbon cycle by Chamberlin and others, he concluded that "the percentage of carbonic acid in the air must be increasing at a constant rate as long as the consumption of coal, petroleum, etc., is maintained at its present figure, and at a still more rapid rate if this consumption should continue to increase as it does now." Arrhenius considered it likely that in future geological ages the Earth would be "visited by a new ice period that will drive us from our temperate countries into the hotter climates of Africa." On the time scale of hundreds to thousands of years, however, he thought that burning fossil fuels could help prevent a rapid return to the conditions of an ice age, and could perhaps inaugurate a new carboniferous age of enormous plant growth.[58]

Conclusion

John Tyndall's carefully executed laboratory experiments clearly demonstrated that trace atmospheric constituents were active absorbers of heat radiation, at least in the near infrared. His meteorological and climatological speculations kept alive what was called the "hot-house theory," and they suggested to Arrhenius that the Earth's heat budget could be controlled by changes in the carbon dioxide content of the atmosphere. As Elisabeth Crawford has shown in her new biography, Arrhenius did not write his 1896 essay because of any great concern for increasing levels of CO_2 caused by the burning of fossil fuels; instead, he was attempting to explain temperature changes at high latitudes that could account for the onset of ice ages and interglacials. Rather than being unique or especially prophetic, his essay represented one of a number of contributions to the ongoing quest at the Stockholm Physical Society to develop a cosmic physics linking the heavens and the Earth.[59]

By 1904 Arrhenius had suggested that increasing the carbon dioxide content of the atmosphere by burning fossil fuels might be *beneficial*, making the Earth's climates warmer and "more equable," stimulating plant growth, and providing more food for a larger population. His view of "paleotechnic" intervention in the climate system by industrial pollution is quite different from earlier, agriculturally based visions of clearing and cultivation resulting in beneficial changes in the climate (chapters 1 and 2). It also differs radically from current concerns over the harmful effects of a global warming caused by industrial emissions and deforestation.[60]

7

T. C. Chamberlin and the Geological
Agency of the Atmosphere

My views depart very essentially from those urged by Arrhenius,
not only in respect of the geologic modus but in regard to the
cooperation of the ocean with the atmosphere. Arrhenius did not
develop a geological theory but merely made an advance on
Tyndall's suggestion as a physicist, tho' the "advance" proved
unfortunate.

—T. C. Chamberlin (1922)

The earth sciences may have experienced their most recent conceptual revolution in the 1970s with the acceptance of plate tectonics, but
that was by no means their only major revolution. T. C. Chamberlin
(1843–1928), America's most eminent geologist turned geocosmolo-
gist, experienced three major conceptual revolutions in his field. As
a student in the 1860s, he rejected the scriptural geology he had learned
in his youth. As a working geologist interested in multiple glaciations,
he rejected the dominant theories of hot planetary birth and secular
cooling of the Earth as severely lacking in explanatory power. As one
of the leading interdisciplinary scientists of his day, he formulated a
new theory of the origin and evolution of the Earth and solar system—
the planetesimal hypothesis.[1]
    Glacial theories of the late nineteenth and early twentieth centu-
ries appear in three distinct clusters: *astronomical theories* involve
changes in the Sun's luminosity, the passage of the Earth through
opaque regions of space, and the variation of the Earth's tilt and orbital elements; *terrestrial theories* include mountain building, volcanism, and changes in atmospheric and oceanic circulations; and *molecular theories* invoke changes in the water vapor or CO_2 content of
the atmosphere. The favorite among geologists was Charles Lyell's

theory of continental uplift and mountain building. James Croll's theory of periodic changes in solar insolation due to changes in the Earth's orbital elements was tantalizing but did not fit with geological evidence. Speculations about possible changes in the Sun were popular as well but were impossible to prove. Lord Kelvin had decided that the Sun was simply cooling off and the Earth's future climate would be a cold, frozen one. Most theorists focused on a single mechanism of glaciation, with perhaps a secondary cause added in. There was some lip service to but little interest in multiple causation.

Chamberlin tried to keep his options open by advocating his "method of multiple working hypotheses." He was one of the first geologists to see the Ice Age as a series of multiple glaciations, and he was interested in searching for fundamental mechanisms of change that would explain the details, including the repeated oscillations between cold and warm epochs, the timing and duration of these events, and the differences between high and low latitude glaciation. His search led him to view the atmosphere as a fundamental geological agent.[2]

A Biographical Sketch

Thomas Chrowder Chamberlin was born on September 25, 1843, in a pioneer settlement near the present town of Mattoon, Illinois, near the crest of the Shelbyville glacial moraine. He was the third of five sons of John Chamberlin, a farmer and Methodist minister, and Cecilia Gill. After several years, the family moved to Wisconsin territory, settling near the town of Beloit. Chamberlin attended the local grammar school and the Beloit preparatory academy. In 1862, he entered Beloit College, where he followed the prescribed classical curriculum. Chamberlin was a hard worker, both on the family farm and in the local schools, where he taught to raise money for college tuition.

Chamberlin received his introduction to geology and scientific research from Professor Henry Bradford Nason, an authority on chemical methods in mineralogy.[3] Because of his religious upbringing, Chamberlin initially defended the geologic doctrine of catastrophic deluges—the so-called Neptunist or diluvial theory. This theory sought to explain geological phenomena, such as marine fossils found on mountain peaks, by the action of great floods. It also held that the record of the rocks could be read in conformity with the biblical stories of creation and universal deluge. After studying the subject intensely and working with Nason, Chamberlin rejected this position as unscientific, and he decided to pursue a career as an educator and geologist.

After graduating in 1866, Chamberlin served for two years as the high school principal in Delavan, Wisconsin, where he introduced natural sciences into the curriculum. In 1867, he married Alma Isabel

Wilson of Beloit, and they had one child, Rollin Thomas. The following year, Chamberlin took graduate courses at the University of Michigan, where he studied with the noted geologist Alexander Winchell. His first college teaching position was at the State Normal School at Whitewater, Wisconsin, where he taught natural sciences, including geology, from 1869 to 1873. Several of his students later became professional geologists, notably his lifelong colleague Rollin D. Salisbury, after whom his son was named.

In 1873, Chamberlin joined the Wisconsin Geological Survey as assistant geologist responsible for the southeastern portion of the state, a region poor in mineral resources but rich in glacial deposits. From 1876 to the survey's completion in 1882, he served as chief geologist in charge of it and oversaw publication of *Geology of Wisconsin*, a comprehensive report issued in four large volumes. Chamberlin also served his alma mater, Beloit College, as a well-liked professor of geology, zoology, and biology.

In 1881, Chamberlin was appointed chief geologist of the pleistocene division of the United States Geological Survey, a position he held for the next twenty-three years. As a result of this work, he became an authority on glaciers, and he was able to identify a series of multiple glaciations in North America. At the invitation of James Geikie, a noted Scottish geologist, he prepared two chapters on the glacial phenomena of North America for the third edition of *The Great Ice Age* (1879).

In 1887, Chamberlin was appointed president of the University of Wisconsin, where he instituted many reforms. He diversified the curriculum, doubled the enrollment, eliminated hazing, expanded graduate and professional education, insisted on faculty research, and promoted public service to the state and its people. Under his presidency, Wisconsin began its transition to a modern university. He found administrative work wearying, however, and much preferred research.[4]

In 1892, Chamberlin moved to the new University of Chicago as professor of geology and chair of the geology department. Chicago offered him more time and excellent resources for research, administrative control, and a significantly higher salary. In his new position, Chamberlin assembled a distinguished geology faculty, including petrologist J. P. Iddings, economic geologist R. A. F. Penrose, Jr., and his former student Rollin D. Salisbury. He also established and edited the *Journal of Geology*, directed the Walker Museum, and supervised the construction of Rosenwald Hall, the department's new home. His three-volume college textbook *Geology* (1904) and its successors, written with Salisbury, remained in use for more than three decades. His son, Rollin, earned a Ph.D. in geology from Chicago in 1908 and took a place on its faculty.

Chamberlin served as president of a number of scientific societies, including the Geological Society of America (1895) and the American Association for the Advancement of Science (1908–9). He was a fellow of the National Academy of Sciences, the American Academy of Arts and Sciences, and the American Philosophical Society, and a corresponding member of many European scientific societies. He was awarded several honorary doctoral degrees and earned a number of major research awards.

Chamberlin retired from the University of Chicago in 1918, but he remained senior editor of the *Journal of Geology* and continued his study of the "fundamental problems of geology," which he had begun in 1903 under the sponsorship of the Carnegie Institution of Washington. His final book, *The Two Solar Families*, was published a few weeks before his death. Chamberlin died November 15, 1928, of bronchial pneumonia and heart disease.

Working Methods in Geology

Each year at the University of Chicago, Chamberlin taught a graduate seminar in problems on the forefront of geology. Course notes from his 1896 seminar, "A Course in Working Methods in Geology," indicate that he was developing his views on the global carbon cycle and the possible role of CO_2 as an agent of climatic change. He was also developing arguments against the nebular hypothesis and beginning to formulate his planetesimal hypothesis of solar system formation.[5]

One of the primary themes of the course was the geological significance of the atmosphere and its relationship to the great unsolved problems of the earth sciences. Chamberlin listed the latter as follows:

> (1) great variations in the temperature of the earth's surface, as revealed by glacial deposits, (2) great variations in humidity, as evidenced by deposits of salt and gypsum, (3) great variations in preserved organic matter (e.g., coal deposits), and (4) great variations in numbers of species, as documented in paleontological collections.

For Chamberlin, these problems were directly connected with variations in the composition of the Earth's atmosphere and changes in the climates of the geological past, and were probably interrelated. In his 1896 course, Chamberlin outlined a CO_2 theory of glaciation and published this idea a year later.[6] Following the suggestions of Tyndall and Arrhenius, Chamberlin proposed that variations of the carbon dioxide content of the atmosphere combined with water vapor feedbacks could account for the advance and retreat of the ice sheets and other geological puzzles. However, as noted in chapter 6, he found the hypothesis of Arrhenius and Högbom—that variations in the supply of atmospheric CO_2 could be attributed to volcanism—overly simplistic and not "clearly and inevitably connected with the known current of geological events."

> I have been unable to find good geological grounds for applying this specifically to the actual history of glaciation. Our knowledge of

volcanism in its worldwide aspects in geological times is very limited on the land and practically *nil* for the ocean areas, so that a final opinion is impracticable but even so as far as the evidence goes, I have been unable to detect a relationship between volcanic activity and the extraordinary climatic episodes of geological history.

In contrast to these ideas, Chamberlin assumed a uniform supply of chemically and thermally active atmospheric constituents, notably CO_2, that varied with the contact of the atmosphere with the rock surface, that is, with the area exposed and the elevation of the land. "The hypothesis is thus connected back with the most fundamental geological events and hence with the great current of events."[7]

Chamberlin's Carbon Cycle

Chamberlin outlined for his students a simple version of the carbon cycle in which sources (mountain building and volcanic outgassing) were dynamically balanced by sinks (erosion and coal and limestone formation). He introduced the question of how much carbon was contained in the various reservoirs, including the oceans, atmosphere, solid earth, and biosphere. He also explored the relative stability of the global carbon cycle and described how various components of the Earth's system were linked into a system of feedbacks. According to Chamberlin, the atmosphere contained approximately three to four hundred parts per million, or 3×10^{12} tons, of carbon dioxide, which is very close to modern estimates for that time.[8]

The carbon cycle had both organic and inorganic components. Chamberlin held that the ratio of gases in the atmosphere to those in the ocean "is a function of the ratio of animal to vegetable life."[9] He believed that disruption of the organic carbon cycle could significantly influence atmospheric carbon dioxide levels in the short run but was less important on geologic time scales. Inorganic carbon sources and sinks were much larger than organic ones. He taught that over geologic time, the Earth had sequestered fantastic amounts of CO_2 in various repositories. He estimated that the sedimentary rocks contain sixteen thousand atmospheric equivalents of carbon dioxide, coal beds four thousand, oceans eighteen to twenty-two, and deep sea sediments one.

In 1896, it was known that the weathering of rocks generally consumes carbon dioxide and converts it to aqueous bicarbonates, for example $Ca(HCO_3)_2$, whereas the precipitation of calcium carbonates liberates carbon dioxide. It was also known that warm, shallow, carbon dioxide–depleted waters are prime locations for calcium carbonate deposition. Chamberlin was aware of essentially four different forms in which carbon dioxide could be stored in solution:

1. as physically absorbed CO_2;
2. as the union of carbon dioxide with water to form H_2CO_3;

3. in the bicarbonate form (e.g., $Ca(HCO_3)_2$); and
4. in the so-called simple carbonate form (e.g., $CaCO_3$).

The dissociation of carbonic acid (2) was known to cause the ratio of the partial pressure of carbon dioxide to all other gases to be greater in the oceans than in the atmosphere. The amount of carbon dioxide dissolved in the oceans was also known to be inversely proportional to salinity. It is apparent from studying Chamberlin's course notes and other papers of the time that there was some uncertainty as to the dominant chemical form assumed by carbon upon solution in water. There was some belief that sulfates bind to carbon dioxide in solution. Chamberlin and others (e.g., Tolman, 1899) maintained that, upon dissolution, carbon dioxide resides primarily in the form of bicarbonate compounds of magnesium and calcium.[10]

Chamberlin attributed the drawdown of atmospheric carbon dioxide primarily to the weathering of rocks. Following periods of vigorous diastrophism, or crustal uplift, when mountain ranges were extensive, the overall rate of weathering would be greater than those times when the topographic relief approached base level. Rapid weathering during periods of high relief would remove carbon from the atmosphere that was generated during mountain building episodes and transfer it in the form of bicarbonates to the oceans. The result would be a surface cooling and possibly a glaciation, due to the diminished atmospheric absorption of heat by carbon dioxide and water vapor.

At the end of a glacial epoch the following mechanisms would increase atmospheric carbon dioxide once warming began:

1. Greater oxidation of organic matter.
2. Greater discharge of CO_2 from ocean water.
3. Increased formation of sulfates at the expense of carbonates in the sea.
4. Water vapor feedbacks. (As CO_2 increases, the temperature increases, adding more water vapor to the atmosphere, which also increases temperature and CO_2.)

Glaciation might also be arrested by the build-up of extensive ice cover that would hinder weathering and allow CO_2 to increase in the atmosphere.[11]

After the glaciers withdraw, the once ice-covered surface would be so greatly scoured as to increase the area available to weathering, possibly leading to another episode of carbon dioxide drawdown and glaciation. This oscillatory cycle might continue until the land surface was reduced close to base level, at which time weathering would slow down, atmospheric carbon dioxide would build up, and the climate would ultimately warm. As the global land surface elevation approached base level, the deposition of calcium carbonates would increase, thereby releasing carbon dioxide to the atmosphere, further enhancing the warming.

In summary, the major aspects of Chamberlin's mature climate theory were as follows:

1. Diastrophism is the *leading cause* and *initiating event* in climate change, elevating the land and modifying the currents of the atmosphere and ocean.
2. Diastrophism enhances the atmosphere's contact with the rocks, resulting in a gradual depletion of the CO_2 in the atmosphere, a gradual cooling of the earth, and a consequent reduction in water vapor.
3. A vital factor in initiating a glacial period is the reversal of the deep-sea circulation, which in mild geologic periods is driven by evaporation and concentration of salinity in low latitudes. Deep ocean currents transfer heat to high latitudes, preserve the warm temperature of the polar regions during the long six-month night, and make temperate life possible there.
4. The first general glaciation was caused by a reversal of preglacial oceanic circulation. This resulted in cold polar waters becoming enriched in CO_2 at the expense of the CO_2 content of the atmosphere. As the temperature fell, so did the water vapor content. Warmer waters rising and establishing equilibrium with the atmosphere in lower latitudes were relatively depleted in CO_2, thus accelerating the process.
5. An interglacial period began when the cold water occupied the ocean floor and began to reach the surface in low latitudes. The ocean then began to release more CO_2 to the atmosphere than the polar waters were absorbing. Successive periods of enrichment and depletion of the ocean water—of glaciation and deglaciation—followed one another.[12]

Water Vapor Feedbacks

Chamberlin was convinced that variations in atmospheric carbon dioxide *and* water vapor were significant. In fact, he was certain that increased amounts of CO_2 would increase the surface temperature, thus enhancing evaporation and playing a crucial role in augmenting the effects of water vapor. For Chamberlin, the radiative effects of these two gases largely explained the change of ten to twelve degrees Celsius between the global mean temperature of glacial and interglacial periods. He wrote about the positive feedback mechanism between CO_2 and water vapor in a 1905 letter to Charles Greely Abbot at the Smithsonian Institution. The context of this letter was Abbot's insistence on the primacy of water vapor as an infrared absorber:

> [W]ater vapor, confessedly the greatest thermal absorbent in the atmosphere, is dependent on temperature for its amount, and if another agent, as CO_2, not so dependent, raises the temperature of the surface, it calls into function a certain amount of water vapor

which further absorbs heat, raises the temperature and calls forth more vapor, thus building a dynamic pyramid on its apex with consequent instability and demonstrative effects that attend the aqueous phenomena of the atmosphere.[13]

In this letter Chamberlin acknowledged that water vapor also responded to changes in temperature from other mechanisms. He cited James Croll's idea that orbital variations and the cooling effect of glaciers themselves could cause an increase in fogs and clouds, resulting in additional cooling. Chamberlin considered these ideas, though "probably sound," to be incidental to the glaciation itself and inoperative without the fundamental agency of CO_2-H_2O feedbacks.[14]

Later, Chamberlin speculated on negative climate feedbacks, which he called "the adverse effect of H_2O." He published his mature view on water vapor in 1923 in the *Year Book* of the Carnegie Institution of Washington. After considering the thermal properties of the permanent gaseous constituents of the atmosphere, including, notably, carbon dioxide, he examined water vapor, a variable constituent. Water vapor (1) consumes heat in the process of evaporation; (2) readily absorbs and radiates terrestrial radiation, but is transparent to solar radiation; (3) releases latent heat in passing to the liquid or solid state; (4) efficiently reflects solar radiation in the liquid or solid state; and (5) forms an immense thermal reservoir in the oceans.[15]

Regrets over the CO_2 Theory

Two decades after Chamberlin's initial work on the subject, the CO_2 climate theory had fallen out of favor. He repeatedly expressed his regrets that, following Arrhenius's lead, he had jumped too hastily into the issue. He wrote the following in 1913 in a long letter to Charles Schuchert of Yale's Peabody Museum:

> I have no doubt that you may be correct in thinking that the number who accept the CO_2 theory is less now than a few years ago. The original suggestion of Tyndall that a deficiency of CO_2 might be the cause of the glacial period received little attention and seems to have been so nearly forgotten that when Arrhenius made a similar claim it seemed to most scientists new and original and, as it seemed to be founded on mathematical deductions from Langley's observations and to come with a high authority, it drew a large following. Unfortunately, however, Arrhenius' deductions from Langley's observations appear to have been unwarranted and when this was discovered a reaction was inevitable. . . . I greatly regret that I was among the early victims of Arrhenius' error.[16]

Chamberlin had nearly completed his 1897 article, "A Group of Hypotheses Bearing on Climatic Changes," when he encountered Arrhenius's first essay.[17] Before completing the paper, he abandoned

his "very conservative statement relative to CO_2" and accepted
Arrhenius's conclusions based on his "supposed high authority."
Chamberlin regretted that his views had been conflated with those of
Arrhenius, which he thought were "in some features antipodal."[18] In
a letter written to Ellsworth Huntington in 1922, Chamberlin again
expressed his deep regrets that he had overeagerly accepted Arrhenius's numerical results and that his "personal demon" had not kept
Arrhenius's essay out of his way until after his article had gone to press.
Chamberlin thought that the role of CO_2 in the atmosphere had been
overemphasized and that not enough attention had been given to the
role of the ocean, which he considered "my distinct contribution to
the subject."[19]

Speculative Cosmogony

Chamberlin's work on the early atmosphere, glaciation, and the carbon cycle led him into the realm of speculative cosmogony, and together with F. R. Moulton, he proposed the planetesimal hypothesis
of the Earth's formation.[20] By doing so, he issued a challenge to the
Laplacian or nebular hypothesis of the origin and early history of the
Earth, which presumed a very hot early Earth, massive protoatmo-
sphere, progressive secular cooling, and gradual loss of the atmosphere. The consequences of the nebular hypothesis were not attractive to Chamberlin, either as a geologist or as an optimistic Christian
who believed in progress. The Earth's thin crust would shrink and
crack as it cooled, its surface features being shaped by lava outflows
from the molten interior, its atmosphere gradually slipping away into
space as the Earth headed toward the "final winter." The Sun, too,
would have the same fate, destined by the laws of thermodynamics to
become a dark cinder. It was a depressing theory of rapid decline, from
a fiery origin to a frigid end, from a thick atmosphere of carbon compounds to a thin sheet of cold nitrogen, from an abode of life to a dead
world.

Chamberlin needed a new cosmogony that allowed a cool birth for
the Earth and the gradual accretion (and secular variation) of its atmosphere. He used the newly formulated kinetic theory of gases to
calculate that molecules at the high temperatures assumed by the nebular hypothesis would be moving so fast that they would be able to
escape the Earth's gravitational attraction. This convinced him that
the Earth's atmosphere was not originally superheated and was not
the remnant of a solar-planetary nebula.[21]

According to Chamberlin, the planetary family was called into being
by a dynamic encounter between the Sun and a passing star. Their
mutual gravitational attraction gave rise to eruptions of large rotating
"solar bolts"—planetary material—that has continually orbited the Sun

and shows promise of doing so for an "indefinite eon to come." Chamberlin was telling a planetary nativity story. The "orderly planetary family" evolved from the condensing bolts that were slowly gathered into planets, planetoids, and satellites. He considered his mechanism markedly superior to others because kinetic energy added by the passing star helped account for the angular momentum of the system.[22]

Chamberlin endowed his theory with paternalistic moral implications drawn, perhaps unconsciously, from his progressive Christianity. If the passing star was the solar system's father, the Sun was the mother, and the planets were their orderly children. Comets were like unruly urchins. Our Sun's encounter with a second passing star, like infidelity, would "necessarily destroy the previous family."

> The symmetry and harmony of our planetary system is specific evidence that no star has come within a seriously disturbing distance since our planetary system was formed. . . . Supplementing this fundamental basis for future endurance, the superior massiveness of the system, its vast hidden stores of energy, and its orderly, harmonious habits combine to give our planetary family an outlook for the future far surpassing that of the current stage of the cometary family.

Chamberlin's nativity story ensured the unity of origin of the planetary familiy, as well as its celestial "harmony, orderliness, stability, and longevity."[23]

Conclusion

Over the course of his long career, T. C. Chamberlin moved from field geology to interdisciplinary earth science and then into speculative cosmology. His work on the geological agency of the atmosphere informed his understanding of the carbon cycle and led him to propose a new theory of the formation of the Earth and the solar system. Chamberlin's scientific contributions are generally underrecognized. We occasionally hear critiques of his method of multiple working hypotheses and his "outmoded" planetesimal hypothesis, and we also hear that he was rather stern and moralistic—yet these criticisms are anachronistic and ring hollow. Chamberlin possessed deep physical insights and made fundamental contributions to his field of geology and to interdisciplinary scientific research. He was admired in Europe and held major administrative posts in America; he was innovative in methodology and engaged in interdisciplinary team research.

The ice ages form a central theme in Chamberlin's career. He was prescient on multiple glaciation, on the geological agency of the atmosphere, and on the role of deep oceanic circulation. Several of his hypotheses, in particular those concerning the inorganic carbon cycle and reversals of deep-sea circulation, have been rediscovered in the past two decades. Perhaps Chamberlin's greatest contribution was his understanding of the interconnections of the Earth's dynamic systems. Currently, one of our most difficult scientific challenges is to understand the complex stabilizing and destabilizing forces operative in the Earth's system, many of which were first described by Chamberlin. His work, from an era long before the rise of climate dynamics as a field, was filled with fundamentally sound scientific insights and represents a surprisingly modern voice from the past. A combination of keen perception, methodology, and teamwork enabled him to make scientific sense out of a plethora of complex phenomena.

8

The Climatic Determinism
of Ellsworth Huntington

Sometimes I wonder whether I shall someday wake up and find my
whole scheme of the universe crashing down like a house of cards.
—Ellsworth Huntington (1914)

The climate work of the unrestrained and undisciplined geographic
determinist, eugenicist, and popular writer Ellsworth Huntington
(1876–1947) can be categorized into three large themes: the influence
of weather and weather changes on workers and students, the influence of climate on world civilizations, and the influence of solar variations on climate change. The first represented a sort of meteorological Taylorism, the second a reprise of enlightenment determinism, and
the third a simplistic and wholly unrealistic pseudoscientific theory.
Why, then, should we bother with him? One answer was provided by
the historian Arnold Toynbee, who was "enormously influenced" by
Huntington's ideas about the relation between human beings and their
physical environments. It was Toynbee's opinion that "[s]tudents of
human affairs may agree or disagree with Huntington, but in either
case they will be influenced by him, so it is better that they should be
aware of him."[1] Although Huntington's thought was indeed influential in its time, since then his racial bias and crude determinisms have
been largely rejected. Nonetheless, his categorical errors seem destined
to be repeated by those who make overly dramatic claims for weather
and climatic influences.[2]

The First Three Decades

Ellsworth Huntington was born in Galesburg, Illinois, on September 16, 1876, the third child and eldest son of Henry Strong Huntington, a Congregationalist minister, and Mary Lawrence Herbert.[3] The Huntingtons were proud of their Puritan ancestry, which they traced to 1633. Following the call of the ministry, the family moved to Gorham, Maine, in 1877 and then in 1889 to Milton, Massachusetts, a wealthy suburb of Boston. Ellsworth attended the public high school, where he excelled in athletics and academics. His biographers have called him reclusive, but his brother suggested that perhaps he was humble rather than shy.

Huntington passed the Harvard entrance examinations, but family finances precluded his enrollment there. Instead, he attended Beloit College, where he boarded with a maternal aunt, from 1893 to 1897. Following in the footsteps of T. C. Chamberlin (Beloit 1866), Huntington studied both classics and geology, publishing his first article, on local road-making materials, in the *Transactions of the Wisconsin Academy of Sciences*.

Huntington's church connections landed him his first job—in Turkey, where he served as an instructor and assistant to the president of Euphrates College, a small missionary school in Harpoot. There he investigated the culture of the region, mapped the area around Harpoot, and attempted to establish a local weather station. In 1901, in the company of the U.S. consul at Harpoot, he shot the rapids of the upper Euphrates River in a raft made of inflated goatskins. For this feat he was awarded the Gill Memorial of the Royal Geographical Society.

In 1901, Huntington returned to the United States to study physiography at Harvard under William Morris Davis, who impressed upon him the importance of climatic influences.[4] He received an M.A. in 1902 and spent that summer in fieldwork with Davis in Utah and Arizona. After graduation, Huntington received and rejected two offers: one to return to Euphrates College in Harpoot, and a second to serve as the consul at Erzerum. In 1903, he returned to Asia as Davis's assistant with the Carnegie-sponsored expedition to central Asia led by Raphael Pumpelly.[5] The expedition was seeking the remains of a lost Aryan civilization thought to have inhabited a Mediterranean-sized sea left by the melt waters of the retreating glaciers of Eurasia. All that remained now, however, was a desiccated land, nomadic inhabitants, and the Caspian and Aral seas. Huntington's early views on climate, culture, and civilization were undoubtedly shaped by this experience. He remained in Turkestan and Persia for sixteen months; then he returned to the United States, where he joined an expedition, led and financed by R. L. Barrett and sponsored by the Association of American Geographers, through the Himalayas into the Tarim Basin of inner Asia (1905–6).

According to Huntington, these trips and his four years of life in Asiatic Turkey impressed upon him the importance of the geographic basis of the study of anthropology and "the immense influence which changes of climate have exerted on history." Among the ruins of ancient civilizations, Huntington found clear evidence of progressive desiccation and historical climatic changes or, as he called them, "pulsations." The result was his first book, *The Pulse of Asia* (1907), written while he was a Hooper Fellow at Harvard. In the concluding chapter of the book, Huntington revealed his propensity for circular argumentation in summarizing what he considered to be the three major themes of his research: (1) the power of physiography, especially climate, to mold the habits and character of peoples; (2) the fact that climates vary over historic times; and (3) the power of climatic changes to cause corresponding changes in population distribution and in human occupations, habits, and even character. He went on to deduce from these conclusions that "geography . . . is the basis of history in a way that is not generally recognized; and that climatic changes have been one of the greatest factors in determining the course of human progress." Going even further out on a limb, Huntington universalized the results of his research in central Asia to include all the nations of the world:

> To-day, the strongest nations of the world live where the climatic conditions are most propitious. Japan and north China in Asia; Russia, Austria, Germany, France, and England in Europe; and the United States and Canada in America, all occupy regions where the climate is of the kind which we have defined as most favorable to the progress of mankind. Much as these nations differ in race, in ideals, and in type of civilization, they all agree in possessing a high degree of will-power and energy, and a capacity for making progress and for dominating other races.[6]

Beginning with evidence from dried-up lakes in central Asia, Huntington's overheated imagination led him to conclusions regarding the overall course of world history. Each climatic "pulse" could also be an ominous "throb" that threatened to dislocate the center of civilization. "Each throb has sent pain and decay to the lands whose day was done, life and vigor to those whose day was yet to be."[7] These themes, and the circular reasoning behind them, would haunt his writings for the next four decades.

A Failed Academic

Early in 1907, Huntington passed his preliminary examination at Harvard for the Ph.D. Later that spring, however, he failed to sustain his final Ph.D. examination by a committee vote of four to two with one abstention. Ironically, his examination committee found he was "deficient in his knowledge of climatology and showed great weakness in historical geology." This opinion was probably that of the climatologist Robert DeCourcey Ward who, also ironically, coined the term "anthropo-climatology" and was promoting it as an interdisciplinary field of human-climate interactions.[8] The weaknesses pointed out by Huntington's professors reappeared in later critiques of his work. The day after his examination, his advisor Davis wrote that the outcome was a "horrid shock" and was still tormenting him. "I had anticipated a great pleasure in this natural culmination of our work together. I cannot yet understand, much less accept the ground of the others who placed so much value on elementary matters (which to be sure have their proper place and time) as compared to proved capacity for large accomplishment in the world's work." Davis advised him, "Go on with your work."[9]

Despite this setback, in September 1907, Huntington began his lifelong (albeit tenuous) relationship with Yale and taught his first classes in geography. Although he was hired as an instructor in Asian geography, he considered himself first and foremost an investigator. He admitted he "liked" teaching but "loved research . . . [and] let the research crowd [his] teaching to the wall," filling his time with travel, exploration, and writing.[10] He served on no Yale committees and became known as somewhat of a recluse; he had obvious problems in the classroom. According to Geoffrey Martin, students at Yale's Sheffield School expected geography courses to be easy, with illustrated lectures and little work. Huntington lacked any sense of pedagogical style. He lectured in a quiet, sometimes squeaky, monotone, displaying no drama or other theatrics. He was short, balding, and hard of hearing. Students found it inconceivable that such an unimpressive person could be an accomplished world traveler and geographer. Still, in 1909, Yale awarded Huntington a Ph.D. degree and, a year later, promoted him to the rank of assistant professor. He continued his travels and explorations, visiting western Asia in 1909, the desert Southwest in 1910, California and the Southwest in 1911, Yucatan and California in 1912, Guatemala in 1913, and the Southwest in 1915. His traveling and writing left little time for course preparation, and most of his teaching was confined to the fall semester.

Huntington's application in 1912 for promotion to full professor was seen by Yale as "problematical." A letter of evaluation written by R. S. Woodward of the Carnegie Institution of Washington pointed out that Huntington's work lacked focus; "[he] is here and there in his writings and in his methods of procedure quite naive if not immature." Eduard Brückner of the University of Vienna thought Huntington was industrious, but uncritical in his use of data and sources. His most severe criticism was that Huntington had "shown several times the desire to fit the facts to his theory." Albrecht Penck of the University of Berlin concurred. Professor of Geology E. S. Dana, who had solicited the letters, was of the opinion that Huntington had "brilliancy" but was "immature" (at the age of 36!), and had not yet settled down to produce "steady, sound work." He also thought that Huntington had the disadvantage "of an enormous overestimate of his own importance to the University" and recommended that Yale make no commitment to his future.[11] Rather than a promotion, Huntington received a two-year extension of his appointment and a raise.

Illustrative of Huntington's poor performance in the classroom is a card from the registrar from 1913 informing Huntington that only five students—four seniors and one junior—had chosen his elective courses. In a letter to President A. T. Hadley of Yale in 1914 asking that his promotion be reconsidered, Huntington explained these low enrollments as in part due to a general falling off in numbers of geology majors and in part due to scheduling conflicts that precluded students from electing his courses. He admitted that he had sacrificed his university work "to a certain degree," but only because he had had "such a wealth of new ideas" that he was "almost dazed."[12] Further review of his record, however, was again unfavorable, and in 1915, Huntington left Yale to work from his parents' home in Milton.

A Prolific and Prolix Writer

Huntington's income was based on the royalties from his many books. He was a prolific author whose publications sounded the repetitive theme of climatic determinism. In addition to numerous articles, he published *The Climatic Factor as Illustrated in Arid America* in 1914 and *Civilization and Climate* in 1915. Two more books, *World Power and Evolution* and *Red Man's Continent*, appeared in 1919. Huntington also collaborated with Sumner Cushing, a well-connected high school teacher, on two school geography textbooks that first appeared in 1920 and 1922. *Climatic Changes* (1922), *Earth and Sun* (1923), *The Character of Races* (1924), *West of the Pacific* (1925), *The Pulse of Progress* (1926), *The Human Habitat* (1927), and *The Builders of America* (1927) followed in quick succession.

The academic tone of his work led many to believe it was rigorous and authoritative, while it was neither. Harlan Barrows, a professor of geography at the University of Chicago, wrote to Isaiah Bowman, editor of the *American Geographical Review*, that "Ellsworth [should] write less and think more."[13] Bowman suggested that if Huntington did not shave one morning he could write an article in the time saved. In the midst of this prolific period, Huntington married Rachel Slocum Brewer; during their Christmas 1917 honeymoon, the new couple traveled to Pittsburgh, where Ellsworth was speaking at an academic meeting.

During World War I, Huntington offered his services to the National

Research Council (NRC) to work on his proposed study of the influence of climatic conditions on the mental, moral, and physical health
of the troops in army training camps and hospitals. He thought the
work would "tend to the advancement of scientific knowledge as well
as toward winning of the war."[14] Instead, he was assigned to the Military Intelligence Division of the NRC, where he participated in a team
effort to produce *The Geography of Europe* (1918). In this volume,
Huntington illustrated his theory of environmental determinism with
an example from the Italian peninsula:

> Few countries of equal size are more diverse than Italy. The north
> is among the most prosperous and progressive parts of the world,
> but the south is decidedly backward. In the north not only is agri-
> culture highly developed, but manufacturing is well advanced in
> proportion to the resources of coal and metals, and science and art
> are well established. In the south, on the contrary, there is almost
> nothing in the way of manufacturing, in spite of the fact that water
> transportation is easier than in the north. Instead of science and art
> there is the most widespread illiteracy. Farming is the chief occu-
> pation, but it is carried on much more carelessly than in the north.
> The population is much less dense than in the north, but the people
> are poorer, in spite of the larger amount of land at their disposal.
> Many are undernourished, and this combines with other things to
> cause disease. In order to understand this contrast between the north
> and south the first necessity is to compare the climatic differences.[15]

Huntington turned down several opportunities to teach at universi-
ties in the Midwest and returned to Yale in 1919 as a research assistant with a nominal salary of two hundred dollars a year. He continued to teach courses there, sometimes as much as a half load at far
less than half salary. This tenuous relationship with Yale continued
until his death in 1945.[16]

Meteorological Taylorism

In the spring of 1914, Huntington confided to his former mentor, William Morris Davis, that he was going to write a new book that summer on "the relation of climate and changes of climate to civilization."
Part of the book would be based on correlations he had drawn between
changes in daily weather conditions and the performance of five hundred factory workers and fifteen hundred students.

> Another book is settling in my brain, and I begrudge everything that
> keeps me from it. Each new step makes me modify my ideas a little,
> but at the same time it confirms some of the main principles in a
> way that seems almost like magic. . . . Here are some of my latest
> results: children tested for speed and accuracy on the typewriter
> for a very brief period work fastest at 67°. Girls working for the whole

day at mechanical work do best at about 60°. Adult men doing mechanical work which also demands a little brain power, but not much, are at their best at about 50–55°. Students at Annapolis, 1300 of them, doing prolonged and concentrated brain work are at their best at about 40°. All of these people are equally stimulated by changes of temperature. Do you see what a field that opens?[17]

Huntington was very enthusiastic about these preliminary results.

This indicates that our frequent changes of weather are one of the important elements in causing the nervous activity of America. It is the first time, so far as I know that we have had anything more than mere speculation on this matter. Here, you see, we have an absolute numerical measure on the effect of our climate on activity.[18]

Huntington's ideas were influenced by Charles J. Kullmer, a professor of German at Syracuse University, who suggested to Huntington that weather events profoundly shape human behavior. Kullmer pointed out correlations between high barometric pressure and peaks in library circulation records for nonfiction books as well as correlations between storminess and larger bank deposits. He also suggested that Huntington should consider the psychological effects of atmospheric electricity. Huntington liked these ideas and included a chapter by Kullmer in his 1914 book, *The Climatic Factor as Illustrated in Arid America.*[19]

By the summer of 1914, Huntington had completed *Civilization and Climate*, a book that contained his ideas on the influence of weather on individuals and the influence of climate on world civilizations. It reached a large popular audience and appeared in two new editions in 1922 and 1924. In the first half of the book, Huntington summarized his research on the effects of seasonal and daily weather variations on the health and productivity of students and workers. He had asked a class of one hundred fifty Yale students to keep a record of "their feelings and energy" and the daily weather. From the piecework records at two factories in Connecticut—the Bridgeport Brass Company and the Stanley Iron Works of New Britain—he drew the conclusion that the rate of work varied in response to the *outside* temperature, even though the factories were well heated! Huntington proposed a world map of factory efficiencies as correlated with mean, seasonal, and extreme temperature conditions, humidity, and storminess. He even included correlations of worker efficiency with peak wind velocities and a comparison of human performance with the optimum growing conditions of plants![20]

Huntington also worked on weather, health, and productivity as chair of the Committee on the Atmosphere and Man (CAM) of the NRC. From its inception in 1921 to its demise in 1929, the efforts of the CAM were focused on four projects: an investigation of the influence of meteorological conditions on factory productivity, physiological experiments under laboratory conditions, experiments in hospitals, and an investigation of mortality caused by influenza in New York City. In support of Huntington's investigations of worker efficiency, the CAM distributed meteorological instruments for installation on factory floors. The Taylor Instrument Company provided about twenty-five special wet and dry bulb recording thermometers for this purpose; collecting the data, however, was left to untrained and largely uninterested shop foremen.[21] The NRC granted funds for Huntington to visit factories and attend meetings around the country. The committee also helped legitimate his agenda and provided seed money to support his requests to foundations, municipal health departments, and insurance companies for additional research funds.[22]

The CAM was inactive for several years, particularly during Huntington's trips abroad. It issued only two reports during its eight-year existence: one on the influenza epidemic of 1918 and a more substantial one on the weather and mortality in New York City, completed with the assistance of the Metropolitan Life Insurance Company.[23] The annual report of the CAM for 1927 contains only a brief, "preliminary" (!) account of Huntington's investigations over the past seven years. Yandell Henderson of Yale's Applied Physiology Laboratory thought that Huntington's carelessness as chair of the CAM was impeding progress in the field of experimental and applied meteorology.[24]

Labor and social historians may well profit from examining the Huntington papers at Yale and the official records of the CAM at the National Academy of Sciences. The former contains massive amounts of piecework records gathered directly from a number of factories and a number of reports of experiments done on human subjects. For example, there are records of women garment workers in 1923 and 1924 along with weekly thermographs taken in the workplace that show afternoon peak temperatures typically above one hundred degrees Fahrenheit.[25] Some of the experiments endorsed by the CAM on the efficiency of factory workers were dangerous and degrading. Those conducted by Philip S. Drinker at the Harvard School of Public Health measured increase of worker pulse rate as a function of environmental temperature. Experimental subjects, stripped to the waist, alternated between working frenetically for five minutes and then resting five minutes. The pace was set at ninety thousand foot-pounds per hour—equivalent to shoveling over a ton of coal into a boiler in one five-minute work period. During each rest period, the rectal temperature of the subjects was taken. As the environmental temperature was slowly increased from 60 to 115 degrees Fahrenheit, workers' body temperatures rose at rates as high as twelve degrees per hour (!) and worker pulse rates increased from about seventy beats per minute to a life-threatening four hundred while working at 115 degrees Fahrenheit![26]

Huntington's study of weather and efficiency—his meteorological Taylorism—was not fundamentally motivated by any sense of a progressive desire to improve worker comfort and safety. Rather, he had in mind company executives and insurers interested in a comprehensive survey of the environmental factors influencing factory efficiency.[27] He also had in mind a sweeping argument that began with the weather's influence on individuals and ended with his bigger goal of demonstrating the overarching influence of climate and climatic change on civilization.

Climatic Energy Zones

The second part of *Civilization and Climate* contained Huntington's attempt to map "climatic energy zones" and to explain the rise and fall of world civilizations with his "pulsatory hypothesis" of climatic change. In 1913, he sent out a long questionnaire to over two hundred intellectuals and public figures—anthropologists, geographers, soldiers, and statesmen—mostly from the United States, Great Britain, and Europe, asking their cooperation in the "preparation of a map showing the distribution of the higher elements of civilization throughout the world." His purpose was to map the world's civilizations from highest to lowest and show that regions of "high civilization" were correlated with regions of high "climatic energy." By civilization, Huntington meant:

> the power of initiative, the capacity for formulating new ideas and for carrying them into effect, the power of self-control, high standards of honesty and morality, the power to lead and control other races, the capacity for disseminating ideas, and other similar qualities which will readily suggest themselves. These qualities find expression in high ideals, respect for law, inventiveness, ability to develop philosophical systems, stability and honesty of government, a highly developed system of education, the capacity to dominate the less civilized parts of the world, and the ability to carry out far-reaching enterprises covering long periods of time and great areas of the earth's surface.[28]

Huntington was seeking a "consensus of expert opinion" ranking the "relative civilization" of 185 regions of the world. Apparently, he believed (or hoped) that by averaging the opinions of his correspondents, "individual idiosyncrasies" would disappear. (Two examples of his attempt to map regions of high and low civilization and climatic energy are illustrated in figs. 8-1 and 8-2.) Not surprisingly, instead of mapping civilization and climate, Huntington measured the collective bias of the respondents—twenty-five Americans, sixteen northern Europeans, eight southern Europeans, six Asians, and one Rus-

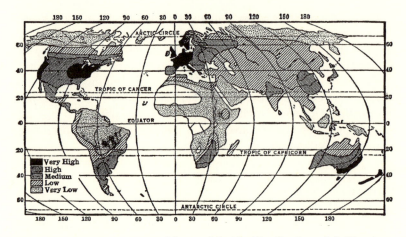

Fig. 8-1. Huntington's map of the worldwide distribution of civilization. *Source:* Ellsworth Huntington, *Civilization and Climate*, 3rd ed. (New Haven: Yale University Press, 1924), 295.

sian. There were no Africans or Latin Americans. Scoring highest on the survey (99–100) were northern regions of Europe—England, Germany, and northern France; and the United States—New England and the North Atlantic States. The lowest scores were given to polar regions—Greenland (17) and northern Siberia (16); deserts—Sahara (19) and Kalahari (12); and the tropics—the Amazon basin (23) and New Guinea (15).[29] Huntington revised and reprinted these maps of civilization and climatic energy in many of his publications, including his last, *Mainsprings of Civilization*, in 1945.

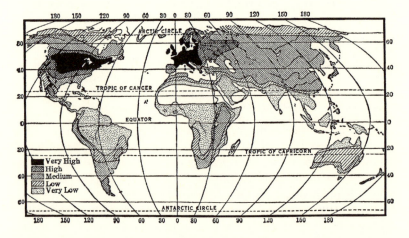

Fig. 8-2. Huntington's map of the worldwide distribution of climatic energy. *Source:* Ellsworth Huntington, *Civilization and Climate*, 3rd ed. (New Haven: Yale University Press, 1924), 295.

Causes of Climatic Change

In 1922 and 1923, Huntington ventured into the realm of astrometeorology with his dual volumes *Climatic Changes: Their Nature and Causes* (with Steven Sargent Visher) and *Earth and Sun: An Hypothesis of Weather and Sun Spots*, both published by Yale University Press. Huntington argued that changes in the Sun were the most effective cause of changes in the Earth's climate. He considered terrestrial factors, such as the form and altitude of the continents, the frequency of volcanic eruptions, and the chemical composition and physical state of the atmosphere and oceans, as secondary causes. Huntington suggested that sunspots, or "solar cyclones," were caused by planetary influences and served both as indicators of solar activity and as the basic mechanism influencing the Earth's climate—diverting storm tracks and controlling glaciation. He ventured the wild speculation that biological evolution was somehow guided by the "influences" of the Sun, planets, and stars through the exchange of electromagnetic radiation.[30]

William Jackson Humphreys of the Weather Bureau despised *Climatic Changes*, noting in two different reviews that "its broader conceptions are mere fantasies, while its details show little regard for facts and none for physics. . . . it is as far from being scientific as *Alice in Wonderland*."[31] Huntington received an advance copy of a review written by his colleague C. F. Brooks at Clark University, an associate editor of the *Monthly Weather Review*. Huntington felt his position had been misrepresented and thought Brooks had supported the "somewhat reactionary policy of the Weather Bureau which opposes everything that is new." Before returning the review to Brooks, Huntington took the liberty of revising it "in such a way as to retain its spirit and yet make it true to the facts."[32]

In 1922, Huntington sent the galley proofs of *Climatic Changes* to T. C. Chamberlin along with a request to dedicate the book to him. Chamberlin acceded to this request "cheerfully" if somewhat reluctantly, since he did not agree with Huntington's emphasis on changes in the Sun or his solar cyclonic mechanism of climatic change. A decade earlier, in 1914, Chamberlin had warned Huntington that his nascent theory did not account for the "orders of magnitude" difference between sunspot cycles and oscillations of the glacial periods.[33] He pointed out that this factor was essential to any serious consideration of the hypothesis. Chamberlin's reply included a very long critical review of the manuscript, taking care to clarify his own views on climatic change (see chapter 7). In the end, Chamberlin's diplomacy overshadowed his criticism. He noted that "although you have pursued a quite independent line of thought and have diverged quite widely in many respects from my own views . . . the fundamental lines of our studies have run in singularly parallel lines."[34] His course notes at the University of Chicago, however, clearly indicate that neither Chamberlin nor his students gave serious consideration to Huntington's theory of climatic change.[35]

Conclusion

Throughout his life, Huntington openly expressed his disdain for what he called "the plain straightforward work of careful men who are competent to develop little ideas but not big ones."[36] But his colleagues characterized him as a "brilliant, erratic, and rather careless man" whose conclusions were frequently "called into question."[37] His enthusiastic but basically unscientific contributions to climate studies cast a long shadow over the field and contributed greatly to the perception, early in the twentieth century, that climatology was not yet ready for an intellectual synthesis and had a healthy population of kooks and cranks.

One historical lesson we can take from Huntington is that our understanding of climate and climatic change is not a story of inevitable progress. There were detours and dead ends. His link to the past—to Du Bos, Montesquieu, and earlier environmental determinists—is obvious. His influence on his own generation was indeed significant and should serve as a warning that environmental determinism may not be dead and may yet again rear its ugly head. Arnold Toynbee's advice that we should be aware (or *beware*) of his influence, is, I think, well taken. Knowing something about him, or at least knowing enough to avoid his categorical errors, may help contemporary students of the human dimensions of global change avoid the pitfalls of environmental determinism.

9

Global Warming?

The Early Twentieth Century

As man is now changing the composition of the atmosphere at a
rate which must be very exceptional on the geological time scale, it
is natural to seek for the probable effects of such a change. From the
best laboratory observations it appears that the principal result of
increasing atmospheric carbon dioxide . . . would be a gradual
increase in the mean temperature of the colder regions of the earth.
—G. S. Callendar (1939)

In the first half of the twentieth century, most scientists did not believe that increased CO_2 levels would result in global warming. It was
thought that at current atmospheric concentrations, the gas already
absorbed all the available long-wave radiation; thus any increases in
CO_2 would not change the radiative heat balance of the planet but
might augment plant growth. Other mechanisms of climatic change,
although highly speculative, were given more credence, especially
changes in solar luminosity, atmospheric transparency, and the Earth's
orbital elements.

By the 1950s, as temperatures around the Northern Hemisphere
reached early-twentieth-century peaks, global warming first found its
way onto the public agenda. Concerns were expressed in both the
scientific and popular press about rising sea levels, loss of habitat, and
shifting agricultural zones. Amid the myriad mechanisms that could
possibly account for climatic changes, several scientists, notably
G. S. Callendar, Gilbert Plass, Hans Suess, and Roger Revelle, focused
on possible links between anthropogenic CO_2 emissions, the geochemical carbon cycle, and climate warming.

A Plethora of Speculative Theories

By 1900, most of the chief theories of climate change had been proposed, if not yet fully explored: changes in solar output; changes in
the Earth's orbital geometry; changes in terrestrial geography, including the form and height of continents and the circulation of the oceans;
and changes in atmospheric transparency and composition, in part due
to human activities.[1] Of course, there were many others. New climate
theories were being proposed and new work was being done on heat
budgets, spectroscopy, and the rising CO_2 content of the atmosphere.
Evidence for glaciation in low latitudes was explained by Wladimir
Köppen and Alfred Wegener as the result of continents drifting north-
ward under climate zones controlled mainly by latitude.[2] Although
this theory was not widely accepted by geologists, it is now seen as a
first step in paleoclimatic reconstruction. In the 1930s, the Serbian
astronomer and geophysicist Milutin Milanković, building on earlier
work, outlined a comprehensive "astronomical theory of the ice ages"
that viewed them as caused by periodic changes in the Earth's orbital
elements.[3] Atmospheric heat budgets were constructed early in the
twentieth century by William Henry Dines and George Clark Simpson,
among others.[4] Measurements of infrared radiation at longer wavelengths, including the eight- to twelve-micron atmospheric "window,"
and at finer band resolutions, were completed in the 1930s.[5] In 1938,
G. S. Callendar read a paper to the Royal Meteorological Society that
argued that CO_2 from fossil fuel consumption had caused a modest
but measurable increase in the Earth's temperature of about one-quarter
of a degree in the previous fifty years.[6] All these issues, especially
whether the Earth would experience a new ice age or would become
warmer, were perennially debated, but no single causal mechanism
was universally accepted.

William Jackson Humphreys, author of *Physics of the Air* and a
strong proponent of the theory that volcanic dust was the leading cause
of ice ages, did not consider any of the current theories adequate:
"Change after change of climate in an almost endless succession, and
even additional ice ages, presumably are still to be experienced, though
. . . when they shall begin, how intense they may be, or how long they
shall last no one can form the slightest idea."[7] Echoing Rudyard
Kipling's "nine and sixty ways of making tribal lays," the climatologist C. E. P. Brooks quipped, "There are at least nine and sixty ways
of constructing a theory of climatic change, and there is probably some
truth in quite a number of them."[8] In a similar lighthearted vein, two
prominent oceanographers, David B. Ericson and Goesta Wollin, wryly
observed: "It has been estimated that a new theory to explain continental glaciations has been published for every year that has passed
since the first recognition of the evidence for past glaciation."[9] Most
scientists of the time supported only one of the major mechanisms of

climatic change; some grudgingly admitted that other mechanisms might play a secondary role.

In 1950, Brooks, who had spent much of his career attempting to sort out the "nine and sixty" theories of climate change, published a selective annotated bibliography on the subject in the first volume of the new journal *Meteorological Abstracts and Bibliography* (table 9-1 is adapted from this work).[10]

Five years after compiling this bibliography, Brooks presented his opinions on the "present position of theories of climatic change" in the *Meteorological Magazine*. He considered variations of solar radiation, "either alone or combined with some other cause," to be a "first favorite," although he had to admit that such theories were, at present,

Table 9-1. Climate change theories as classified by C. E. P. Brooks (1950).

Theory	Author
Changes in elements of the Earth's orbit	Adhémar (1842), Croll (1864, 1875), Drayson (1873), Ekholm (1901), Spitaler (1907), Milanković (1920, 1930, 1941)
Changes of solar radiation	Dubois (1895), Simpson (1930, 1934, 1939–40), Himpel (1937), Hoyle and Lyttleton (1939)
Lunar-solar tidal influences	Pettersson (1914)
Elevation of land masses—mountain building	Lyell (1830–33), Wright (1890), Ramsay (1909–10, 1924), Brooks (1926, 1949)
Changes in atmospheric circulation	Harmer (1901, 1925), Gregory (1908), Hobbs (1926), Flint and Dorsey (1945)
Changes in oceanic circulation	Croll (1875), Hull (1897), Chamberlin (1899), Brooks (1925), Lasareff (1929)
Changes in continent-ocean distribution	Czerney (1881), Harmer (1901, 1925), Gregory (1908), Brooks (1926), Willis (1932)
Changes in atmospheric composition	Arrhenius (1896), Chamberlin (1897, 1899), Ekholm (1901), Callendar (1938, 1939)
Volcanic dust in the atmosphere	Humphreys (1913, 1920), Abbot and Fowle (1913)
Cosmic dust theory	Hoyle and Lyttleton (1939), Himpel (1947)
Sunspot theory	Czerny (1881), Huntington (1915), Huntington and Visher (1922)
Polar migration and continental drift theory	Kreichgauer (1902), Wegener (1920), Köppen and Wegener (1924)

"almost entirely hypothetical with little or no evidence to support them." Other causes were given short shrift. In his opinion, orogenesis and changes of land and sea distribution were not widely accepted, changes in the elements of the Earth's orbit and inclination of the axis were "rather out of favor," and changes in atmospheric composition, given the assumed insufficiency of CO_2 to absorb infrared radiation, "now reduce almost entirely to the effects of volcanic dust."[11]

In his 1956 article in the popular journal *Weatherwise*, respected meteorologist Hans Panofsky located the question of climatic changes on a vast spectrum of atmospheric fluctuations that ranged from seconds (turbulence) to millions of years. Pointing out that the shorter period fluctuations of the atmosphere are not due to a single cause, Panofsky thought it reasonable that longer period climatic changes might also have multiple explanations. His classification of the most important types of climatic change theories included changes in the Earth's crust, astronomical influences, and changes in atmospheric composition.[12]

Panofsky selected three theories involving changes in the Earth's crust for further examination: migration of the Earth's axis, mountain building, and volcanism. His article did not mention Alfred Wegener's theory of continental drift. Polar wandering, which he traced to Joseph Adhémar, assumes that the Earth's axis has taken different positions relative to the crust. The main difficulty of this theory is that polar shifts would produce glaciation in different regions of the globe at different times, while the evidence seemed to indicate simultaneous advance and retreat of the glaciers. Mountain building, a preferred mechanism of Charles Lyell and many other geologists, may produce glaciation over the longest time scales, but Panofsky considered simple diastrophism inadequate to explain the ice ages of the past million years. Climate changes caused by the reduction of solar insolation following the injection of volcanic dust high into the atmosphere was (as noted earlier) a favored mechanism of William Jackson Humphreys. Historic eruptions have indeed measurably reduced solar radiation and temperatures, at least for several years following the events, but Panofsky was not convinced that volcanism was sufficient to cause widespread glaciation.

Panofsky next reviewed theories of astronomical influence, including variations in solar luminosity and the Earth's orbit. Changes in solar output were favored by many climatologists and astronomers, perhaps influenced by C. G. Abbott's measurements of the varying "solar constant." Panofsky found no evidence that the Sun was a variable star, especially if the effect of atmospheric absorption at all wavelengths was taken into account. The theory that the Sun may occasionally increase its luminosity due to encounters with clouds of interstellar dust seemed both ad hoc and quantitatively inadequate. Panofsky noted two basic (and opposing) opinions on the climatic effects of a hotter Sun: One school believed it would cause a direct temperature rise and *decreased* glaciation; the other school thought it would cause a greater pole-to-equator temperature gradient, increased atmospheric circulation, increased evaporation, increased precipitation, and *increased* glaciation.

Although orbital changes, as calculated by Milanković, were not widely accepted in the 1950s as causes of climatic change, Panofsky thought they caused important changes in solar insolation that would alter atmospheric dynamics as well as climate. He presented the following arguments in favor of this mechanism: (1) Variations in the obliquity of the ecliptic, the angle between the plane of the Earth's orbit and the plane of the equator, result in greater contrasts between seasons. When the obliquity is large this could lead to increased temperature gradients, a more energetic general circulation, and perhaps an ice age. (2) Variations in the eccentricity of the Earth's orbit can result in significant differences between solar insolation received by the Earth at perihelion and aphelion. (3) The precession of the equinoxes causes systematic variations in the seasons. Currently the Earth is closest to the Sun in January; in ten thousand years this will occur in July. Currently the northern hemisphere has less contrast between winter and summer than the southern hemisphere; this will be reversed in ten thousand years.

Most of Panofsky's contemporaries favored a combination of solar activity and mountain building as the causes of major climatic changes. Panofsky himself favored the orbital theory combined with mountain building.

Doubts about CO_2

In 1899, Nils Eckholm, an early and eager spokesman for anthropogenic climate control, pointed out that at present rates, the burning of pit coal could double the concentration of atmospheric CO_2. This would "undoubtedly cause a very obvious rise of the mean temperature of the Earth." By controlling the production and consumption of carbonic acid, he thought humans would be able to "regulate the future climate of the Earth and consequently prevent the arrival of a new Ice Age." Eckholm, like his lifelong friend and colleague Svante Arrhenius, thought that warmer was better. An increasing concentration of CO_2 would counteract the expected deterioration of the climate of the northern and Arctic regions, as predicted by James Croll's astronomical theory of the Ice Age.[13]

Soon, however, the efficacy of CO_2 as an infrared absorber was challenged. In 1900 Knut Ångström concluded that CO_2 and water vapor absorb infrared radiation in the same spectral regions. The amount of carbon dioxide in the atmosphere was thought to be equivalent to a column of the pure gas 250 centimeters in length at STP. Experiments done in 1905 demonstrated that a column of carbon dioxide fifty centimeters long was ample for maximum absorption. Any additional CO_2, it was argued, would have little or no effect. Humphreys used these results to argue that a doubling or halving of CO_2, as proposed by Arrhenius, would make no difference in the amount of infrared radiation absorbed by the atmosphere and could not appreciably change the average temperature of the Earth or be at all effective in the production of marked climatic changes. Such negative assessments of CO_2 were amplified by Charles Greely Abbot and his assistant F. E. Fowle, Jr., who insisted on the primacy of water vapor as an infrared absorber.[14]

T. C. Chamberlin considered the view of Humphreys "absurd" and found the contention of Abbot and Fowle "strange." He thought their positions were in direct violation of the "fundamental principle of spectroscopy that each element radiates or absorbs its own lines exclusively."[15] He considered CO_2 an "innocent party" in the matter and did not approve of Abbot "throw[ing] so much (cold) water vapor over so worthy a member of the atmospheric family." It was Chamberlin's view that each atmospheric constituent interacted with all others and all were ultimately controlled by diastrophism, "the most basal and independent agency" of atmospheric change.[16]

Doubts about CO_2 continued, however. In 1929, G. C. Simpson pointed out that it was "now generally accepted that variations in carbon-dioxide in the atmosphere, even if they do occur, can have no appreciable effect on the climate." He provided three reasons why this was so: "(1) [T]he absorption band of carbon-dioxide is too narrow to have a significant effect on terrestrial radiation; (2) the current amount of atmospheric CO_2 exerts its full effect and any further addition would have little or no influence; (3) the water vapor absorption band overlaps and dominates the CO_2 band."[17] The third edition of Humphreys's *Physics of the Air* appeared in 1940, and an article on climatic change in the *U.S.D.A. Yearbook* for 1941 echoed his negative assessment of CO_2:

> Much has been written about varying amounts of carbon dioxide in the atmosphere as a possible cause of glacial climates. The theory received a fatal blow when it was realized that carbon dioxide is very selective as to the wavelengths of radiant energy it will absorb, filtering out only such waves as even very minute quantities of water vapor dispose of anyway. No possible increase in atmospheric carbon dioxide could materially affect either the amount of insolation reaching the surface or the amount of terrestrial radiation lost to space.[18]

One investigator allowed that the equilibrium of the carbon cycle might be disturbed over periods of several centuries, causing temperature fluctuations, but pointed out that the quantity of CO_2 produced by photosynthesis in three days was greater than that produced by industrial activity in a year. C. E. P. Brooks, writing in the *Compendium of Meteorology* (1951), observed that the CO_2 theory of climate change, advanced by Arrhenius and Chamberlin, "was never widely accepted and was abandoned when it was found that all the long-wave radiation absorbed by CO_2 is also absorbed by water vapour." He considered the recent rise in both CO_2 and global temperature as documented by Callendar to be nothing more than a "coincidence."[19]

Concerning changes in atmospheric composition, Panofsky's 1956 article focused on the effects of increased levels of carbon dioxide and increased cloudiness. The radiative effects of CO_2 were well known by this time, but its meteorological effects were not. Panofsky was quite skeptical of the overall efficacy of CO_2 as an agent of climatic change, noting, "Carbon dioxide is such a good absorber in a narrow band of the radiation spectrum, that neither a reduction nor an increase of the existing amount of carbon dioxide would have much effect on the temperature of the atmosphere." He mentioned Arrhenius's hypotheses that a fifty percent reduction of CO_2 might reduce the Earth's temperature by four degrees Celsius, leading to widespread glaciation, but he agreed with T. C. Chamberlin's objection that the oceans contain many times more CO_2 than the atmosphere and could easily correct any CO_2 deficit. He also accepted Chamberlin's view that the slow turnover of ocean water occurring over tens of thousands of years might possibly withdraw and supply atmospheric CO_2 in amounts sufficient to trigger glacial and interglacial periods. Panofsky, representing most meteorologists of the time, was not convinced that "the general rise in temperature in the last 100 years" could be explained by increased industrial activity and carbon emissions, since this theory "omits the possible storage of the additional carbon dioxide in the oceans." Admitting that unknown, internal changes in the atmosphere *might* be operative, Panofsky rightly pointed out the lack of knowledge of the complex interrelationships among atmospheric composition, solar insolation, cloudiness, evaporation, ocean circulation, and glaciation.[20]

G. S. Callendar and Anthropogenic CO_2

Beginning in 1938, the role of anthropogenic carbon dioxide in climate change was reevaluated. G. S. Callendar, a British steam engineer, acknowledged the "checquered history" of the CO_2 theory: "[I]t was abandoned for many years when the prepondering influence of water vapour radiation in the lower atmosphere was first discovered, but was revived again a few years ago when more accurate measurements of the water vapour spectrum became available." Noting that humans had long been able to intervene in and accelerate natural processes, Callendar pointed out that humanity was now intervening heavily in the slow-moving carbon cycle by "throwing some 9,000 tons of carbon dioxide into the air each minute."[21]

Guy Stewart Callendar was born in 1897, the second son of Professor Hugh Longbourne Callendar, F.R.S., and Victoria Mary Stewart. He was educated at St. Paul's School and City and Guilds Engineering College, London. He assisted his father's experiments on steam at high temperatures and pressures at the Royal College of Science from 1923 to 1929 and lectured on the subject following his father's death in 1930. He continued his steam research under the patronage of the British Electrical and Allied Industries Research Association, which represented turbine manufacturers. His research included investigations on the efficiencies of various batteries, particularly fuel cells. From 1942 to 1957, he was a member of the research staff of the Ministry of Supply at Langhurst and subsequently at London. His avocation was meteorology, and he published numerous articles on terrestrial temperature fluctuations and trends in the *Quarterly Journal of the Royal Meteorological Society*, *Tellus*, and *Weather*. He was a member of the Glaciological Society, and he was elected a fellow of the Royal Meteorological Society and served on its council. He died suddenly in October 1964.[22]

Following Eckholm's lead, Callendar examined the role of anthropogenic carbon dioxide in the climate warming experienced during the early decades of the twentieth century (see fig. 10-1). His first article on this subject appeared in 1938. It was followed by articles in successive years on the carbon dioxide content of the atmosphere through the ages, on the current amount of atmospheric carbon dioxide, and on the infrared absorption properties of CO_2. Callendar published articles on the influence of carbon dioxide on climate in 1949 and 1957, reported on the present climatic fluctuation and on a series of important pre–Mauna Loa measurements of atmospheric carbon dioxide in 1958, and, in 1961, reviewed the relationship between temperature trends and CO_2 in light of recent work by others.[23]

In 1938, Callendar pointed out that fuel combustion had generated some one hundred fifty thousand million tons of carbon dioxide in the previous half century, and that three-quarters of it had remained in the atmosphere—an increase of six percent in the CO_2 concentration from 1900 to 1936. Callendar's radiative model calculated "sky radiation" emitted by water vapor and CO_2 in the thirteen- to sixteen-micron band. This is one factor in what is now called greenhouse forcing. As the density of gases increased in the model, the total sky radiation increased, and the height of the effective atmospheric radiating surface decreased. With a hypothesized doubling of the CO_2 concentration, Callendar's model predicted only a small increase in the total sky radiation. This was because radiation from higher, cooler layers of the atmosphere was effectively screened off. Using the best available data for fossil fuel combustion, Callendar calculated that downward or sky radiation generated by these emissions could account for sixty percent of the half-degree Celsius per century rate of temperature increase being measured by meteorological stations. A doubling of CO_2 in his model resulted in an increase in the mean temperature of two degrees Celsius. Callendar noted, however, that the effect of carbon dioxide might be "considerably greater than supposed."

Warmer, however, was still better. Callendar concluded, much as Arrhenius had three decades earlier, "that the combustion of fossil fuel, whether it be peat from the surface or oil from ten thousand feet below, is likely to prove beneficial to mankind in several ways, besides the provision of heat and power." He cited as examples the importance of small increases of mean temperature at the northern margin of cultivation and the idea that the growth of plants is directly proportional to an increase of the partial pressure of carbon dioxide. "In any case," he concluded, "the return of the deadly glaciers should be delayed indefinitely."[24]

During the discussion of this article at the Royal Meteorological Society, Sir George Clark Simpson, who advocated a theory based on changes in solar radiation, pointed out that the atmosphere was not in a state of radiative equilibrium and that convection and other air movements would have to be taken into account. These sentiments were echoed by David Brunt and C. E. P. Brooks. Simpson regarded the recent rise of CO_2 content and temperature as coincidental and pointed to other complicating factors. John Henry Coste questioned the reliability of the early measurements of CO_2 concentration and temperature. Callendar responded by saying that the measurements he used, taken at Kew Observatory, were "probably very accurate."[25] He realized the extreme complexity of the atmospheric heat budget, but noted that "if any substance is added to the atmosphere which delays the transfer of low temperature radiation, without interfering with the arrival or distribution of the heat supply, some rise of temperature appears to be inevitable in those parts which are furthest from outer space." In other words, *the greenhouse effect is real.*[26]

Callendar's 1939 article, "The Composition of the Atmosphere through the Ages," is an account of the atmospheric carbon cycle over geological time. The article contains an early statement of the now familiar claim that humanity is conducting a "grand experiment" and has become an "agent of global change." Callendar considered it a "commonplace" that humanity had sped up natural processes and had interfered with the carbon cycle. According to Callendar, "[t]he five years 1934–38 are easily the warmest such period at several stations whose records commenced up to 180 years ago." The article ends with an argument linking the one-degree Fahrenheit rise in temperature from 1900 to 1938 to the concurrent increase in industrial emissions of carbon dioxide (fig. 9-1).[27]

In 1941, Callendar published a review of spectroscopic measurements on the absorption bands of CO_2 and the effect of pressure broad-

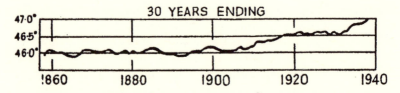

Fig. 9-1. Rising temperatures circa 1858 to 1939. Original caption: "The 30 year moving average from the combined means at Edinburgh, Oxford, Greenwich, De Bilt, Bergen, Oslo, Stockholm, Copenhagen, Wilno, and Berlin." *Source:* G. S. Callendar, "The Composition of the Atmosphere through the Ages," *Meteorol. Mag.* 74 (1939).

ening on line widths. Of note is his diagram of the infrared spectrum, clearly showing the atmospheric window at eight to twelve microns and the absorption bands of CO_2, H_2O, N_2O, and O_3 (fig. 9-2). All this fit well with Callendar's stated research agenda, which was to "reconsider the difficult problem of the effect of changes in the amount of carbon dioxide on the temperature of the atmosphere with the aid of the much more accurate absorption values given here."[28]

A discussion of this article at the Royal Meteorological Society revealed significant changes in opinion caused by Callendar's work. Brunt thought Callendar had made it clear that "CO_2 absorption was rather more important than had been thought in the past." The noted geophysicist Sidney Chapman pointed out, as Tyndall had known a century earlier, that the polyatomic gases in the atmosphere were the chief absorbers and emitters of radiation and suggested that meteo-

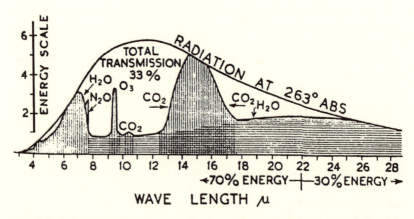

Fig. 9-2. The generalized atmospheric spectrum in infrared wavelengths. *Source:* G. S. Callendar, "Infra-red Absorption by Carbon Dioxide, with Special Reference to Atmospheric Radiation," *Quart. J. Roy. Meteorol. Soc.* 67 (1941).

rologists should conduct an organized research program on atmospheric radiation.[29]

Callendar's 1949 article, "Can Carbon Dioxide Influence Climate?" provided the following values from various sources for the observed CO_2 content of the atmosphere:

Date	Observed CO_2 content (ppm)
Pre-1900	290
1910	303
1922	305
1931	310
1935	320

These figures indicated a ten percent rise in observed CO_2 content in the previous thirty-five years. One might predict from this about a twenty-five percent increase in CO_2 per century. Callendar noted, however, that the *rate* of CO_2 increase had been accelerating recently, perhaps due to the expansion of industry.[30]

In his 1958 article on the amount of carbon dioxide in the atmosphere, Callendar provided a chart of the CO_2 levels in the free air of the North Atlantic region since 1870 (fig. 9-3) and a full discussion of its implications.[31] He called the solid line the "fuel line" noting that the rise of fossil fuel emissions was in "close agreement" with the rise in measured ambient CO_2 concentrations. He considered this agreement possibly coincidental, but potentially significant, pending the outcome of further investigations.

By 1961, Callendar had completed his remarkable series of essays on atmospheric warming and anthropogenic CO_2. He concluded that the trend toward higher temperatures was significant, especially north of the forty-fifth parallel; that increased use of fossil fuels had caused

G. S. CALLENDAR

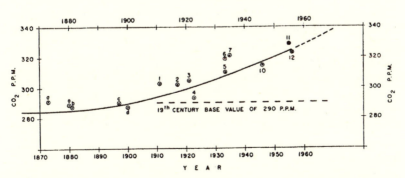

Fig. 9-3. "Amount of CO_2 in the free air of the N. Atlantic region, 1870–1956. Data points indicate individual measurements; the solid line represents the amount from fossil fuel." *Source:* G. S. Callendar, "On the Amount of Carbon Dioxide in the Atmosphere," *Tellus* 10 (1958).

a rise of the concentration of CO_2 in the atmosphere of about seven percent from pre-1920 levels; and that increased sky radiation from the extra CO_2 was linked to the rising temperature trend. Although he was an amateur meteorologist, Callendar's work, contrary to the assertions of some, was not "largely ignored because of World War II," nor was he quite the obscure figure some make him out to be.[32] In 1944, Gordon Manley noted Callendar's valuable contributions to the study of climatic change. A decade later, Gilbert Plass and Charles Keeling consulted with Callendar before beginning their research programs.

In 1953, Hans Suess, one of the founders of radiocarbon dating, pointed out that according to Callendar,

> The average CO_2 concentration in the atmosphere has increased over the past 50 years by approximately 10 percent. This can be seen from a comparison of CO_2 analyses of air carried out in the 19th century with those of more recent years . . . this increase corresponds very closely to the amount of carbon dioxide added to the atmosphere by artificial coal combustion.

Suess and Roger Revelle even referred to rising levels of atmospheric CO_2 caused by industrial fuel combustion as the Callendar effect.[33]

The Public Agenda on Warming

Global warming was on the public agenda in the late 1940s and early 1950s, as Northern Hemisphere temperatures reached an early-twentieth-century peak (see fig. 10-1). Hans Ahlmann, a climatologist at Stockholm University, reported in the *Geographic Journal* that Iceland had experienced a 1.3-degree Celsius warming from the period 1872–1925, when the average annual temperature was 4.1 degrees, to the period 1926–47, when the average annual temperature had risen to 5.7 degrees. His article contained photographs documenting the retreat of the Áobrekke glacier since 1869.[34] In 1950, based on his analysis of meteorological records, the meteorologist Hurd C. Willet told the Royal Meteorological Society that the global temperature trend was "significantly upward" since 1885, with most of the warming occurring north of the fiftieth parallel.[35] Subsequent studies confirmed that from 1890 to 1940, the mean thickness of Arctic ice decreased by about thirty percent, and the area covered decreased by as much as fifteen percent; the intensity of the global circulation increased markedly, and the Earth became warmer—ten degrees warmer in the Norwegian Sea.[36]

In the 1950s, several developments combined to increase public awareness of geophysical issues. Many people were certain that atmospheric nuclear testing was changing the Earth's weather. Weather bureau officials dismissed such speculation, arguing that the impact of the tests on the atmosphere was primarily local and temporary. Radioactive fallout posed far more insidious dangers to human health and environmental quality. Radioactive materials in the environment, however, provided new tools for ecologists and geophysicists to trace the flow of materials through the biosphere, atmosphere, and oceans. The International Geophysical Year (IGY), in 1957–58, provided an organizational and financial boost to academic geophysics, including meteorology. The successful launch of the Soviet IGY satellite *Sputnik*, however, combined with the failure of the U.S. Vanguard launch vehicle program, precipitated a crisis in public confidence, a "race" to close a perceived missile gap, and an increase in Cold War tensions. *Newsweek* announced a weather modification "Race with the Reds," and some even wanted to use weather control as a weapon of war.[37]

Concerns were also being expressed in the popular press about changing climates, rising sea levels, loss of habitat, and shifting agricultural zones. In 1950, the *Saturday Evening Post* asked, "Is the World Getting Warmer?" The article cited three January thaws in succession on the Penobscot River near Old Town, Maine, an unprecedented event that marooned the Indians living on an island and prompted the state to build a new bridge across the river. Average February temperatures in Spitzbergen, Norway, had risen seven degrees in twenty-six years. Hans Ahlmann believed this climatic fluctuation was the first in history that we could "measure, investigate, and possibly also explain." He was of the opinion that "if older people say that they have lived through many more hard winters in their youth, they are stating a real fact." Thomas Jefferson would have concurred. In fact, there is little that is actually new or unique in popular climate discourse. Topics of climatic speculation cited in the article included a warmer planet; rising sea levels; shifts of agriculture; the retreat of the Greenland ice cap and other glaciers; changes in ocean fisheries, perhaps due to changes in the Gulf Stream; and the migration of millions of people displaced by climate change. Ahlmann was concerned about the unprecedented rate of change. He pointed out that the climate was now changing so fast that "each new contribution to the subject is out of date almost as soon as it is published." Perhaps he also meant to say that *climatology* was experiencing unprecedented rates of change.[38]

The famous cartoonist Virgil Partch (a.k.a. VIP) illustrated contemporary climate concerns in *Today's Revolution in Weather!*, a 1953 compilation of news items on weather extremes and global warming. These concerns included sea level rise, migration of plant and animal species, regional winners and losers, and psychological and social influences of climatic change (fig. 9-4). The compiler, economic forecaster William J. Baxter, predicted a climate-induced real estate boom in the north and advised, "Go north-west young man."

Why was the climate getting warmer? Scientists, inspired by Callendar, began to investigate in greater detail the linkages between ris-

The 4-H'S": Holland Housewives
Hanging Wash in Hipboots

Did You Ever See A Tree Walking?

Chapter III

Make Room For Trees, Grains, Vegetables
and Bugs on the North Express!

Nature at Last Smiles on the Russians

One Over-Peppy Milwaukee Industrialist Plus 2
Weeks of 90° Temperature in The South Equals
a New, Lazy "Chinaman Type" of Bird Watcher

Fig. 9-4. Four global warming cartoons by Virgil Partch (VIP) published in 1953 illustrating sea level rise, migration of plant and animal species, regional winners and losers, and psychological and social influences of climatic change. *Source:* William J. Baxter, *Today's Revolution in Weather!* (New York: International Economic Research Bureau, 1953).

ing CO_2 levels and rising temperatures. His early results were revised and extended by the work of others, notably Gilbert Plass, an infrared physicist who developed an early computer model of infrared radiative transfer and published a number of articles on carbon dioxide and climate between 1953 and 1959.

Gilbert Plass

Gilbert Plass built bridges—between the physics of infrared absorption and the geochemistry of the carbon cycle and between geophysics and computer modeling. According to Plass, "all sorts of things came together." New detailed spectroscopic measurements of the absorption bands of water vapor, carbon dioxide, and ozone; new information on the carbon cycle and industrial emissions; and newly available digital computers meant that more realistic models of radiative transfer would soon replace the older, graphical approximations. Plass's new carbon dioxide theory meant that old objections, like those of Humphreys, were no longer valid.[39]

Gilbert Norman Plass was born in Toronto, Ontario, on March 22, 1920. He received a B.S. from Harvard University in 1941, where he recalled that his courses on geology, chemistry, and physics provided an interdisciplinary foundation for his later work. He was particularly impressed by the experimental techniques of John Strong, one of his physics professors. Plass received his Ph.D. in physics from Princeton University in 1947 and worked as an associate physicist at the Metallurgical Laboratory (Manhattan District) of the University of Chicago from 1942 to 1945. He became an instructor of physics at Johns Hopkins University in 1946 and was subsequently promoted to assistant and then associate professor. At Hopkins he conducted research on infrared radiation with funds provided by the Office of Naval Research. During his sabbatical year, at Michigan State University in 1954–55, he gained access to a large computer and realized it offered the perfect way to construct a better model of radiative transfer. In 1955, Plass moved out of academics, serving for a year as a staff scientist with Lockheed Aircraft Corporation. He then joined the advanced research staff of the aeronutronic division of the Ford Motor Company. Ford provided him with excellent laboratory facilities where he could continue his experimental work on infrared physics. In 1960, he became manager of the research lab at Ford's theoretical physics department and a consulting editor of the journal *Infrared Physics*. In 1963, he accepted a position as the first professor of atmospheric and space science at the Southwest Center for Advanced Studies (now the University of Texas, Arlington) where he remained for five years. In 1968, he arrived at Texas A&M University, where he served as professor of physics and head of the department. He is the author of *Infrared Physics and Engineering* (1963).[40] Plass is well known for his research in radiative transfer and planetary atmospheres, especially infrared absorption and emission by molecules and the carbon dioxide theory of climate. He also worked on nuclear fission and neutron physics, electromagnetic and gravitational action at a distance, electron emission, and electrostatic electron lenses. As of this writing, he is retired and living in Bryan, Texas.

Before the advent of numerical models of radiative transfer that included the detailed infrared spectrum of CO_2 and water vapor, meteorologists used a simplified atmospheric radiation chart and tables developed by Walter M. Elsasser in 1942 and Arent Bruinenberg in 1946.[41] The Elsasser Chart assumed that CO_2 was a perfect "black body" absorber at all altitudes, but only for wavelengths between 13.1 to 16.9 microns. Other simplifying assumptions were made for water vapor.[42]

Plass used his more sophisticated theory to warn that accumulation of carbon dioxide in the atmosphere from anthropogenic sources could become a serious problem in the near future. He pointed out in 1956 that humanity was conducting a large-scale experiment on the atmosphere, the results of which would not be available for several generations: "If at the end of this century, measurements show that the carbon dioxide content of the atmosphere has risen appreciably and at the same time the temperature has continued to rise throughout the world, it will be firmly established that carbon dioxide is an important factor in causing climatic change."[43] According to the IPCC scientific assessment, published in 1995, "[t]he balance of evidence suggests a discernible human influence on global climate."[44] Many would say that the uncontrolled "experiment" pointed out by Callendar in 1939 and revisited by Plass in 1956 has been verified.

Roger Revelle

Roger Revelle, statesman of science and public policy, convinced himself that he was the "granddaddy" of the theory of global warming.[45] Although this claim cannot be supported historically, the popular press and many geophysicists have kept the notion alive. A survey of the obituary notices of Roger Revelle reveals his considerable reputation in this area. The *New York Times* referred to him as "an early predictor of global warming"; the *Boston Globe* called him the "grandfather of the greenhouse effect" and the "godfather of global warming"; and his hometown paper, the San Diego County edition of the *Los Angeles Times*, began its front page coverage as follows: "Roger Revelle, the internationally renowned oceanographer who warned of global warming 30 years before greenhouse effect became a household term, died Monday of complications related to a heart attack. He was 82."[46]

Such renown may be attributed in part to Revelle's family ties, social standing, and the high academic, administrative, and political positions he held at the University of California at San Diego (UCSD), at Harvard University, and in the federal government. G. S. Callendar was, after all, just a "steam engineer," and Gilbert Plass was a junior professor who moved to industry just as his articles on CO_2 and climate were appearing in the scholarly journals. In contrast, in his lifetime Revelle attained godlike status at his home institution and served on national climate panels such as the National Academy of Sciences Climate Research Board and the Committee on Climate of the American Association for the Advancement of Science.

Revelle also had loyal colleagues at the Scripps Institution of Oceography (SIO) who were not shy about embellishing his reputation. One of them, the noted oceanographer Walter Munk, told an interviewer in 1990:

> For Roger, one scientific idea led to another. . . . Typical of this was the greenhouse effect, which he *really invented*, which he was the first to sense was happening, to consider the implications. . . . If it weren't for him getting the carbon dioxide observation started . . . there would be significant differences today at the highest levels of world governments in terms of how they approach global warming.[47]

Roger Randall Dougan Revelle was born March 7, 1909, in Seattle, Washington, and was raised in Pasadena, California. He earned a B.A. in geology from Pomona College in 1929 and a Ph.D. in 1936 from the University of California at Berkeley in conjunction with the SIO. Early in his graduate studies, in 1931, he married Ellen Virginia Clark, a member of the prominent Scripps publishing family and a grandniece of the original benefactors of the SIO. He was appointed as an instructor at Scripps after graduation. During World War II, he served as commander of the oceanographic section of the navy's Bureau of Ships and was involved in the establishment of the Office of Naval Research, where he became head of the geophysics branch in 1946. One of his projects there involved monitoring the effects on the ocean of the atomic bomb tests at Bikini Atoll.

Revelle returned to Scripps as a professor in 1948, working first as its associate director and, from 1951 to 1964, as its director. He held a number of prominent positions during this period, serving on the organizing committee of the IGY (1957–58), as president of the first International Oceanographic Congress (1959), and in the Kennedy administration as the science advisor to Secretary of the Interior Stewart Udall (1961–63). Under his administration, the SIO grew dramatically in size and reputation and became part of UCSD. He was disappointed in 1963, however, when he failed in his bid to become chancellor of UCSD, a campus he had done much to establish. He took a leave of absence and formally switched fields from oceanography to public policy. He became the founding director of the Center for Population Studies at Harvard University in 1964, where he supervised research on population issues in relation to economic and natural resources development. In 1975, he began splitting his time between Harvard and UCSD; he returned to Scripps permanently in 1978. He continued to teach one undergraduate course at UCSD, met with students during office hours, and spent much of his time answering his correspondence. Among his many honors, he received the National Medal of Science in 1990 for his work on carbon dioxide and climate, oceanographic exploration, radiation in the marine environment, and global population and food studies. In 1991, he died of complications following cardiac arrest at the UCSD Medical Center, which he cofounded.[48]

Carbon Dioxide Exchange between Atmosphere and Ocean

In the mid-1950s, Revelle first became concerned about the increase in carbon dioxide in the atmosphere caused by the burning of fossil fuels. In 1957, he and Hans Suess published an oft-cited article in *Tellus* on the exchange of carbon dioxide between the atmosphere and ocean. They began by citing Callendar, who maintained that most of the carbon dioxide produced by fossil fuel combustion had remained in the atmosphere (see fig. 9-3), and that increasing levels of CO_2 may account for the recent warming in high latitudes. They also cited calculations by Plass, who found that a ten percent increase in atmospheric carbon dioxide would increase the average temperature by 0.36 degrees Celsius. As did T. C. Chamberlin at the turn of the century, Revelle and Suess thought that positive feedback processes, such as an increase in atmospheric water vapor content, could result in a more pronounced effect, but they emphasized that so little was known about the thermodynamics of the atmosphere that "it is not certain whether or how a change in infrared back radiation from the upper air would affect the temperature near the surface."[49]

The authors were concerned, however, about a possible increase in worldwide fuel and power consumption. They tabulated United Nations estimates of increasing concentrations of atmospheric CO_2 caused by exponentially increasing fossil fuel consumption. The United Nations figures indicated a worst-case seventy-four percent increase in atmospheric CO_2 concentration over preindustrial levels by the first decade of the twenty-first century. This would be about a sixty percent increase over the 1955 level. Based on these estimates and the

observation that the production of industrial CO_2 is probably two orders of magnitude greater than the natural rate of CO_2 production from
volcanoes, the authors ventured their memorable statement that

> human beings are now carrying out a large scale geophysical ex-
> periment of a kind that could not have happened in the past nor be
> reproduced in the future. Within a few centuries we are returning
> to the atmosphere and oceans the concentrated organic carbon
> stored in sedimentary rocks over hundreds of millions of years. This
> experiment, if adequately documented, may yield a far-reaching
> insight into the processes determining weather and climate.[50]

This statement is reminiscent of Plass's a year earlier and Callendar's
statements earlier still.[51]

The balance of their essay is a calibration of the "carbon cycle" and
an estimate of the sequestering of CO_2 in the atmosphere, oceans, biosphere, and lithosphere using C^{14} techniques pioneered by Suess. As
did many others before them, notably Arvid Högbom and T. C. Chamberlin, Revelle and Suess reported ocean carbon reservoirs two orders
of magnitude larger than those of the atmosphere, and carbonates in
sediments two to three orders of magnitude larger than those of the
ocean. In the 1950s, estimates of CO_2 exchange rates ranged over six
orders of magnitude. Theirs was one hundred times larger than the
one used by Plass in 1956, yet ten thousand times smaller than that
deduced by H. N. Dingle in 1954.[52] Clearly the carbon *fluxes* were not
well known. This fact severely limited their conclusions.

Revelle and Suess thought that the Callendar effect, their term for
a ten percent increase in atmospheric CO_2 concentration caused by
industrial fuel combustion during the past century, was "quite improb-
able" on its own and was probably augmented by a number of factors.
These included a slight increase of ocean temperature (not more than
0.05 degrees Celsius), a decrease in the carbon content of soils due to
clearing of the forests and increased cultivation (shades of colonial
America), and a possible change of organic matter in the oceans.[53]
Using results published in the 1930s by Kurt Buch on the absorption
of CO_2 by sea water and estimates of the average lifetime of a CO_2
molecule in the atmosphere of ten to thirty years, Revelle and Suess
calculated secular increases in atmospheric CO_2 of only two to about
ten percent *per century*. Their final estimates, a compromise between
their own calculations and United Nations projections, was a twenty
to forty percent increase by the end of the century. This, they said,
would "allow a determination of the effects, *if any*, of changes in atmospheric carbon dioxide on weather and climate throughout the earth."
With a rhetorical flourish, they pointed to current uncertainties and
new work that needed to be done.

> Present data on the total amount of CO_2 in the atmosphere, on the
> rates and mechanisms of CO_2 exchange between the sea and the air,

and between the air and the soils, and on possible fluctuations in marine organic carbon are insufficient to give an accurate base line for measurement of future changes in atmospheric CO_2. An opportunity exists during the International Geophysical Year to obtain much of the necessary information.[54]

Revelle and Suess concluded by acknowledging an article "on the same subject" in the same issue of *Tellus* by James R. Arnold and Ernest C. Anderson. These authors made several references to the "Suess effect," the recent secular decreases of C^{14} in the biosphere. They explained this effect by noting that industrial combustion of fossil carbon had now reached "truly geochemical proportions" and had exceeded natural production of current carbon by two orders of magnitude.[55] The matter, however, was far from settled.

During the IGY, Harry Wexler of the U. S. Weather Bureau succeeded in establishing a series of accurate measurements of carbon dioxide. Following a meeting with Revelle in October 1956, Wexler provided initial funding to the Mauna Loa Observatory for an infrared gas analyzer "to keep a continuous record of CO_2 at the Observatory."[56] These measurements were accurately and faithfully executed by Charles David Keeling, then an assistant research chemist at Scripps.[57] The measurements at Mauna Loa almost did not happen as planned, however. As Keeling recalls, "[Revelle] wouldn't sign my travel orders to go out and set up my measurements at the Mauna Loa Observatory because he wanted me to do it his way first."[58] "His way" was a geographical survey over large expanses of the ocean, based on an older notion that CO_2 varies by location. Wexler and Keeling prevailed, however, and as Keeling recalled two decades later:

> The first unmistakable evidence of atmospheric CO_2 increase was furnished by continuous measurements made at [the Mauna Loa Observatory] and by measurements of flask samples collected periodically at the South Pole. These data, obtained in connection with the [IGY], were precise enough to indicate a rise in concentration in 1959 when compared with the results of the previous year. Further measurements have shown a persistent year-to-year increase.[59]

Since then, the Keeling curve, the famous saw-toothed curve of rising CO_2 concentrations, has become *the* environmental icon of the century (fig. 9-5).

It is important to note, however, that measurements of the concentration of CO_2 in the atmosphere did not begin in 1958. They had been made, with varying degrees of accuracy, since the beginning of the nineteenth century by John Dalton and others. Callendar reported background measurements from as early as the 1870s in his essays and estimated that the concentration of CO_2 in the late nineteenth century was close to 290 parts per million. This result was later confirmed by Eric From and Charles Keeling.[60] It is also important to note that

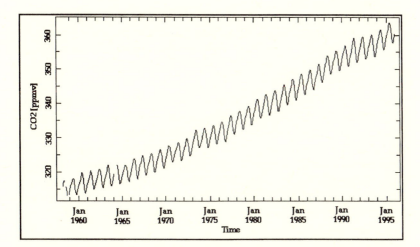

Fig. 9-5. The Keeling curve, 1958–1996: an icon of global warming. Adapted from "Mauna Loa CO₂ Data," http://ingrid.ldgo.columbia.edu/ SOURCES/.KEELING/ (February 27, 1997).

Callendar's curve (fig. 9-3), which ends at about 325 parts per million in the mid-1950s, fits closely with the Keeling curve, which started at 315 parts per million in 1958.

Roger Revelle was a formidable figure in academic and political circles. By his own admission, however, he was not educated enough to tackle the modern rigors of the geophysical sciences he had done so much to promote. "I was never very well-educated," he told an interviewer in 1990 after President George Bush awarded him the National Medal of Science. "Geologists in those days didn't get much physics or mathematics." He called oceanography a "young man's game—not because it's physically demanding, but because it requires a lot of mathematics now."[61] His role in the global warming issue can largely be understood as an advocate for carbon cycle monitoring.[62]

The 1957 article of Revelle and Suess, so widely cited as launching Revelle's claim to being the father of the theory of the greenhouse effect, focused on geophysical and anthropogenic carbon sources and sinks. It was not a clarion call on the dangers of global warming. Clearly, it was the product of two separate authors—Suess's work on the carbon cycle as calibrated by C[14] and Revelle's work on the chemistry of sea water. While it enhanced the luster of Revelle, publishing an article in *Tellus* was all in a day's work for Suess.

G. S. Callendar pointed out in 1961 that "this matter of atmospheric CO_2 increase is highly controversial at the present time, and several authors have expressed doubts as to the possibility of a CO_2 increase approaching the amount . . . added by fossil-fuel combustion."[63] He was referring to the 1957 article by Revelle and Suess in which they had argued that "most of the CO_2 released by artificial fuel combustion since the beginning of the industrial revolution must have been absorbed by the oceans." Clearly their work was not the dramatic turning point in our awareness of the risk of global warming that later authors perceived it to be.

In 1985, Revelle wrote a short, revisionist "scientific history of carbon dioxide" in which he *failed to mention the contributions of Callendar and Plass*. His account jumps from T. C. Chamberlin directly to areas of current concern.[64] Perhaps this omission was simply an oversight in a brief essay. More likely, it was based on Revelle's need to place himself at the center of the carbon dioxide theory of climate as a way of maintaining his larger-than-life legend.

Conclusion

Global warming and the carbon dioxide theory of climate change are not new issues. In the 1940s and 1950s, doubts about the efficacy of CO_2 as an agent of climatic change gave way to new theories and observations. Rising temperatures, expanding carbon emissions, new measurements of the radiative properties of trace gases, and new models of the Earth's heat budget and carbon cycle convinced a number of scientists that the carbon dioxide theory needed to be taken seriously. By the late 1940s and early 1950s, as Northern Hemisphere temperatures continued to rise, global warming was on the public agenda.

However, scientific work done in the mid-1950s did not seem to make much of an impression on the general public, whose awareness of climate issues seemed to rise and fall with the temperature trends. With the exception perhaps of Revelle's policy initiatives and Keeling's curve of CO_2 concentration, which continues its snakelike rise, early twentieth century concerns about global warming are not continuous with later climate research.

10

Global Cooling, Global Warming

Historical Dimensions

> At certain revolutions all the damned
> Are brought: and feel by turns the bitter change
> Of fierce extremes, extremes by change more fierce,
> From beds of raging fire to starve in ice
> Their soft ethereal warmth, and there to pine
> Immovable, infixed, and frozen round,
> Periods of time, thence hurried back to fire.
> —John Milton, *Paradise Lost*, bk 2, ll. 597–603.

I have chosen to conclude these essays just as the well-known IGY was getting started. Of course, much has changed since then. There is little to gain, however, by attempting to recount the recent policy history of global change, at least from my perspective as a historian of science and technology. I have tried in this book to provide fresh perspectives on the more distant past, not to replicate the recent literature on global change. Although I am actively engaged in projects sponsored by the American Meteorological Society and the American Geophysical Union that document the recent past, I have little inclination to attempt to interpret it. Consequently I include in this chapter only the briefest sketch of the global cooling scare after 1958 and the return of a global warming discourse in the 1980s. I believe the metaphor of apprehension (awareness, understanding, fear, intervention) applies quite well to a number of current environmental issues, and I will point to some of them by way of conclusion.

I was asked once after a seminar whether, as a historian, I could predict the eventual demise of today's global change discourse, since there had been so many changes in the past. I responded that history has no predictive value, but does indeed provide valuable perspectives to its readers. History is first and foremost the study of change.

For students of global change, history can serve as an inspirational story of how far we have come. It can also serve as a humbling reminder that change is indeed inevitable in our lives, in the Earth system, and in our ideas and institutions. Although I am professionally engaged with the past, I am still a citizen of my own age—an age of vastly enhanced environmental awareness. Like many of my contemporaries, I believe that humanity is a part of, not apart from, nature; that human activity is placing tremendous stress on global biophysical systems; and that we have an ethical responsibility to each other and to future generations to live sustainably, in harmony with the Earth. Your guesses about the future are probably as good as and perhaps better than mine.

New Privileged Positions

In the second half of the twentieth century, computers and satellites have offered new privileged perspectives on the climate. Developing a numerical climate experiment to run on a digital electronic computer and launching a new satellite remote sensing experiment have become the preferred ways of establishing privileged perspectives or making authoritative claims about the climate. For centuries, meteorologists have employed calculating devices to aid them in analyzing large amounts of weather and climate data. These included paper forms—tables, graphs, nomograms, and mechanical, electrical, and electronic devices—special slide rules, punched-card tabulating machines, analog computers, and digital computers. The first large-scale electronic digital computer, ENIAC, was completed just as World War II ended. Numerical weather prediction was attempted using this machine as early as 1950, and within several years, similar efforts were being made at the Institute for Advanced Study, the Air Force Cambridge Research Laboratory, the Napier Shaw Laboratory of the British Meteorological Office, and the International Meteorological Institute at the University of Stockholm.[1]

As noted earlier, Gilbert Plass developed a computer model of infrared radiative transfer in the mid-1950s that supported his research on carbon dioxide and climate. Several years later, in the interest of national security, a model known as Nile Blue was developed by the Advanced Research Projects Administration (ARPA) in the Department of Defense. It was hoped that this model could be used to test the sensitivity of the climate to major perturbations, including Soviet tinkering and those that could result from a major environmental war. F. Kenneth Hare pointed out in the *Geographical Review* in 1964:

> The work of Joseph Smagorinsky at the United States Weather Bureau, and of Norman A. Phillips, E. N. Lorenz, and Jule G. Charney at the Massachusetts Institute of Technology has brought us within

distant sight of a genuine theory of present-day climate. Hence it becomes more profitable to speculate about the causes of past and present climatic change; we may soon have something to test these speculations against.[2]

In 1967, Syukuro Manabe and Richard T. Wetherald published the computerized equivalent of Arrhenius's much earlier exercise in cosmic physics. Their one-dimensional model included the effects of both radiation and convection to calculate temperature as a function of latitude. It predicted a mean warming of 2.3 degrees Celsius for a doubling of CO_2. Two years later Manabe and Kirk Bryan added basic oceanic features to the model.[3]

By 1970, the Rand Corporation, fearful that the United States might be harmed either inadvertently or maliciously by changes in the climate, developed a program on "climate dynamics for environmental security." Their goal was to learn how to anticipate and detect climatic changes. Rand scientists, in conjunction with the modeling community, constructed climate models with doubled levels of CO_2. Boundary conditions in the models could also be altered to represent variations in solar output or changes in the Earth's surface features, if, for example, the Soviets dammed the Bering Strait. Rand was hoping to run more complex models on ARPA's new computer, the ILLIAC-IV, and was prepared to use it "as soon as somebody throws the switch."[4]

The first meteorological experiment conducted in outer space was a "heat-budget package" designed by Verner Suomi and Robert Parent at the University of Wisconsin and flown on *Explorer 7* in 1959. This experiment indicated that heat losses near the equator were approximately twenty-five percent greater than heat losses in polar latitudes. Since 1974, estimates of the Earth's albedo and outgoing long-wave radiation have been derived from data collected by operational polar orbiting satellites. A decade later, the Earth Radiation Budget Experiment was developed to measure by satellite the incoming solar radiation and outgoing shortwave and long-wave radiation at the top of the atmosphere. As satellite specialists James F. W. Purdom and W. Paul Menzel pointed out, "[s]atellites are the only platform capable of measuring the global distribution of the radiation budget in space and time."[5]

Global Cooling and Global Warming

As public awareness of global warming reached an early peak in the mid-1950s, the popular press began to carry articles on climate cooling. *Fortune* published an article in 1954 entitled "Climate: The Heat May Be Off," and in 1958, just as the IGY was winding down, journalist Betty Friedan wrote an article for *Harper's Magazine* on the coming of a new ice age. Her article was a review of a recent theory by

Maurice Ewing and William Donn which held that climate warming could lead to a breakup of the Arctic ice pack. This event would result in an open Arctic Ocean, increased snowfall in high latitudes, a glacial advance, global cooling, and perhaps a new ice age. Rather than a "silent spring," Friedan sketched a glacial nightmare in which spring might *never* come:

> If [Ewing and Donn] are right, for the first time in the history of the world, the victims of an Ice Age are going to see it coming. Television cameramen will be ranging all over the far north . . . looking for the first dirty summer slush. For the Ice Age will dawn, not in crashing glacial terror, but in slush . . . on a summer vacation up north, you will simply see a lot of dirty slush, winter's snow that for the first time in thousands of years didn't quite melt.[6]

All these changes already seemed to be occurring. The Arctic ice pack was reported to be twelve percent smaller and forty percent thinner in 1958 than it had been fifteen years before, and the U. S. Geological Survey estimated that sea level was rising at a rate of two feet per century (their former estimate had been six inches per century). They predicted coastal flooding, beach erosion, and possibly the loss or abandonment of some cities. Friedan editorialized that human intervention in the climate or mass migrations (in the opposite direction recommended by Baxter) may be the only solution: "If man finds no way to switch the glacial thermostat, there may well be a real estate boom in the Sahara."

By the mid-1970s global cooling was an observable trend (see fig. 10-1). The U. S. National Science Board pointed out that during the last twenty to thirty years, world temperature had fallen, "irregularly at first but more sharply over the last decade."[7] The leading culprits in a global cooling were thought to be particulates from industrial sources, increased cirrus clouds due to jet airplane contrails, and the configuration of the Earth's orbital elements according to the astronomical theory of the ice ages. Reid Bryson of the University of Wisconsin was concerned about anthropogenic increases of the Earth's albedo. He called the overall climatic effect of human activities a "human volcano" that could upset the climatic "balance," and warned that even minor changes in agriculture could plunge an overcrowded world into starvation and ultimate tragedy.

Such concerns brought together atmospheric scientists and the Central Intelligence Agency (CIA) in an attempt to determine the geopolitical consequences of a sudden onset of global cooling.[8] Responding to recently released official CIA documents, journalist George Will warned of possible "megadeaths and social upheaval" if the cooling continued:

> Some climatologists believe that the average temperature in the Northern Hemisphere, at least, may decline two or three degrees

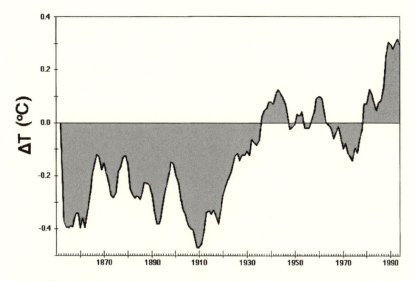

Fig. 10-1. Combined land air and sea surface temperature anomalies for the Northern Hemisphere. Plot indicates a five year running average of annual temperature difference, in degrees Celsius, from 1853 to 1994. The line of zero temperature anomaly is the 1961–1990 average. *Source:* "Hadley Centre for Climate Prediction and Research, Historical temperature records," http://www.meto.gov.uk/sec5/CR_div/Tempertr/lsst_ vals_nh.html (November 20, 1997).

Throughout most of the nineteenth century the climate was considered to be generally stable (see chapter 4); from 1910 through the 1950s the climate was warming (see chapter 9); global cooling was on the public agenda in the 1970s and global warming in the 1980s (see chapter 10).

by the end of the century. If that climate change occurs, there will be megadeaths and social upheaval because grain production in high latitudes (Canada, northern regions of China and the Soviet Union) will decrease. Monsoons will be disrupted and droughts will increase in nations (especially in southern Asia) where monsoons are vital to agriculture. Only the U.S. and Argentina, of the major grain-growing nations, will not be adversely affected. What is happening now to the poor in India and in drought-stricken Africa is probably a pale sample of what the food deficit areas might then experience.[9]

Another journalist, Lowell Ponte, turned the twenty-year cooling trend in the Northern Hemisphere into an exaggerated, apocalyptic, cold war scare in his book *The Cooling* (1976). According to Ponte, a collapse of the Soviet grain harvest might trigger a land invasion of Western Europe, perhaps resulting in World War III.

Modest advances in cloud seeding suggested to some that weather modification techniques might be extended and applied to the climate.

In an era of cold war competition, climate prediction and control became a national security issue. In his 1955 *Fortune* article "Can We Survive Technology?" the noted mathematician John von Neumann listed global climate control among the "mortal technological dangers to world civilization," because it was in fundamental conflict with traditional geographical units and political concepts.[10]

One widely discussed proposal involved damming the Bering Strait. The idea was to isolate the Arctic Ocean from the cold waters of the North Atlantic, pump in warmer water from the Kurishiro current in the North Pacific, and melt some of the glaciers. Most scientists believed a milder Arctic would favor the Soviet Union. Mikhail Budyko, a well-respected Soviet climatologist, proposed melting the ice by dusting it with soot from airplanes. Other Soviet scientists favored the use of underground nuclear explosions to cut canals and reroute the course of rivers, saving water and perhaps ameliorating the climate. The most outrageous proposal was that of Valentin Chernkov, who wanted to use rockets to construct a ring of potassium dust around the Earth similar to the rings of Saturn. Chernkov felt this would result in a "perpetual summer" and lead to agricultural improvements. Such uncontrolled experiments, of course, would have indefinite costs and unpredictable effects, and would be likely to generate unwanted side effects.[11]

From the U. S. government and the United Nations came proposals to limit population growth. A cooler world could mean reduced agricultural productivity and a reduced food supply. Some even went so far as to propose injecting sterility drugs into food exports to underdeveloped, overpopulated countries. Even the "green revolution" was in part cast as a solution to global cooling. Buckminster Fuller proposed "migrating like birds" if the cold weather continued. He also speculated on a growing form of social Darwinism caused by climatic change. It was thought that the strongest nations, rather than engaging in a nuclear war, would instead fight for land near the equator in order to survive the "big chill."[12] In the early 1980s, a hypothetical large-scale exchange of nuclear weapons by the superpowers came to be viewed as a potent agent of global cooling and a potentially lethal threat to the Earth's population. A "nuclear winter" caused by a forest of mushroom clouds would indeed constitute a very powerful human volcano.

Since the mid-1980s, the dominant concern has been global warming from rising concentrations of CO_2 and other greenhouse gases (see fig. 10-1). In 1988, scientist James Hansen of the National Aeronautics and Space Administration announced to Congress and the world, "Global warming has begun."[13] He went on to report that, at least to his satisfaction, he had seen the "signal" in the climate noise and we were in for a hell of a warming, perhaps in the form of a runaway greenhouse effect. Hansen later revised his remarks, but his statement remains the starting point of recent widespread concerns over global warming. This revelation, combined with a continual stream of negative news about the stratospheric ozone layer since 1985, has resulted in a major shift in humanity's relationship with the Earth's atmosphere. The clear blue sky now seems menacing. How can you enjoy a day at the beach if you know that a sunburn could lead to skin cancer? Were the killer hurricanes Gilbert, Hugo, and Andrew a result of human intervention in the climate? Probably not. What about the heat wave of 1988, the midwestern floods of 1993, or El Niño of 1997–98? Again, probably not. Still, there is no way around it for the realist or the skeptic—human activities have indeed altered the chemical composition and radiation budget of the atmosphere. The question is not whether human agency has contributed to global change. That question has been answered in the affirmative throughout history. More significant questions today involve the magnitude, consequences, and even the direction of global changes caused by anthropogenic stresses.

Although in 1992 the IPCC supplementary report concluded that "the unequivocal detection of the enhanced greenhouse effect from observations is not likely for a decade or more," a widely cited conclusion of the 1995 report was that "[t]he balance of evidence suggests a discernible human influence on global climate."[14] On the social end, the United Nations Environmental Program recently asked, "Are we overlooking the social and political implications of climate change?" pointing out that if scientific predictions about climate change hold true, it seems "likely" that political structures and social bonds will be subjected to additional stresses.[15] Several strategies of climate intervention are being pursued. The Montreal Protocol and the United Nations Framework Convention on Climate Change represent geopolitical interventions in the climate system. Many more policy initiatives are underway. Economics has also begun to play a role as taxes and incentives are put in place to reduce unwanted emissions. Meanwhile, green social engineers are attempting to convince the general public to save the planet by reducing, reusing, and recycling.

The most immodest of the new intervention strategies involves "geoengineering" massive technical fixes for the climate system. A recent National Academy of Sciences report, *Policy Implications of Greenhouse Warming,* advised that the United States should conduct research in schemes to cool the Earth if global warming gets out of hand. Proposals included orbiting a fleet of space mirrors or spraying sulfur dioxide into the stratosphere to reflect solar radiation back to space, turning the oceans into soupy green algae blooms to sequester excess carbon, or setting up gigantic "soot generators" to shade the Earth. Other scholars have taken a recent "serious look" at geoengineering and find it attractive, because in their words, "Doubt about the prospects for cooperative abatement of global greenhouse gas emissions is a pragmatic reason to consider geoengineering, whose implementation requires fewer cooperating actors than abatement."[16] If this does not invoke apprehension, I don't know what will.

Conclusion

The study of the history of global change reminds us that there have been many global changes in our relationship to nature and that history, climate, and culture are closely interwoven. Climate apprehensions did not begin in 1988 or in 1957, or even in 1896. There were colonial, early modern, and even ancient precedents. From a climate discourse steeped in the tradition of literary analogy, through a long and continuing effort to establish positive climate science, we have arrived, late in the twentieth century, at a climate discourse that is again saturated with metaphor, values, and apprehensions. As Jerome Namias pointed out in 1989, "the greenhouse effect is now firmly part of our collective angst, along with nuclear winter, asteroid collisions, and other widely bruited global nightmares."[17]

The Abbé Du Bos's book on poetry and painting argued for a link between changes in the climate and the rise and fall of creative genius. His theory of climatic influence, although based on shaky philosophical and literary foundations, continued in the work of Montesquieu, Gibbon, and others. It found a receptive audience among American colonists and early patriots who hoped that the climate of the New World was being improved by settlement and cultivation. In the nineteenth and twentieth centuries this culture-bound discussion of climatic change was superseded by more or less objective attempts to examine the atmosphere and its changes. The modern, scientific description of weather and climate has been gradually established since about the mid–nineteenth century. Like most sciences, it has focused on understanding, prediction, and control, attempting to reduce atmospheric phenomena to their equations of motion, chemical constituents, or other "manageable" components. The atmosphere, however, is not so easily characterized.

Today we are probably more aware than ever before of the risks posed by climate change. There are more atmospheric scientists than ever before, employing more sophisticated tools than ever before, and publishing more studies than ever before. Policymakers have been establishing treaties, laws, and policies that attempt to reduce human interference in the climate system and mitigate the impact of unwanted global changes. Recently, because of pessimistic forecasts of economic and other dislocations related to global change, social scientists and policymakers have returned to the "human dimensions" of the atmosphere. There is a flood of new literature on "managing" planet Earth.[18] Isn't it time for historical, literary, and other humanistic explorations and reevaluations of environmental change as well?

As both our technical prowess and our capacity to pollute increase, it is crucial that we understand how civilizations have perceived and have related to the natural world. The scientific challenge of global change is to understand and predict the response of a large, complex, potentially chaotic system to small changes in forcing factors; the political challenge is how to make prudent, fair, and effective decisions concerning the modification of human activities in order to mitigate climate impacts or adapt to possible global changes. Historical studies can make particularly valuable contributions by elucidating the intellectual, social, and cultural roots of environmental issues. The result should be better scientific understanding, more effective policies, and a view of the human dimensions of global changes rendered more complete by a study of the past.

Notes

Introduction

1. For example, John A. Dutton, "The Challenges of Global Change," in *Science, Technology, and the Environment: Multidisciplinary Perspectives*, ed. James Rodger Fleming and Henry A. Gemery (Akron: University of Akron Press, 1994), 53–111, has a scientific focus; Robert G. Fleagle, *Global Environmental Change: Interactions of Science, Policy, and Politics in the United States* (Westport, Conn.: Praeger, 1994) is more policy oriented; Harold K. Jacobson and Martin F. Price, *A Framework for Research on the Human Dimensions of Global Environmental Change* (Paris: UNESCO, 1991) discusses the contributions of social scientists but excludes history and the humanities; Mats Rolén and Bo Heurling, eds., *Environmental Change: A Challenge for Social Science and the Humanities* (Stockholm: Norstedts, 1994) is much broader but is restricted to Swedish examples; Leo Marx, "The Environment and the 'Two Cultures' Divide," in Fleming and Gemery, *Technology, and the Environment*, 3–21 is a fruitful approach for humanists.

2. For a scientific reconstruction of the recent climate record see Raymond S. Bradley and Philip D. Jones, eds., *Climate since A.D. 1500.* (London: Routledge, 1992); and Philip D. Jones, Raymond S. Bradley, and Jean Jouzel, eds., *Climatic Variations and Forcing Mechanisms of the Last 2000 Years* (Berlin: Springer, 1996). On historians' interpretations of climatic

changes see, for example, Emmanuel Le Roy Ladurie, *Times of Feast, Times of Famine: A History of Climate since the Year 1000*, trans. Barbara Bray (Garden City, N.Y.: Doubleday, 1971); Robert I. Rotberg and Theodore K. Rabb, eds., *Climate and History: Studies in Interdisciplinary History* (Princeton: Princeton University Press, 1981); T. M. L. Wigley, M. J. Ingram, and G. Farmer, eds., *Climate and History: Studies in Past Climates and Their Impact on Man* (Cambridge: Cambridge University Press, 1981); and H. H. Lamb, *Climate, History and the Modern World*, 2nd ed. (London: Routledge, 1995).

3. *The Oxford English Dictionary*, CD Rom version 1.0b (New York: Oxford University Press, 1993), s.v. "apprehension."

4. Yi-fu Tuan, *Landscapes of Fear* (New York: Pantheon Books, 1979), 6.

5. Nico Stehr, "Trust and Climate," typescript paper prepared for the fourteenth International Congress of Biometeorology, Ljubljana, Slovenia, September 1996. United Nations, Information Unit on Climate Change, "Are we overlooking the social and political implications of climate change?" http://www.unep.ch/iucc/fs108.html (September 26, 1996).

1. Climate and Culture in Enlightenment Thought

1. D. Diderot and J. D'Alembert, eds., *Encyclopdédie, ou Dictionnaire Raisonné des Sciences, des Arts et des Métiers* (Paris, 1779), 8:280–86.

2. Abbé Jean-Baptiste Du Bos, *Réflexions critiques sur la poësie et sur la peinture*, 2 vols. (Paris, 1719); and numerous subsequent editions in 3 vols., e.g., Paris (1733), Utrecht (1732, 1736), Paris (1740). According to his English translator, Thomas Nugent (London, 1748), "there have been very few books published of late years that have met with a better reception, or attained to a greater reputation in the learned world, than the following Critical Reflections." Voltaire was cited in *Dictionnaire de Biographie Français*, s.v. "Du Bos," 1967.

Du Bos was perpetual secretary of the French Academy from 1722 to 1742. On his life see Auguste Morel, *Etude sur l'abbé Dubos* (Paris, 1850); and Alfred Lombard, *L'Abbé Du Bos: Un initiateur de la pensée moderne (1670–1742)* (Paris, 1913; Geneva: Slatkine Reprints, 1969).

3. Du Bos, *Critical Reflections*, vol. 2 (1748), 99–100.

4. Ibid., 225.

5. Ibid., 177–78.

6. Ibid., 179.

7. Ibid., 217–18.

8. Cited in Armin Hajman Koller, *The Abbé du Bos: His Advocacy of the Theory of Climate, a Precursor of Johann Gottfried Herder* (Champaign, Ill.: Garrard Press, 1937), 110.

9. Du Bos, *Critical Reflections*, vol. 2 (1748), 177–78.

10. Ibid., 224.

11. Ibid., 206.

12. These ideas were developed further by John Arbuthnot, *An Essay Concerning the Effects of Air on Human Bodies* (London, 1733).

13. Cited in Koller, *Abbé du Bos*, 67–68.

14. Ibid., 183. Julian Offreay de la Mettrie (1709–51) also cited this anecdote in his *Man a Machine* (LaSalle, Ill.: Open Court, 1912), 96.

15. Koller, *Abbé du Bos*, 185–86.

16. Du Bos, *Critical Reflections*, vol. 2 (1748), 214–215.

17. Ibid., 224–225.

18. Clarence J. Glacken, *Traces on the Rhodian Shore: Nature and Culture in Western Thought from Ancient Times to the End of the Eighteenth Century* (Berkeley: University of California Press, 1967), 434. See also Marian J. Tooley, "Bodin and the Mediaeval Theory of Climate," *Speculum* 28 (1953): 64–83 and E. Fournol, *Bodin prédécesseur de Montesquieu* (Paris, 1896).

19. Sir John Chardin, *Travels in Persia* (London: Argonaut Press, 1927), 134.

20. Argued in Warren E. Gates, "The Spread of Ibn Khaldûn's Ideas on Climate and Culture," *Journal of the History of Ideas* 28 (1967): 416–17.

21. Chardin, *Travels in Persia*, 131–34; 226–27. The influence of Chardin's work on Montesquieu, Jean Jacques Rousseau, and Edward Gibbon is mentioned in the introduction to the volume by Percy Sykes, xv. A complete argument for Chardin's influence on Montesquieu is found in Muriel Dodds, *Les récites des voyages, sources de l'Esprit des Lois de Montesquieu* (Paris: H. Champion, 1929).

22. For example, Frank T. H. Fletcher, "Climate and Law: Influence of Montesquieu on British Writers," *Geography* 19 (1934): 29–36; and Gordon Manley, "The Revival of Climatic Determinism," *Geogr. Rev.* 48 (1958): 98–105.

23. Robert Shackleton, "The Evolution of Montesquieu's Theory of Climate," *Rev. intl. phil.* 9 (1955): 318.

24. Montesquieu, *The Spirit of Laws: A Compendium of the First English Edition*, ed. D. W. Carrithers (Berkeley: University of California Press, 1977), pt. 3, bk. 17, chap. 2, 276.

25. Montesquieu, *Persian Letters*, trans. C. J. Betts (Baltimore: Penguin, 1973). For a similar view see Abbé Guillaume-Thomas François Raynal, *A Philosophical and Political History of the Settlements and Trade of the Europeans in the East and West Indies*, 8 vols., trans. J. O. Justamond (London, 1783).

26. Johann Gottfried von Herder, cited in Koller, *Abbé du Bos*, 6.

27. Abbé Dedieu, *Montesquieu et la tradition politique anglaise en France* (Paris: J. Gabalda, 1909), citing Arbuthnot, *Effects of Air on Human Bodies*.

28. François-Ignace Espiard de La Borde, *Essais sur le génie et la caractère des nations*, 3 vols. (Brussels, 1743), 1: 60, 87 and 3: 5, quoted in Shackleton, "Montesquieu's Theory of Climate," 327.

29. Ernst Cassirer, *The Philosophy of the Enlightenment* (Boston: Beacon Press, 1955), 214; cited in Montesquieu, *Spirit of Laws*, ed. D. W. Carrithers, 50.

30. Montesquieu to Hume, May 19, 1749, Letters to Hume 6: 46, Montesquieu to Hume, Sept. 3, 1749, 6: 47, MS. 23156, David Hume Correspondence and Papers, National Library of Scotland, Edinburgh. See also *Correspondance de Montesquieu*, ed. François Gebelin and André Morize, 2 vols. (Paris: Imprimeries Gounouilhou, 1914), 222–23.

Du Bos also influenced other famous authors, including Edward Gibbon and Johann Gottfried von Herder; Koller, *Abbé Du Bos*, 67–68, 109–

10. For more on climate in the eighteenth century, see Glacken, *Traces on the Rhodian Shore*, especially 552 and passim.

31. David Hume, "Of the Populousness of Ancient Nations," in Hume, *Essays: Moral, Political, and Literary*, ed. T. H. Green and T. H. Grose (London, 1875), 1: 432–33.

32. Ibid., 434.

33. For example, William Wood, *New England's Prospect* (London, 1634); and Cotton Mather, *The Christian Philosopher* (London, 1721).

34. Thomas Jefferson to Lewis E. Beck, July 16, 1824, in *The Writings of Thomas Jefferson*, ed. Andrew A. Lipscomb and Albert Ellery Bergh, vol. 15 (Washington, D.C.: Thomas Jefferson Memorial Association of the United States, 1907), 71–72.

2. The Great Climate Debate in Colonial and Early America

1. For details see James Rodger Fleming, *Meteorology in America, 1800–1870* (Baltimore: Johns Hopkins University Press, 1990), 2–3. See also Karen Ordahl Kupperman, "The Puzzle of the American Climate in the Early Colonial Period," *Amer. Hist. Rev.* 87 (1982): 1270.

2. Rev. John Campanius, quoted in Oliver L. Fassig, "A Sketch of the Progress of Meteorology in Maryland and Delaware," *Maryland Weather Service* 1 (1899): 333–34.

3. Thomas Campanius Holm, *Kort Beskrifning om Nya Sverige* (Stockholm, 1702). See also Nicholas Collin, "Observations Made at an Early Period on the Climate of the Country Along the River Delaware, Collected from the Records of the Swedish Colony," *Trans. Amer. Philos. Soc.* n.s. 1 (1818): 340–52.

4. James MacSparran, *America Dissected, being a full and true account of all the American Colonies, shewing the intemperance of the climates, excessive heat and cold, and sudden violent changes of weather, terrible and mischievous thunder and lightning, bad and unwholesome air, destructive to human bodies, etc.* (Dublin, 1753).

5. Alexander Hewatt, *An Historical Account of the Rise and Progress of the Colonies of South Carolina and Georgia*, 2 vols. (London, 1779), 1: 49–50, 79.

6. Kenneth C. Crawford and Edwin Kessler, "Severe Convective Storms: A Brief History of Science and Practice," in *Historical Essays on Meteorology, 1919–1995*, ed. James Rodger Fleming (Boston: American Meteorological Society, 1996), 307–19.

7. Thomas Hariot, *A Brief and True Report of the New Found Land of Virginia* (London, 1588; New York: History Book Club, 1951), conclusion (no pagination).

8. William Strachey, *The History of Travell into Virginia Britania*, ed. Louis B. Wright and Virginia Freund (London: Printed for the Hakluyt Society, 1953), 37–38.

9. Quoted in Kupperman, "Puzzle of the American Climate," 1270.

10. Edward Antill, "An Essay on the cultivation of the VINE, and the making and preserving of Wine, suited to the different Climates in North-America, *Trans. Amer. Philos. Soc.* 1 (1771): 117–97; quote from 120.

11. Cited in Peter Eisenstadt, "The Weather and Weather Forecasting in Colonial America" (Ph.D. diss., New York University, 1990), 232.

12. Edmund Halley, "Some Considerations About the Cause of the Universal Deluge" (read December 12, 1694), *Phil. Trans.* 33 (1724–35): 118–23; and in the same issue, Halley, "Some Farther Thoughts Upon the Same Subject, Delivered on the 19th of the Same Month. By the Same," 123–25. See also Journal Book of the Royal Society, vol. 9, 1690–1696, December 12, 1694, 175–76, MS in Royal Society Library, London. Buffon, *Histoire naturelle*, 26 vols. (Paris, 1802) and Peter Kalm, *Travels in North America*, 2 vols. (New York: Wilson-Erickson, 1937), both cited in Durand Echeverria, *Mirage in the West: A History of the French Image of American Society to 1815* (Princeton: Princeton University Press, 1957), 8–9.

13. Benjamin Franklin noted De Pauw's low opinion of Americans, but he certainly did not agree with it. *The Papers of Benjamin Franklin*, vol. 19, ed. William B. Willcox (New Haven: Yale University Press, 1959–95), 197. See also Gilbert Chinard, "Eighteenth Century Theories on America as a Human Habitat," *Proc. Amer. Philos. Soc.* 91 (1947): 35–6; and Echeverria, *Mirage in the West*, 10–13.

14. Abbé Guillaume-Thomas François Raynal, *A Philosophical and Political History of the Settlements and Trade of the Europeans in the East and West Indies*, trans. J. O. Justamond (London, 1783), vol. 7, bk. 17, 161.

15. Both quotes are from Echeverria, *Mirage in the West*, 14.

16. Cotton Mather, "Essay XIX. Of Cold," in *The Christian Philosopher* (London, 1721), 81.

17. Benjamin Franklin to Ezra Stiles, May 29, 1763, in *The Papers of Benjamin Franklin*, vol. 10, ed. Leonard W. Labaree (New Haven: Yale University Press, 1959–95), 264–67.

18. Hugh Williamson, "An Attempt to Account for the Change of Climate, Which Has Been Observed in the Middle Colonies in North-America," *Trans. Amer. Philos. Soc.* 1 (1771): 272–80.

19. Hugh Williamson, *Observations on the Climate in Different Parts of America, Compared with the climate in corresponding parts of the other continent. To which are added remarks on the different complexions of the human race; with some account of the aborigines of America. Being an introductory discourse to the history of North-Carolina* (New York, 1811), 9–10.

20. Ibid., 24.

21. Ibid., 72. Williamson supported his contention with wind data from Philadelphia comparing the prevalence of easterly and westerly winds for 1748–49 and 1772.

22. Ibid., 174–78.

23. Samuel Williams, *The Natural and Civil History of Vermont* (Walpole, N.H., 1794), cited in Eisenstadt, "Weather and Weather Forecasting," 233.

24. Thomas Jefferson, *Notes on the State of Virginia* (Paris, 1785; Gloucester, Mass.: Peter Smith, 1976), 79; for similar sentiments see James Winthrop, "Some account of the Amelioration of climate in Mass.," 28 May 1804, Verbal Communications, 1801–7, American Philosophical Society Archives.

25. Thomas Jefferson, "Weather memorandum book," MS, Library of Congress, quoted in David M. Ludlum, *Early American Winters, 1604–1820* (Boston: American Meteorological Society, 1966), 1: 214.

26. Constantin-François Volney, *A View of the Soil and Climate of the United States of America* . . . (Philadelphia, 1804), cited in Michael Williams, *Americans and Their Forests* (New York: Cambridge University Press, 1989), 144.

27. W. R. Baron, "Historical Climate Records from the Northeastern United States, 1640 to 1900," in *Climate Since A.D. 1500*, ed. Raymond S. Bradley and Philip D. Jones (London: Routledge, 1992), 82–83.

28. Kenneth Thompson, "Forests and Climate Change in America: Some Early Views," *Climatic Change* 3 (1980): 47–64. Ferdinand Columbus, *The Life of the Admiral Christopher Columbus by his son Ferdinand*, trans. B. Keen (New Brunswick, N.J.: Rutgers University Press, 1959), 142–43.

29. William Wood, *New England's Prospect* (London, 1634), 7–8.

30. John Evelyn (1620–1706), *Silva, or, A discourse of forest-trees, and the propagation of timber in His Majesties dominions* (London, 1664), 1:26. See also Eisenstadt, "Weather and Weather Forecasting," 230–31.

31. John Woodward, *An essay toward a natural history of the earth and terrestrial bodies, especially minerals, as also of the sea, rivers, and springs, with an account of the universal deluge, and of the effects that it had upon the earth* (1st ed. London, 1695; London: British Museum Photo Services, 1972), cited in Eisenstadt, "Weather and Weather Forecasting," 231.

32. For eighteenth-century chemists, "phlogiston" was the substance emitted during combustion. A loss of phlogiston, for example, would represent a gain in oxygen. Edward A. Holyoke, "An Estimate of the Excess of the Heat and Cold of the American Atmosphere Beyond the European, in the Same Parallel of Latitude; To which are added, some thoughts on the causes of this excess," (read 1788), *Mem. Amer. Acad. Arts Sci.* 2, pt. 1 (1793): 65–92; see also Eisenstadt, "Weather and Weather Forecasting," 232–33.

33. Noah Webster, "On the Effects of Evergreens on Climate, " *Trans. Soc. Promotion of Useful Arts* 1, pt. 4 (Albany, 1799): 51–52; Parker Cleaveland, "Meteorological Observations Made at Bowdoin College," *Mem. Amer. Acad. Arts Sci.* 3, pt. 1 (1809): 119–21.

34. Jefferson, *Notes on the State of Virginia*, 74.

35. Thomas Jefferson to Jean Baptiste Le Roy, November 13, 1786, in *The Papers of Thomas Jefferson*, vol. 10, ed. Julian P. Boyd (Princeton: Princeton University Press, 1950–95), 524–28.

36. Ibid., 529–30.

37. J. Henry Smyth, Jr., ed., *The Amazing Benjamin Franklin* (New York: Frederick A. Stokes, 1929), 8: 597–98. See also A. Fothergill, "Animadversions on the dangerous practice of sleeping on the damp ground and of exposure to the night air, particularly where the animal powers are diminished; illustrated on philosophical principles," *Mem. Amer. Acad. Arts Sci.* 2, pt. 1 (1793): 206.

38. Thomas Wright, "On the Mode Most Easily and Effectually Practicable of Drying Up the Marshes of the Maritime Parts of North America,"

Trans. Amer. Philos. Soc. 4 (1799): 246. See also William Currie, "An Enquiry into the Causes of the Insalubrity of Flat and Marshy Situations; And directions for preventing or correcting the effects thereof," *Trans. Amer. Philos. Soc.* 4 (1799): 127–42.

39. Benjamin Rush, "An Enquiry into the Cause of the Increase of Bilious and Intermitting Fevers in Pennsylvania, With Hints for Preventing Them," *Trans. Amer. Philos. Soc.* 2 (1786): 206–12; quotes from 207, 25; see also Eisenstadt, "Weather and Weather Forecasting," 234–235.

40. Thomas Jefferson, "Petition to the Senate and House of Representatives of the U.S.," January 17, 1800, MS Communications, no. 3, 1, American Philosophical Society Archives.

41. Job Wilson, "A Meteorological Synopsis, in connection with the prevailing diseases for sixteen years, as they occurred at Salisbury, Massachusetts," *Medical Repository* 22, n.s. 7 (1822): 409–13.

42. William Dunbar to Thomas Jefferson (1801); quoted in Ludlum, *Early American Winters*, 1: 63; see David M. Ludlum, "Thomas Jefferson and the American Climate," *Bull. Amer. Meteorol. Soc.* 47 (1966): 974–75. William Dunbar, "Meteorological Observations," *Trans. Amer. Philos. Soc.* 4 (1809): 48.

43. David Ramsay, *The History of South-Carolina: From Its First Settlement in 1670, to the year 1808* (Charleston, S.C., 1809), quoted in Ludlum, *Early American Winters*, 1: 162.

44. Johann David Schoepf, *The Climate and Diseases of America During the Revolution*, trans. James Read Chadwick (Boston, 1875), 26.

45. Noah Webster, "On the Supposed Change in the Temperature of Winter," in *A Collection of Papers on Political, Literary, and Moral Subjects* (New York, 1843), 138.

46. *New Edinburgh Encyclopedia*, 30 vols., conducted by David Brewster, American ed. (Philadelphia, 1808–24), 1:583, cited in Chinard, "Eighteenth Century Theories," 41.

3. Privileged Positions

1. Many of the diaries have been preserved, for example, James Madison, "Meteorological journals kept at his plantation, with notes on sowing and harvesting, migration of birds, etc., 1784–93, 1798–1802," 2 vols., MS, American Philosophical Society Library, cited in *A New Guide to the Collections in the Library of the American Philosophical Society*, ed. Stephen J. Catlett (Philadelphia: American Philosophical Society, 1987), entry 718.

2. Thomas Jefferson to Lewis E. Beck, July 16, 1824, in *The Writings of Thomas Jefferson*, ed. Andrew A. Lipscomb and Albert Ellery Bergh (Washington, D.C.: Thomas Jefferson Memorial Association of the United States, 1904–7), 15: 71–72.

3. On instruments, see W. E. Knowles Middleton, *The History of the Barometer* (Baltimore: Johns Hopkins Press, 1964); Middleton, *A History of the Thermometer and Its Use in Meteorology* (Baltimore: Johns Hopkins Press, 1966); and Middleton, *Invention of the Meteorological Instruments* (Baltimore: Johns Hopkins Press, 1969).

4. "Dichiarazione d'alcun Istrumenti per conoscer l'Alterazioni dell'-

Aria," *Saggi di naturali esperienze fatte nell'Accademia del Cimento* (Firenze, 1666).

5. *Archivo Meteorologico Centrale Italiano* (Firenze, 1858), reproduced in G. Hellmann, *Neudrucke von Schriften und Karten über Meteorologie und Erdmagnetismus* no. 7 (Berlin, 1897), 9–17. Brief mention of this system also appears in H. H. Frisinger, *The History of Meteorology to 1800* (New York: Science History Publications, 1977).

6. Thomas Sprat, *History of the Royal Society* (London, 1667); reprint, ed. J. I. Cope and H. W. Jones (St. Louis: Washington University Press, 1958), 173–79. See also Theodore Feldman, "The Origin of Institutional Weather Diaries at the Royal Society," unpublished manuscript, 1997.

7. James Jurin, "Invitatio ad Observationes Meteorologicas communi consilio instituendas," *Phil. Trans.* 32 (1723): 422–27.

8. See, for example, William Derham, "An Abstract of the Meteorological Diaries," *Phil. Trans.* (1733–34): 101–5.

9. Roger Pickering, "Scheme of a Diary of the Weather, together with draughts and descriptions of Machines subservient thereunto," *Phil. Trans.* 43 (May 3, 1744).

10. George J. Symons, "History of English Meteorological Societies, 1823 to 1880," *Quart. J. Roy. Meteorol. Soc.* 7 (1881): 65–98. See also Robert Watson-Watt, "The Evolution of Meteorological Institutions in the United Kingdom," *Quart. J. Roy. Meteorol. Soc.* 76 (1950): 115–24; and Richard Corless, "A Brief History of the Royal Meteorological Society," *Weather* 5 (1950): 78–83.

11. Symons, "English Meteorological Societies," 76. Symons provides a useful summary of the minutes of the proceedings of the society for 1823–24 and 1836–43.

12. John Ruskin, "Remarks on the Present State of Meteorological Science," *Trans. Meteorol. Soc. Lond.* 1 (1839): 56–59.

13. *The Quarterly Journal of Meteorology* was published from 1841 to 1843.

14. Symons, "English Meteorological Societies," 93.

15. Ibid., 88.

16. George J. Symons, "The First Daily Weather Map," *Meteorol. Mag.* 32 (1897): 133–35; a copy of this map was published in *Meteorol. Mag.* 31 (1896): 113. Bernard Ashley, *Weather Men* (London: Allman, 1974), 39–41, says it was August 31, 1848, but provides no references.

17. Jim Burton, "Robert Fitzroy and the Early History of the Meteorological Office," *Brit. J. Hist. Sci.* 19 (1986): 147–76. Other short articles include the following: "Meteorological Office Centenary, 1855–1955," *Meteorol. Mag.* 84 (1955): 161–98; David Brunt, "A Hundred Years of Meteorology, 1851–1951," *Adv. Sci.* 8 (1951): 114–24; Brunt, "The Centenary of the Meteorological Office: Retrospect and Prospect," *Sci. Prog.* 44 (1956): 193–207; G. A. Bull, "Short History of the Meteorological Office," *Meteorol. Mag.* 83 (1955): 163–67; R. P. W. Lewis, "The Founding of the Meteorological Office, 1854–55," *Meteorol. Mag.* 110 (1981): 221–27; "Meteorological Office, 1855–1955," *Nature* 175 (1955): 963–65.

18. Edme Mariotte, *Oeuvres de Mariotte*, 2 vols. in 1 (Leiden, 1717). Gustav Hellmann, "Die Ältesten instrumentellen meteorologischen

Beobachtungen in Deutchland," *Beitr. Gesch. Meteorol.*, bd. 1, nr. 2 (Berlin, 1914), 103–7.

19. Charles C. Gillispie, *Science and Polity in France at the End of the Old Regime* (Princeton: Princeton University Press, 1980), 226–29. On Cotte see J. A. Kington, "A Late Eighteenth-Century Source of Meteorological Data," *Weather* 25 (1970): 169–75; Theodore S. Feldman, "The History of Meteorology, 1750–1800: A Case Study in the Quantification of Experimental Physics" (Ph.D. diss., University of California, Berkeley, 1983), 214.

20. Lavoisier to Blondeau, November 16, 1776, in *Oeuvres de Lavoisier*, vol. 3, *Correspondence*, ed. R. Fric (Paris: Imprimerie Imperiale, 1964), 658; also Lavoisier, "Règles pour Prédire le Changement de Temps," *Literary Magazine* (1790).

21. Lambert, "Exposé de quelques observations . . . por répondre du jour sur la métérologie," *Nouv. mém. Acad. Roy. Sci. Belles-Let.* (Berlin) (1773): 60–65; Condorcet, "Equisse d'un tableau historique . . ." (1795), in *Oeuvres complètes de Condorcet*, vol. 8 (Paris, 1804).

22. Alfred Angot, "Premier catalogue des observations météorologiques faites en France depuis l'origine jusqu'en 1850," in *Annales du Bureau Central Météorologique de France, 1895*, vol. 1, *Mémoires* (Paris, 1897), 89–146.

23. Doublet, "La météorologie en France et en Allemagne," *Revue philomathique de Bordeaux et du Sud Ouest* 14 (1911): 213–32, 250–67; 15 (1912): 103–28, 169–86. See also *Ce qu'est la météorologie française* (Paris: Bureau central météorologique de France, 1952): and John L. Davis, "Weather Forecasting and the Development of Meteorological Theory at the Paris Observatory, 1853–1878," *Ann. Sci.* 41 (1984): 359–82.

24. Or *Sammlung von Natur- und Medicin-, wie auch hiezu gehörigen Kunst- und Literatur-Geschichten* (1718–30). Gustav Hellmann, "Die Vorläuffer der Societas Meteorologica Palatina," *Beitr. Gesch. Meteorol.*, bd. 1, nr. 5 (Berlin, 1914), 139–47; Hellmann, "Umriss einer Geschichte der meteorologischen Beobachtungen in Deutchland," *Repertorium der Deutchen Meteorologie* (Leipzig, 1883): 884–86; Abraham Wolf, *A History of Science, Technology, and Philosophy in the Eighteenth Century* (New York: Macmillan, 1939), 284; and Emil J. Walter, "Technische Bedingungen in der historichen Entwicklung der Meteorologie," *Gesnerus* 9 (1952): 55–66.

25. David C. Cassidy, "Meteorology in Mannheim: The Palatine Meteorological Society, 1780–1795," *Sudhoffs Archiv: Zeitschrift für Wissenschaftsgeschichte* 69 (1985): 8–25; Albert Cappel, "Societas Meteorologica Palatina (1780–1795)," *Annalen der Meteorologie* n.s. 16 (1980): 10–27, 255–61; Friedrich Traumüller, *Die Mannheimer meteorologische Gesellschaft (1780–1795): Ein Beitrag zur Geschichte der Meteorologie* (Leipzig, 1885).

26. J. J. Hemmer, "Historia Societas Meteorologicae Palatinae," in Societatis Meteorologicae Palatinae, *Ephemerides*, vol. 1, *1781* (1783): 1–54, cited by Cassidy, "Meteorology in Mannheim," 15.

27. Societatis Meteorologicae Palatinae, *Ephemerides*, 12 vols. (1783–95).

28. Hellmann, "Umriss einer Geschichte." Data from the Verein appear in *Annalen für Meteorologie, Erdmagnetismus und verwandte*

Gegenstände beginning in 1842. See also Hellmann, "Die Entwicklung der meteorologischen Beobachtungen in Deutchland von der ersten Anfängen bis zur Einrichtung staatlicher Beobachtungsnetze," *Abh. Preuss. Akad. Wiss. Phys.-math. Kl.*, no. 1 (Berlin, 1926).

29. Gustav Hellmann, *Geschichte des Königlich Preussischen Meteorologischen Instituts von seiner Gründing im Jahre 1847 bis zu seiner Reorganisation im Jahre 1885* (Berlin, 1887). See also Hellmann, "Katalogen der Schriften und Erfindungen," *Repertorium der Deutchen Meteorologie*, 1–744. A bibliography of 208 of Dove's works appears on pages 93–103.

30. E. Doublet, "La météorologie en France et en Allemagne," *Revue philomathique de Bordeaux et sud ouest* 15 (1912): 173; Heinrich Seilkopf, "Zur Geschichte der meteorologischen Arbeit an der Deutchen Seewarte, Hamburg," *Annalen der Meteorologie* 3 (1950): 53–56.

31. E. I. Tichomirov, "Instructions for Russian Meteorological Stations of the 18th Century," (in Russian, English summary) *Proc. Central Geophys. Obs.* (1932): 3–12.

32. Alexander Woeikof, "Meteorology in Russia," *Smithson. Rept.* (1872): 267–98; F. Clawer, *Catalog der Meteorologischen Beobachtungen im Russichen Reich Zusammengestelt*, in *Repertorium für Meteorologie*, ed. H. Wild, vol. 2 (St. Petersburg, 1872), contains information on meteorological observations at 330 locations in Russia from 1726. See also Pavel Nikolaevich Tverskoi, *Razvitie Meteorologii v U.S.S.R.* [Development of meteorology in the U.S.S.R.] (Leningrad, 1949).

33. Woeikof, "Meteorology in Russia."

34. Cleveland Abbe, "Meteorology in Russia," *Monthly Weather Rev.* 27 (1899): 106.

35. Alexsandr Khristoforovich Khrgian, "The History of Meteorology in Russia," *Actes du VIIIe Congrès International d'Histoire des Sciences* (Paris, 1958): 446. A book-length treatment by the same author with international comparisons is *Meteorology: A Historical Survey*, 2nd. ed., vol. 1., trans. Ron Hardin (Jerusalem: Israel Program for Scientific Translations, 1970).

36. See Alfred J. Henry, "Early Individual Observers in the United States," *Bull. U. S. Weather Bureau* 11 (1893): 291–302; and James M. Havens, ed., *An Annotated Bibliography of Meteorological Observations in the United States, 1731–1818*, Florida State University Department of Meteorology Technical Rept. no. 5 (Tallahassee, Fla., 1956).

37. [R. M. Patterson], "Suggestions for the expedition on meteorological observations, topography, traverse distances, knowledge of the Indians in astronomy, etc." MS, n.d., but ca. 1819, B P274, American Philosophical Society Archives.

38. "Concerning Inquiries to be Made of Major Long of the Indians," March 30, 1819, draft MS-A and B, 28pp., MS Communications, American Philosophical Society Archives.

39. William Stanton, *American Scientific Exploration, 1803–1860* (Philadelphia: American Philosophical Society Library, 1991), 50.

40. For details see James Rodger Fleming, *Meteorology in America, 1800–1870* (Baltimore: Johns Hopkins University Press, 1990), 9–19 and passim.

41. Josiah Meigs to John Vaughan, September 6, 1821, MS Communications, American Philosophical Society Archives. Josiah Meigs, "Geo-

metric exemplification of temperature, winds, and weather for 1820 at Washington City," *Minutes Amer. Philos. Soc.* (October 19, 1821): 505.

42. See Fleming, *Meteorology in America* for details.

43. [Matthew Fontaine Maury], *On the Establishment of an Universal System of Meteorological Observations by Sea and Land* (Washington, D.C., 1851). Maury's role in the history of science is ambiguous. Frances Leigh Williams, *Matthew Fontaine Maury: Scientist of the Sea* (New Brunswick, N.J.: Rutgers University Press, 1963), praises him. John Leighly, in his introduction to Maury, *The Physical Geography of the Sea and Its Meteorology* (Cambridge, Mass.: Belknap Press of Harvard University Press, 1963), pp. ix–xxx, is highly critical.

44. John F. Crampton, Britain's Chargé d'Affairs to Daniel Webster, Secretary of State, November 13, 1851; transmitted to Secretary of the Navy William A. Graham, November 14, 1851; Charles Morris, Chief of Bureau of Ordnance and Hydrography to Maury, November 19, 1851; Maury to Morris, November 21, 1851, all letters quoted in [Maury], *Establishment of an Universal System.*

45. Maury to the Foreign Ministers of Belgium, Austria, Netherlands, Sweden and Norway, Two Sicilies and Parma, Sardinia, Guatemala, Argentina, Chile, Mexico, Nicaragua, Venezuela, and Peru, December 23, 1851, Letters Sent, Naval Observatory Records, U.S. National Archives and Records Administration (hereafter NARA).

46. *Maritime Conference held at Brussels for devising an uniform system of meteorological observations at sea, August and September 1853* (Brussels, 1853), published in both English and French.

47. Maury to Lieut. Marin Jansen, Royal Dutch Navy, November 8, 1853, September 2, 1858, Box KN, Naval Records Collection, NARA. [Johann von] Lamont to Maury, n.d. ca. 1853, Letters Received, Naval Observatory Records, NARA. According to Lamont, the same noncooperation hampered the "Magnetic Conference" in England in 1845.

48. For details, see Fleming, *Meteorology in America*, 106–10.

49. Most of these international meetings are well documented. See, for example, *Meteorological Conference Proceedings* 12 vols. in 1 (London, 1873–81), which contains reports on meetings from Leipzig (1872) through Bern (1880). Also see O. L. Fassig, ed., *Report of the International Meteorological Congress held at Chicago, Ill., August 21–24, 1893, under the auspices of the congress auxiliary of the World's Columbian Exposition*, U. S. Dept. of Agriculture, *Bull. U. S. Weather Bureau* 11 (Washington, D.C., 1894, 1896), 772 pp.

50. Myer, *U. S. Army Signal Office Report* (1874): 505.

51. Bruno Latour, "Visualization and Cognition: Thinking with Eyes and Hands," *Knowledge and Society: Studies in the Sociology of Culture Past and Present* 6 (1986): 22–23.

4. Climate Discourse Transformed

1. Noah Webster, "On the Supposed Change in the Temperature of Winter," *Mem. Conn. Acad. Arts Sci.* 1, pt. 1 (1810): 216–60; reprinted in Webster, *A Collection of Papers on Political, Literary, and Moral Subjects* (New York, 1843), 119–62, quote from 136.

2. Webster, "Temperature of Winter," 127–34, 138.

3. Ibid., 145.

4. Luke Howard, *The Climate of London*, 2nd ed. (London, 1820), cited in Joseph M'Sweeny, "An Essay on the Climate of Ireland," *Trans. Roy. Irish Acad.* 17 (1837): 193.

5. Webster, "Temperature of Winter," 162; quote from 148. See also Peter Eisenstadt, "The Weather and Weather Forecasting in Colonial America" (Ph.D. diss., New York University, 1990), 236–37.

6. William Cronon, *Changes in the Land: Indians, Colonists, and the Ecology of New England* (New York: Hill and Wang, 1983), 122–26 discusses the ecology of these changes.

7. U. S. Army Medical Department, *Meteorological Register for the Years 1822, 1823, 1824, and 1825 from Observations made by the Surgeons of the Army at the Military Posts of the United States* (Washington, D.C., 1826).

8. Ibid., 1–2.

9. "Notice of a Meteorological Register for the years 1822, 1823, 1824 and 1825; from observations made by the Surgeons of the Army, at the Military Posts of the United States," *Amer. J. Sci.* 12 (1827): 149–54.

10. Alexander von Humboldt, "Uber die Haupt-Ursachen der Temperatur-Verschiedenheit auf dem Erdköper" (1827), quoted and translated in H. E. Landsberg, "Early Stages of Climatology in the United States," *Bull. Amer. Meteorol. Soc.* 45 (1964): 270.

11. Samuel Forry, "Researches in Elucidation of the Distribution of Heat over the Globe, and Especially of the Climatic Features Peculiar to the Region of the United States," *Amer. J. Sci.* 47 (1844): 227.

12. Ibid., 240. Forry was citing Conrad Malte-Brun, *A System of Universal Geography*, 3 vols. (Boston, 1834).

13. Forry, "Distribution of Heat over the Globe," 236.

14. Ibid., 239.

15. Alexander von Humboldt, *Views of Nature: Or Contemplations on the Sublime Phenomena of Creation; with Scientific Illustrations*, trans. E. C. Otté and Henry G. Bohn (London, 1850), 103–4.

16. Humboldt, cited in M. Becquerel, "Forests and Their Climatic Influence," *Smithson. Rept.* (1869): 408–9.

17. Lorin Blodget, *Climatology of the United States* (Philadelphia, 1857), chap. 17, 481–92, quotes from 481, 484.

18. Elias Loomis and H. A. Newton, "On the Mean Temperature, and On the Fluctuations of Temperature, at New Haven, Conn., Lat. 41° 18' N., Long. 72° 55' W. of Greenwich," *Trans. Conn. Acad. Arts Sci.* 1, pt. 1 (1866): 194–246.

19. Cleveland Abbe, "Biographical Memoir of Charles Anthony Schott," *Biog. Mem. Natl. Acad. Sci.* 8 (1915): 87–133.

20. Charles A. Schott, "Tables and Results of the Precipitation, in Rain and Snow, in the United States and at Some Stations in Adjacent Parts of North America and in Central and South America," *Smithson. Contrib.* 18 (1872), article 2; Schott, "Tables, Distribution, and Variations of the Atmospheric Temperature in the United States and Some Adjacent Parts of North America," *Smithson. Contrib.* 21 (1876), article

5; the manuscript copy of this work is in RG-27, NARA. Curves of secular change in the mean annual temperature are facing p. 310; the quote is from 311. Schott's charts are reproduced in James Rodger Fleming, *Meteorology in America 1800–1870* (Baltimore: Johns Hopkins University Press, 1990), 130–32.

21. William Ferrel, "Note on the Influence of Forests upon Rainfall," *Amer. Meteorol. J.* 5 (1888–89): 433–35. Charles D. Wilber, *Great Valleys and Prairies of Nebraska and the Northwest* (Omaha, 1881), 68, cited in Charles R. Kutzler, "Can Forests Bring Rain to the Plains?" *Forest History* 15, no. 3 (October 1971): 14–21.

22. William Ferrel, *Temperature of the Atmosphere and Earth's Surface*, Professional Papers of the Signal Service, no. 13 (Washington, D.C., 1884), 20–21, 52, emphasis added.

23. Cleveland Abbe, "Is Our Climate Changing?" *Forum* 6 (1889): 679.

24. Ibid., 683–84.

25. Ibid., 687–88.

5. Joseph Fourier's Theory of Terrestrial Temperatures

1. I. Grattan-Guinness, with J. Ravitz, *Joseph Fourier, 1768–1830: A survey of his life and work, based on a critical edition of his monograph on the propagation of heat presented to the Institute of France in 1807* (Cambridge, Mass.: MIT Press, 1972); John Herivel, *Joseph Fourier: The Man and the Physicist* (Oxford: Clarendon Press, 1975); David A. Keston, "Joseph Fourier—Politician and Scientist," http: //www.astro.gla.ac.uk/ ~davidk/fourier.htm (October 29, 1996).

2. Joseph Fourier, "Remarques générales sur les températures du globe terrestre et des espaces planétaires," *Ann. chim. phys.* (Paris) 2nd ser., 27 (1824): 136–67. This essay was reprinted, with slight changes, as Fourier, "Mémoire sur les températures du globe terrestre et des espaces planétaires," *Mém. Acad. Sci.* 2d ser., 7 (1827): 569–604. The English translation of Fourier's 1824 article, by Ebeneser Burgess, appears in the *Amer. J. Sci.* 32 (1837): 1–20.

3. V. Ramanathan, "The Greenhouse Theory of Climate Change: A Test by Inadvertent Global Experiment," *Science* 240 (1988): 293–299, quote from 293.

4. V. Ramanathan, "The Radiative and Climatic Consequences of the Changing Atmospheric Composition of Trace Gases," in *The Changing Atmosphere*, ed. F. S. Rowland and I. S. A. Isaksen (New York: Wiley, 1988), 159–186, quote from 160.

5. M. D. H. Jones and A. Henderson-Sellers, "History of the Greenhouse Effect," *Prog. Phys. Geog.* 14, no. 1 (1990): 5.

6. Michael Oppenheimer and Robert H. Boyle, *Dead Heat: The Race Against the Greenhouse Effect* (New York: Basic Books, 1990), 34. The following citation is on p. 222: "Les Temperatures [sic] du Globe Terrestre et des Espaces Planétaires," *Memoires* [sic] *de L'Academe* [sic] *Royal des Sciences de L'Institut de France* 7 (1824) [sic], 569–604. The correct citation is given in note 2.

7. Joseph Fourier, 1824, 153; see note 2. "L'effet de la chaleur solaire

sur l'air contenu par des enveloppes transparentes avait été depuis long-
temps observé" (my translation).

8. Ian H. Rowlands, *The Politics of Global Atmospheric Change* (Manchester: Manchester University Press, 1995), 66.

9. Roger Revelle, "Introduction: The Scientific History of Carbon Dioxide," in *The Carbon Cycle and Atmospheric CO_2: Natural Variations Archean to Present*, ed. E. T. Sundquist and W. S. Broecker, Geophysical Monographs, vol. 32 (Washington, D.C.: American Geophysical Union, 1985), 1–4. William W. Kellogg, "Mankind's Impact on Climate: The Evolution of an Awareness," *Climatic Change* 10 (1987): 113–136. Wilfrid Bach, *Our Threatened Climate: Ways of Averting the CO_2 Problem through Rational Energy Use*, trans. Jill Jäger (Dordrecht: D. Reidel, 1984), 320.

10. Spencer Weart, "From the Nuclear Frying Pan into the Global Fire," *Bull. Atom. Sci.* (June 1992): 19–27; Weart, "The Discovery of the Risk of Global Warming," *Physics Today* (January 1997): 36 also wrongly cites Fourier (1827).

11. M. D. Handel and J. S. Risbey, "An Annotated Bibliography on the Greenhouse Effect and Climate Change," *Climatic Change* 21, no. 2 (1992): 97–255.

12. *Oeuvres de Fourier*, ed. Gaston Darboux (Paris, 1890), 2: 97ff.

13. Theophrastus, cited in Clarence J. Glacken, *Traces on the Rhodian Shore: Nature and Culture in Western Thought from Ancient Times to the End of the Eighteenth Century* (Berkeley: University of California Press, 1967), 130.

14. David Hume, "Of the Populousness of Ancient Nations," (ca. 1750), in Hume, *Essays: Moral, Political, and Literary*, ed. T. H. Green and T. H. Grose (London, 1875), 1: 432–39.

15. Thomas Jefferson, *Notes on the State of Virginia* (Paris, 1785; Gloucester, Mass.: Peter Smith, 1976), 79.

16. Jones and Henderson-Sellers, "History of the Greenhouse Effect," 5.

17. Svante Arrhenius, "On the Influence of Carbonic Acid in the Air upon the Temperature of the Ground," *Phil. Mag.* ser. 5 (1896): 237.

18. John Tyndall, "On the Absorption and Radiation of Heat by Gases and Vapours, and on the Physical Connection of Radiation, Absorption, and Conduction," *Phil. Mag.* ser. 4 (1861): 22, 169–94, 273–85. References to Fourier are on 169 and 277. The geologist T. C. Chamberlin followed Tyndall's suggestion. See T. C. Chamberlin, "A Group of Hypotheses Bearing on Climatic Changes," *J. Geol.* 5 (1897): 653–83; and James R. Fleming, "T. C. Chamberlin and H_2O Climate Feedbacks: A Voice from the Past," *EOS, Trans. Amer. Geophys. Union* 73 (1992): 505, 509.

19. C. S. M. Pouillet, "Memoir on the Solar Heat, on the Radiating and Absorbing Powers of the Atmospheric Air, and on the Temperature of Space," trans. Richard Taylor, *Scientific Memoirs* 4 (1846): 68–69.

20. M. Melloni, "Memoir on the Free Transmission of Radiant Heat through Different Solid and Liquid Bodies," trans. Richard Taylor, *Scientific Memoirs* 1 (1837): 1–5. Melloni, "Proposal of a New Nomenclature for the Science of Calorific Radiations," trans. Richard Taylor, *Scientific Memoirs* 3 (1843): 527–36.

21. Pouillet, "Memoir on the Solar Heat."

22. Fourier, "Températures du globe terrestre et des espaces planétaires," 136.

23. Herivel, *Joseph Fourier*, 197.

24. Joseph Fourier, "Sur la propagation de la chaleur, présenté à l'Institut le 21 décembre 1807, avec notes présentées en 1808 et 1809," reproduced as an appendix in Grattan-Guinness, *Joseph Fourier, 1768–1830*.

25. Joseph Fourier, "Remarques générales," 151–53; Burgess translation, 10–11.

26. Ibid., 155; Burgess translation, 13.

27. H. B. de Saussure, [letter dated March 30, 1784], *Journal de Paris* no. 108 (1784): 475–78; Saussure, *Voyages dans les Alpes*, vol. 4 (Neuchâtel-Geneva, 1779–96), section 932, pp. 136–39; Alexsandr Khristoforovich Khrgian, *Meteorology: A Historical Survey*, 2nd ed., vol. 1; trans. Ron Hardin (Jerusalem: Israel Program for Scientific Translations, 1970), 336.

28. Joseph Fourier, "Remarques générales," 154; Burgess translation, 12.

29. Ibid., 163–64; Burgess translation, 17–18.

30. Ibid., 165; Burgess translation, 19.

31. Ibid., 166–67; Burgess translation, 19.

32. Joseph Fourier, *Théorie analytique de la chaleur* (Paris, 1822); Fourier, *The Analytical Theory of Heat*, trans. Alexander Freeman (Cambridge, 1878), 9.

33. Ibid., 72–73. The translator used the term "diathermanous," which is anachronistic. The adjective used by Fourier in 1822 was "diaphanes," meaning diaphanous or almost transparent.

34. Joseph Fourier, "Sur la température des habitations et sur le mouvement varié de la chaleur dans les prismes rectangulaires," *Bull. Soc. Philomath.* (1818): 1–11, reprinted in *Oeuvres de Fourier*, 2: 225–39.

35. Joseph Fourier, "Questions sur la théorie physique de la chaleur rayonnante," *Ann. chim. phys.* (Paris) 2nd ser., 6 (1817): 259–303, quoted in Fourier, *Oeuvres*, 2: 364.

36. Joseph Fourier, "Extrait d'une mémoire sur l'état actual de la théorie physique et mathematique de chaleur," n.d., Théorie de la chaleur 7. Ouvrages sur la chaleur, MS, Collection des papiers du mathématicién Fourier 29 (MSS français 22529), 79, Bibliothèque nationale, Paris (hereafter Fourier Papers). My translation. The five laws of radiant heat are enumerated in Joseph Fourier, "Precis historique sur la théorie de la chaleur," n.d., Théorie de la chaleur 3, Histoire de la Théorie, Fourier Papers 25 (MSS français 22525), 168.

37. Fourier, "Extrait d'une mémoire," 80–83. My translation. See Fourier, *Analytical Theory of Heat*, 3.

38. Fourier, "Extrait d'une mémoire," 87. My translation.

39. Reference to his 650-page manuscript is in Joseph Fourier, "Théorie de la chaleur" (Extrait), *Ann. chim. phys.* (Paris) 2d ser., 3 (1816): 350–76.

40. Fourier, "Precis historique sur la théorie de la chaleur," 163–64.

41. Edme Mariotte, "Traite de la nature des couleurs," (1681), in *Oeuvres de M. Mariotte* 2nd ed., 2 vols. in 1 (The Hague, 1740), 288.

6. John Tyndall, Svante Arrhenius, and Early Research on Carbon Dioxide and Climate

1. The standard biography of Tyndall is by Arthur Stewart Eve and Clarence Hamilton Cressey, *The Life and Work of John Tyndall* (London: Macmillan, 1945). Tyndall's manuscripts, some eight thousand items, are in the John Tyndall Collection, Royal Institution of Great Britain, London (hereafter Tyndall Collection). A comprehensive guide to Tyndall manuscripts is James R. Friday, Roy M. MacLeod, and Phillipa Shepherd, *John Tyndall: Natural Philosopher, 1820–1893: Catalog of Correspondence, Journals and Collected Papers* (London: Mansell, 1974). Tyndall's publications are listed in *A Record of the Scientific Work of John Tyndall, D.C.L., L.L.D., F.R.S. (1850–1888)* (London: Chiswick, 1935). This biographical sketch is based on these sources and on the *Dictionary of Scientific Biography*.

2. John Tyndall to Michael Faraday, July 20, 1851, Tyndall Collection.

3. Tyndall to Faraday, July 22, 1862, Tyndall Collection 12: 4114–18.

4. Tyndall to Herschel, November 17, 1864, Letters and Papers of Sir John Herschel, Royal Society of London 17: 397 (hereafter John Herschel Papers, Royal Society); copy in Tyndall Collection 2: 533.

5. Tyndall to Herschel, January 4, [1863], John Herschel Papers, Royal Society 17: 392; copy in Tyndall Collection 2: 520.

6. Herschel to Tyndall, January 5, 1863, Tyndall Collection 2: 521–22; copy in John Herschel Papers, Royal Society 17: 392a.

7. In 1863, on the occasion of Tyndall's receipt of the Royal Medal of the Royal Society, Sir George Gabriel Stokes prepared a ten-page written summary and evaluation of Tyndall's research over the past ten years. Papers of Sir George Gabriel Stokes, Add. MS 7656, Tyndall-Stokes, T555 [c. 1863], Department of Manuscripts and University Archives, Cambridge University Library (hereafter Stokes Papers).

8. Rough Draft of Notes," (for 1882 lecture on heat/sound), Tyndall Collection.

9. John Tyndall, Journal 8a, Wednesday 18th May [1859], Tyndall Collection.

10. E. S. Barr, "The Infrared Pioneers II," *Infrared Phys.* 2 (1962): 67–73. Maurizio Torrini, *Scienziati a Napoli, 1830–1845* (Napoli: CUEN, 1989). Gino Tarozzi, ed., *Leopoldo Nobili e la cultura scientifica del suo tempo* (Bologna: Nuova Alfa Editoriale, 1985).

11. Tyndall recounts the history of his own discovery many times. One example is Tyndall, [Making wave of radiant heat sonorous], MS 1881, Tyndall Collection.

12. John Tyndall, "Note on the Transmission of Heat Through Gaseous Bodies," *Proc. Roy. Soc. Lond.* 10 (1859): 37; Tyndall, "Transmission of Heat of Different Qualities," 155–58.

13. Tyndall, "On the Absorption and Radiation of Heat by Gases and Vapours, and on the Physical Connection of Radiation, Absorption, and Conduction," *Phil. Mag.* ser. 4, 22 (1861): 169–94, 273–85.

14. John Tyndall, "On Radiation through the Earth's Atmosphere," *Phil. Mag.* ser. 4, 125 (1862): 202–3.

15. *Professor Tyndall's Lectures on Heat*, Lecture 11, April 3, 1862, and Lecture 12, April 10, 1862, pamphlet, Tyndall Collection.

16. [John Tyndall], "Making wave of radiant heat sonorous," MS, p. 2, 1881, Tyndall Collection.

17. John Tyndall, "Action of Free Molecules on Radiant Heat, and Its Conversion thereby into Sound" [abstract], *Proc. Roy. Soc. Lond.* 216 (1881): 5.

18. John Tyndall, "On Radiation through the Earth's Atmosphere," Friday, January 23, 1863, *Proc. Roy. Inst. Gt. Br.* 4 (1851–66): 4–8; quote from 8. This wording is also in the article of the same title published in *Phil. Mag.* ser. 4, 25 (1862): 200–206. See also John Tyndall to James Croll, ca. 1865–1868, Letters to Croll, f. 150, Additional MS 41,077, Department of Manuscripts, British Library, London.

19. *Tyndall's Lectures on Heat*, Lecture 12.

20. Tyndall, "Radiation through the Earth's Atmosphere," 204–5.

21. William Wells, *An Essay on Dew* (London, 1814); *Tyndall's Lectures on Heat*, Lecture 12; [John Tyndall], "Action of Molecules, Free and Constrained, on Radiant Heat," MS, p. 21, n.d., Tyndall Collection.

22. Tyndall to Herschel, November 21, 1861, John Herschel Papers, Royal Society 17: 389; copy in Tyndall Collection 2: 509–10.

23. Herschel to Tyndall, November 22, 1861, Tyndall Collection 2: 512–13.

24. Herschel to Tyndall, November 24, 1861, Tyndall Collection 2: 515; copy in John Herschel Papers, Royal Society 23: 350.

25. Herschel to Tyndall, April 12, 1862, Tyndall Collection 2: 516–17; copy in John Herschel Papers, Royal Society 7: 390a. This was also G. B. Airy's opinion. See, for example, Tyndall to [J. D.] Hooker, Friday, n.d. [late 1862?], Tyndall Collection, 8: 2561.

26. Stokes Papers, Add. MS 7656, Tyndall-Stokes, T555 [c. 1863].

27. Tyndall, "Radiation through the Earth's Atmosphere," 205.

28. John Tyndall, "On the Passage of Radiant Heat through Dry and Humid Air," *Phil. Mag.* ser. 4, 26 (1863): 54.

29. Tyndall, "Action of Molecules," 24–25.

30. Samuel P. Langley to John Tyndall, September 10, 1881, cited in Tyndall, "Action of Free Molecules on Radiant Heat," 6. See also S. P. Langley, "The Bolometer," *Nature* (1881): 14–16.

31. Tyndall, "Absorption and Radiation of Heat," 276–77.

32. John Tyndall, "On the Transmission of Heat of Different Qualities through Gases of Different Kinds," *Proc. Roy. Inst. Gt. Br.* 3 (1858–62): 156.

33. Charles Lyell to John Tyndall, February 28, 1865, Tyndall Collection, 3: 849. See also James Rodger Fleming, "Charles Lyell and Climatic Change: Speculation and Certainty," in *Lyell: The past is the key to the present*, ed. D. J. Blundell and A. C. Scott (London: Geological Society, 1998).

34. Tyndall to Lyell, March 2, 1865, Tyndall Collection, 3: 839.

35. Tyndall to Lyell, June 1, 1866, Tyndall Collection, 3: 839–40.

36. This biographical sketch is based on George B. Kauffman, "Svante August Arrhenius, Swedish Pioneer in Physical Chemistry," *J. Chem. Ed.* 65 (1988): 437–38; the *Dictionary of Scientific Biography* entry; and the authoritative new biography by Elisabeth Crawford, *Arrhenius: From Ionic*

Theory to the Greenhouse Effect (Canton, Mass.: Science History Publications, 1996).

37. Crawford, *Arrhenius*, 51.

38. A list of Arrhenius's publications in earth science and cosmology appears in Gustaf O. S. Arrhenius, "Svante Arrhenius' Contribution to Earth Science and Cosmology," in *Svante Arrhenius: till 100–årsminnet av hans födelse* (Uppsala: Almqvist and Wiksells, 1959), 65–81. I thank Jan Nolin for bringing this reference to my attention.

39. Ibid, 65.

40. Svante Arrhenius, "Über den Einfluss des atmosphärischen Kohlensäuregehalts auf die Temperatur der Erdoberfläche," *Bihang* 22, no. 1 (1896): 102ff.; "On the Influence of Carbonic Acid in the Air upon the Temperature of the Ground," *Phil. Mag.* ser. 5, 41 (1896): 237–76.

41. Arrhenius, "Influence of Carbonic Acid," 254.

42. Crawford said the effect was greater in summer. Crawford, *Arrhenius*, 152–53; Arrhenius, "Influence of Carbonic Acid," 265–66, emphasis added.

43. Högbom, *Svensk kemisk Tidskrift* 4 (1894): 169ff.; translated in Arrhenius, "Influence of Carbonic Acid," 269–73. A recent treatment of Högbom's contribution is Robert A. Berner, "A. G. Högbom and the Development of the Concept of the Geochemical Carbon Cycle," *Amer. J. Sci.* 295 (1995): 491–95.

44. Arrhenius, *Influence of Carbonic Acid*, 269–71; citing Högbom.

45. Ibid., 271–73.

46. Luigi De Marchi, *Le cause dell' era glaciale* (Pavia, 1895), cited in Arrhenius, "Influence of Carbonic Acid," 273–75. A review of both Arrhenius and De Marchi is included in T. C. Chamberlin's 1896 course notes (see chapter 8).

47. Arrhenius, "Influence of Carbonic Acid," 275 and 268.

48. Gustaf O. S. Arrhenius, "Svante Arrhenius' Contribution," 76–77.

49. T. C. Chamberlin to Charles Greely Abbot, February 27, 1905, letterbook 18, Papers of Thomas Chrowder Chamberlin, Department of Special Collections, Joseph Regenstein Library, University of Chicago (hereafter Chamberlin Papers).

50. Spencer Weart, "From the Nuclear Frying Pan into the Global Fire," *Bull. Atom. Sci.* (June 1992): 19–27; emphasis added.

51. Arrhenius, "Influence of Carbonic Acid," 248.

52. Svante Arrhenius, "Uber die Wärmeabsorption durch Kohlensäure und ihre Einfluss auf die Temperatur der Erdoberfläche," *Ann. Physik* 4 (1901): 690–705; Arrhenius, *Lehrbuch der kosmischen Physik* (Leipzig: S. Hirzel, 1903); Arrhenius, *Worlds in the Making: The Evolution of the Universe*, trans. H. Borns (New York: Harper and brothers, 1908).

53. Craig F. Bohren, *Clouds in a Glass of Beer: Simple Experiments in Atmospheric Physics* (New York: Wiley, 1987), 83–84.

54. Arrhenius, *Worlds in the Making*, 51–52.

55. Tyndall, "Transmission of Heat of Different Qualities"; Arrhenius, *Worlds in the Making*, 48.

56. Arrhenius, *Worlds in the Making*, 52.

57. Julia Uppenbrink, "Arrhenius and Global Warming," *Science* 272 (1996): 1122. J. E. Kutzbach, "Steps in the Evolution of Climatology: From

Descriptive to Analytic," in *Historical Essays on Meteorology, 1919–1995*, ed. James Rodger Fleming (Boston: American Meteorological Society, 1996), 357; emphasis added.

58. See the epigraph to this section. Arrhenius, *Worlds in the Making*, 54–63.

59. Elisabeth Crawford, "Not Warm but Cold: The Genesis of Arrhenius's 1896 Work on the Greenhouse Effect," paper presented at American Geophysical Union, Baltimore, spring 1996; and Crawford, *Arrhenius*, 145–55. Recently Spencer Weart has followed Crawford's lead and has changed some of his opinions about Arrhenius; see Weart, "The Discovery of the Risk of Global Warming," *Physics Today* (Jan. 1997): 34–40.

60. The term "paleotechnic" comes from Lewis Mumford, *Technics and Civilization* (London: G. Routledge and Sons, 1934).

7. T. C. Chamberlin and the Geological Agency of the Atmosphere

1. "Thomas Chrowder Chamberlin," *Dictionary of Scientific Biography*, ed. Charles C. Gillispie (New York: Scribner, 1970–80). Susan F. Schultz, "Thomas C. Chamberlin: An Intellectual Biography of a Geologist and Educator" (Ph.D. diss., University of Wisconsin, Madison, 1976).

2. T. C. Chamberlin, "The Method of Multiple Working Hypotheses," *J. Geol.* 5 (1897): 837–48. See T. C. Chamberlin and Rollin D. Salisbury, *Geology*, vol. 3, *Earth History*, 2nd ed. rev. (New York: H. Holt, 1907), 424–46.

3. Nason came to Beloit in 1858 with a Ph.D. in chemistry from Göttingen. He was an organizer and later president of the American Chemical Society and the editor of two manuals on chemical methods in mineralogy.

4. Schultz, "Thomas C. Chamberlin," 31–68.

5. T. C. Chamberlin, "A Course in Working Methods in Geology," University of Chicago, fall quarter 1896, J. Paul Goode, scribe [bound volume of lecture notes], 185 pp., dated February 22, 1897, folder 4, 9, Chamberlin Papers.

6. Ibid., 2–6. T. C. Chamberlin, "A Group of Hypotheses Bearing on Climatic Changes," *J. Geol.* 5 (1897): 653–83.

7. T. C. Chamberlin to Charles Greely Abbot, February 27, 1905, letterbook 18, Chamberlin Papers.

8. H. Oeschger, "Information on the History of Atmospheric CO_2 and the Carbon Cycle from Ice Cores," in *Carbon Dioxide and Other Greenhouse Gases: Climatic and Associated Impacts*, ed. R. Fantechi and A. Ghazi (Dordrecht: Kluwer Academic, 1987).

9. Chamberlin, "Course in Working Methods," 29.

10. Ibid., 14–16. C. R. Tolman, "The Carbon Dioxide of the Ocean and Its Relations to the Carbon Dioxide of the Atmosphere," *J. Geol.* 7 (1899): 585–618.

11. T. C. Chamberlin, "An Attempt to Frame a Working Hypothesis of the Cause of Glacial Periods on an Atmospheric Basis," *J. Geol.* 7 (1899): 545–84, 667–85, 751–87.

12. T. C. Chamberlin to E. Huntington, May 20, 1922, series 5, box 11, folder 77, Ellsworth Huntington Papers, Manuscripts and Archives,

Sterling Memorial Library, Yale University (hereafter Huntington Papers).

13. T. C. Chamberlin to Charles Greely Abbot, February 27, 1905, letterbook 18, Chamberlin Papers. Although the term "dynamic pyramids" has a nice ring to it, amplifying processes are not always unstable.

14. James Croll, *Climate and Time in their Geological Relations: A Theory of Secular Changes of the Earth's Climate* (London, 1875).

15. T. C. Chamberlin, "Study of the Fundamental Problems of Geology," Carnegie Institution *Year Book*, no. 22 (1923): 325 and 330–32. James R. Fleming, "T. C. Chamberlin and H_2O Climate Feedbacks: A Voice from the Past," *EOS, Trans. Amer. Geophys. Union*, 505, 509.

16. T. C. Chamberlin to Charles Schuchert, October 27, 1913, addenda box 3, folder 5, Chamberlin Papers.

17. Chamberlin, "Hypotheses Bearing on Climatic Changes," 653–83.

18. Chamberlin to Schuchert, October 27, 1913.

19. See chapter epigraph. Chamberlin to Huntington, May 20, 1922.

20. Stephen G. Brush, *Fruitful Encounters: The Origin of the Solar System and of the Moon from Chamberlin to Apollo* (New York: Cambridge University Press, 1996), 49–67, contains a detailed description of the planetesimal hypothesis and its reception.

21. A summary of hot earth cosmology is given by M. Faye, "Concordance des époques géologiques avec les époques cosmogoniques," *Compt. rend. acad, sci.* 100 (1895): 926–31.

22. T. C. Chamberlin, *The Two Solar Families: The Sun's Children* (Chicago: University of Chicago Press, 1928), 297–301.

23. Ibid.

8. The Climatic Determinism of Ellsworth Huntington

1. Arnold J. Toynbee, foreword to Geoffrey J. Martin, *Ellsworth Huntington: His Life and Thought* (Hamden, Conn.: Archon Books, 1973), ix.

2. See J. B. Rigg, "Climatic Determinism," *Weather* 16 (1961): 255–60, 298–303, 327–33.

3. This sketch of Huntington's life is drawn from Martin, *Ellsworth Huntington*; John E. Chappell, Jr., "Huntington and His Critics: The Influence of Climate on Civilization" (Ph.D. diss., University of Kansas, 1968); and the *Dictionary of American Biography,* 10 vols., ed. Allen Johnson and Dumas Malone (New York: Scribner, 1964).

4. See William Morris Davis, *Elementary Meteorology* (Boston, 1894), 345.

5. See Peggy Champlin, *Raphael Pumpelly: Gentleman Geologist of the Gilded Age* (Tuscaloosa: University of Alabama Press, 1994).

6. Ellsworth Huntington, *The Pulse of Asia: A Journey in Central Asia Illustrating the Geographic Basis of History* (Boston: Houghton Mifflin, 1907), 359.

7. Ibid, 384–85.

8. Chappell, "Huntington and His Critics," 67; Robert DeCourcey Ward, "Climate and Man," *Science* n.s. 4 (1896): 749.

9. Davis to Huntington, May 26, 1907, cited in Martin, *Ellsworth Huntington*, 65.

10. Martin, *Ellsworth Huntington*, 73.

11. R. S. Woodward to E. S. Dana, November 16, 1912; E. Brückner to Dana, November 26, 1912; A. Penck to Dana, November 26, 1912; Dana to H. Oertel, December 30, 1912, all cited in Martin, *Ellsworth Huntington*, 85–87.

12. Card from the registrar to Huntington, April 16, 1913, series 9, box 6, folder 28, Huntington Papers; Huntington to President A. T. Hadley, October 22, 1914, cited in Martin, *Ellsworth Huntington*, 87–89.

13. Harlan H. Barrows to Isaiah Bowman, June 15, 1921; Bowman, cited in Martin, *Ellsworth Huntington*, 134, 142.

14. Huntington to George Ellery Hale, April 4, 1917, cited in Martin, *Ellsworth Huntington*,, 148.

15. National Research Council, *The Geography of Europe*, ed. Ellsworth Huntington and Herbert E. Gregory (New Haven: Yale University Press, 1918), 87.

16. Martin, *Ellsworth Huntington*, 159–60.

17. Ellsworth Huntington to William Morris Davis, April 5, and June 25, 1914, series 3, box 32, folder 664, Huntington Papers.

18. Huntington to Caroll Alden, April 29, 1912, cited in Martin, *Ellsworth Huntington*, 111.

19. Martin, *Ellsworth Huntington*, 102–3. Ellsworth Huntington, *The Climatic Factor as Illustrated in Arid America*, with contributions by Charles Schuchert, Andrew E. Douglass, and Charles J. Kullmer. Carnegie Institution of Washington, pub. no. 192 (Washington, D. C., 1914).

20. Huntington to A. R. Wallace, mimeo, marked ansd. December 4, 1913, add. MS 46438, ff. 273–278, Alfred Russell Wallace Papers, Department of Manuscripts, British Library, London (hereafter Wallace Papers).

21. Minutes of the meeting of the Committee on the Atmosphere and Man, October 22, 1921, Division of Biology and Agriculture, Committee on the Atmosphere and Man, U. S. National Academy of Sciences Archives (hereafter NAS Archives); CAM, "Report of the CAM," April 10, 1922, NAS Archives.

22. The New York City Department of Health, the New York Life Insurance Company, and the Metropolitan Life Insurance Company, to name three.

23. U. S. National Research Council, Committee on the Atmosphere and Man, "Causes of Geographical Variations in the Influenza Epidemic of 1918 in the Cities of the United States," (Washington, D. C., 1923), 36 pp; and, by the same organization, "Weather and Health: A Study of Daily Mortality in New York City," (Washington, D. C., 1930), 161 pp.

24. Yandell Henderson to chairman of Division of Biology and Agriculture, National Academy of Sciences, December 31, 1924, copy, NAS Archives.

25. "Records of Women Garment Workers, 1923 and 1924," series 6, box 3, Huntington Papers. There are many more factory records in the collection.

26. Philip S. Drinker to Huntington, December 25, 1925, series 6, box 11, folder 40, Huntington Papers.

27. "Notes for the study of factory efficiency," folio 7, box 10, folder 37, Huntington Papers.

28. An example of such a request is Huntington to A. R. Wallace, mimeo, marked ansd. December 4, 1913.

29. Ellsworth Huntington, *Civilization and Climate*, 3rd ed. (New Haven: Yale University Press, 1924), 415–27.

30. Martin, *Ellsworth Huntington*, 195.

31. *Science* 57 (March 30, 1923): 386–91; Humphreys to National Book Buyers Service, February 5, 1923, both cited in Martin, *Ellsworth Huntington*, 196.

32. Huntington to C. F. Brooks, February 5, 1923, series 4, box 35, folder 368, Huntington Papers.

33. Chamberlin to Huntington, May 19, 1914, addenda box 2, folder 4, Chamberlin Papers.

34. Chamberlin to Huntington, May 20, 1922, Huntington Papers.

35. T. C. Chamberlin, "Geology 51 Lecture Outline," June 10–14, 1915, addenda box 11, folder 2, Chamberlin Papers.

36. Huntington to William Morris Davis, April 5, 1914, series 3, box 32, folder 664, Huntington Papers.

37. Rollin Salisbury to J. R. Angell, November 25, 1921, cited in Martin, *Ellsworth Huntington*, 163.

9. Global Warming?

1. Many of these theories are surveyed in C. E. P. Brooks, *Climate through the Ages: A Study of the Climatic Factors and Their Variations*, 2nd ed., rev. (New York: McGraw-Hill, 1949).

2. Wladimir Köppen and Alfred Wegener, *Die klimate der geologischen vorzeit* (Berlin: Gebruder Borntraeger, 1924). See also Martin Schwarzbach, *Alfred Wegener: The Father of Continental Drift*, trans. Carla Love (Madison, Wisc.: Science Tech, 1986), 86–101.

3. On Milanković, see John Imbrie and Katherine Palmer Imbrie, *Ice Ages* (Short Hills, N.J.: Enslow Publishers, 1979), and A. Berger, "Milankovitch Theory and Climate," *Rev. Geophys.* 26 (1988): 624–57. Excerpts from his autobiography with comments by his son appear in *Milutin Milanković, 1879–1958* (Katlenburg-Lindau, FRG: European Geophysical Society, 1995).

4. See, for example, W. H. Dines, "The Heat Balance of the Atmosphere," *Quart. J. Roy. Meteorol. Soc.* 43 (1917): 151–58; and G. C. Simpson, "Some Studies in Terrestrial Radiation," *Mem. Roy. Meteorol. Soc.* 2 (1928): 69–95. A review article is Garry E. Hunt, Robert Kandel, and Ann T. Mecherikunnel, "A History of Pre-satellite Investigations of the Earth's Radiation Budget," *Rev. Geophys.* 24 (1986): 351–56.

5. For example, Louis Russell Weber, "The Infrared Absorption Spectrum of Water Vapor beyond 10µ" (Ph.D. diss., University of Michigan, 1932); and Paul Edmund Martin, "Infrared Absorption Spectrum of Carbon Dioxide," *Phys. Rev.* 41 (1932): 291–303. On infrared radiation in the atmosphere circa 1950 see L. Goldberg, "The Absorption Spectrum of the Atmosphere," in *The Earth as a Planet*, ed. G. P. Kuiper (Chicago: University of Chicago Press, 1954), 434ff.

6. G. S. Callendar, "The Artificial Production of Carbon Dioxide and Its Influence on Temperature," *Quart. J. Roy. Meteorol. Soc.* 64 (1938): 223–40.

7. W. J. Humphreys, "Volcanic Dust and Other Factors in the Production of Climatic Changes, and Their Possible Relation to Ice Ages," *J. Frankl. I.* 176 (1913): 132.

8. Brooks, *Climate through the Ages*, 7.

9. David B. Ericson and Goesta Wollin, cited in Samuel W. Matthews, "What's Happening to Our Climate?" *National Geographic* 150 (1976): 590.

10. C. E. P. Brooks, "Selective Annotated Bibliography on Climatic Changes," *Meteorological Abstracts and Bibliography* 1, no. 4 (1950): 446–75. Full citations to the works listed in table 9-1 are found in my bibliography. See also Brooks, *Climate through the Ages*.

11. C. E. P Brooks, "Present Position of Theories of Climatic Change," *Meteorol. Mag.* (June 1955): 204–6.

12. Hans A. Panofsky, "Theories of Climate Change," *Weatherwise* 9 (1956): 183–87, 204. Panofsky's discussion of the astronomical theory of Milanković has been superseded.

13. Nils Ekholm, "On the Variations of the Climate of the Geological and Historical Past and Their Causes," *Quart. J. Roy. Meteorol. Soc.* 27 (1901): 61. This article appeared in Swedish in 1899 and was translated two years later. See also Nils Ekholm, "Über Emission und Absorption der Wärme und deren Bedeutung für die Temperatur der Erdoberfläche," *Meteorol. Z.* 19 (1901): 1–26, 489–505.

14. Knut Ångström, 'Ueber die Bedeutung des Wasserdampfes und der Kohlensäure bei der Absorption der Erdatmosphäre," *Ann Phys.* 4 (1900): 720-33; Abbot and Fowle, *Annals of the Astrophysical Observatory*, Smithsonian Institution, vol. 2 (1908): 172, cited in W. J. Humphreys, "Volcanic Dust and Other Factors," 134–35. See also Humphreys, *Physics of the Air* (Philadelphia: J. B. Lippincott, 1920).

15. T. C. Chamberlin to E. Huntington, May 20, 1922, series 5, box 11, folder 77, Huntington Papers.

16. Chamberlin to Charles Schuchert, October 27, 1913, addenda box 3, folder 5, Chamberlin Papers.

17. G. C. Simpson, "Past Climates," *Manchester Lit. Philos. Soc. Mem.* 74, no. 1 (1929–30): 9–10.

18. Richard Joel Russell, "Climatic Change through the Ages," in U. S. Dept. of Agriculture, *Climate and Man: Yearbook of Agriculture 1941*, House Doc. 27, 77th Cong., 1st sess. (Washington, D.C., 1941), 67–97, quote from 94.

19. C. Kramer, "Carbon Dioxide in the Atmosphere in Relation to Climate," *Hemel en Dampkring* 48 (1950): 189–91; C. E. P. Brooks, "Geological and Historical Aspects of Climatic Change," in *Compendium of Meteorology*, ed. Thomas F. Malone (Boston: American Meteorological Society, 1951), 1015–16.

20. Panofsky, "Theories of Climate Change," 183–87, 204.

21. G. S. Callendar, "Can Carbon Dioxide Influence Climate?" *Weather* 4 (1949): 310–14; quote from 310; and Callendar, "The Composition of the Atmosphere through the Ages," *Meteorol. Mag.* 74 (1939): 38.

22. "Mr. G. S. Callendar," obituary notice, *Quart. J. Roy. Meteorol. Soc.* 91 (1965): 112.

23. Callendar, "Artificial Production of Carbon Dioxide," 233–40;

Callendar, "Composition of the Atmosphere," 33–39; Callendar, "Variation of the Amount of Carbon Dioxide in Different Air Currents," *Quart. J. Roy. Meteorol. Soc.* 66 (1940): 395–400; Callendar, "Infra-red Absorption by Carbon Dioxide with Special Reference to Atmospheric Radiation," *Quart. J. Roy. Meteorol. Soc.* 67 (1941): 263–75; Callendar, "Can Carbon Dioxide Influence Climate?" 310–14; Callendar, "Climatic Changes," *Weather* 12 (1957): 67ff; Callendar, "On the Present Climatic Fluctuation," *Meteorol. Mag.* 87 (1958): 204–07; Callendar, "On the Amount of Carbon Dioxide in the Atmosphere," *Tellus* 10 (1958): 243–48; and Callendar, "Temperature Fluctuations and Trends over the Earth," *Quart. J. Roy. Meteorol. Soc.* 87 (1961): 1–11. After the International Geophysical Year, Charles Keeling's CO_2 measurements became the new standard. See, for example, Charles D. Keeling, "The Concentration and Isotopic Abundances of Carbon Dioxide in the Atmosphere," *Tellus* 12 (1960): 200–203.

24. Callendar, "Artificial Production of Carbon Dioxide," 236.

25. As F. B. Mudge has shown, inaccuracies in the measurement of CO_2 were greatly reduced by 1900 and tended to cluster around 300 parts per million; Mudge, "The Development of the 'Greenhouse' Theory of Global Climate Change from Victorian Times," *Weather* 52 (1997): 13–17.

26. Callendar, "Artificial Production of Carbon Dioxide," 237–40.

27. Callendar, "Composition of the Atmosphere," 38, 39. See also the epigraph to this chapter.

28. Callendar, "Infra-red Absorption by Carbon Dioxide," 274.

29. Ibid., 274–75.

30. Callendar, "Can Carbon Dioxide Influence Climate?" 312. Other investigators reported similar results; for example, Kurt Buch, "Carbon Dioxide Content as an Indicator of Meteorological Condition of the Air," *Geophysica* 3 (1948): 63–79, calculated a fourteen percent increase in thirty-five years, a rate of increase of forty percent per century.

31. Callendar, "Carbon Dioxide in the Atmosphere," 243–48.

32. M. D. Handel and J. S. Risbey, "An Annotated Bibliography on the Greenhouse Effect and Climate Change," *Climatic Change* 21, no. 2 (June 1, 1992): 97–255, say that Callendar's work was "quickly ignored as World War II intervened and northern hemisphere surface temperatures began to decline in the 1940s." Spencer Weart, "From the Nuclear Frying Pan into the Global Fire," *Bull. Atom. Sci.* (June 1992): 19–27, mentions Callendar's 1938 article to the Royal Meteorological Society but indicates that his work was obscure and no one really cared. Spencer Weart, "Global Warming, Cold War, and the Evolution of Research Plans," *Hist. Stud. Phys. Sci.* 27 (1997): 319–56 again emphasizes Callendar's obscurity and amateur status.

33. Gordon Manley, "Some Recent Contributions to the Study of Climatic Change," *Quart. J. Roy. Meteorol. Soc.* 70 (1944): 197–219. Author's interview with Gilbert Plass, February 13, 1997. Hans E. Suess, "Natural Radiocarbon and the Rate of Exchange of Carbon Dioxide Between the Atmosphere and the Sea," *Proc. Conf. Nuclear Processes in Geologic Settings* (Williams Bay, Wisc., Sept. 21–23, 1953), 52.

34. H. W. Ahlmann, "The Present Climatic Fluctuation, " *Geogr. J.* 112, nos. 4–6, (October–December 1948): 165–95.

35. H. C. Willett, "Temperature Trends of the Past Century," *Centennial Proc. Roy. Meteorol. Soc.* (1950), 195–211.

36. J. O. Fletcher, "Climatic Change and Ice Extent on the Sea," Rand Paper P-3831 (April 1968), 22 p.

37. See Charles C. Bates, Thomas F. Glaskell, and Robert B. Rice, *Geophysics in the Affairs of Man* (New York: Pergamon Press, 1982), 133–42 for additional details. "The Weather Weapon: New Race with the Reds," *Newsweek,* January 13, 1958, 54.

38. Ahlmann, quoted in Albert Abarbanel and Thorp McClusky, "Is the World Getting Warmer?" *Saturday Evening Post*, July 1, 1950, 22–23, 57, 60–63.

39. Author's interview with Gilbert Plass, February 13, 1997.

40. *American Men and Women of Science* (New Providence, N.J.: R. R. Bowker, 1995), Lexis/Nexis version; and *Who's Who In Technology*, 6th ed. (Detroit, Mich.: Gale Research, 1989), Lexis/Nexis version, s.v. "Gilbert N. Plass."

41. Walter M. Elsasser, *Heat Transfer by Infrared Radiation in the Atmosphere*, Harvard University and Blue Hill Meteorological Observatory, Milton, Mass., *Harvard Meteorol. Stud.*, no. 6 (1942); and Arent Bruinenberg, *Een numerieke methode voor de bepaling van temperatursveranderingen door straling in de vrije atmosfeer* ('s-Gravenhage, 1946). A revised method appears in Elsasser and Margaret F. Culbertson, *Atmospheric Radiation Tables*, Boston: American Meteorological Society, *Meteorol. Monogr.* 4 (1960).

42. A copy of this chart and an explanation of how it was constructed and used appears in F. A. Berry, Jr., E. Bollay, and Norman R. Beers, eds., *Handbook of Meteorology* (New York: McGraw-Hill, 1945), 301–11. Practical applications of the Elsasser method appear in William D. Sellers, *Physical Climatology* (Chicago: University of Chicago Press, 1965), 47ff.

43. Gilbert N. Plass, "Effect of Carbon Dioxide Variations on Climate," *Amer. J. Phys.* 24 (1956): 387.

44. Intergovernmental Panel on Climate Change, Working Group 1, 1995, "Summary for Policy Makers: The Science of Climate Change," http://www.unep.ch/ipcc/wg1.html (December 5, 1996).

45. Amy Wallace and David Smollar, "Roger Revelle, Founder of UCSD, Is Dead at 82," *Los Angeles Times*, San Diego County edition, July 16, 1991, Lexis/Nexis.

46. Walter Sullivan, "Roger Revelle, 82, Early Theorist in Global Warming and Geology," *New York Times*, July 17, 1991, B-5; Martin F. Nolan, "Taking Time to Toast 1991—Additions to Roll Call of the Great Beyond," *Boston Globe*, January 1, 1992, 1; "Roger Revelle, Oceanographer and Population Expert; at 82," *Boston Globe*, July 17, 1991; Wallace and Smollar, "Roger Revelle, Founder of UCSD." All citations from Lexis/Nexis.

47. Wallace and Smollar, "Roger Revelle, Founder of UCSD," emphasis added.

48. Judith Morgan and Neil Morgan, *Roger: A Biography of Roger Revelle* (San Diego: University of California, San Diego–Scripps Institution of Oceanography, 1996).

49. Roger Revelle and Hans E. Suess, "Carbon Dioxide Exchange be-

tween Atmosphere and Ocean and the Question of an Increase in Atmospheric CO_2 during the Past Decades," *Tellus* 9 (1957): 19.

50. Ibid., 19–20.

51. Revelle's phrase "geophysical experiment" is in U. S. House of Representatives, Committee on Appropriations, *National Science Foundation—International Geophysical Year* (Washington, D.C., 1956), 473. Estimates of carbon dioxide emissions are in United Nations, "World Requirements of Energy, 1975–2000," *International Conference on Peaceful Uses of Atomic Energy*, vol. 1 (Geneva, 1955), 3.

52. Gilbert N. Plass, "The Carbon Dioxide Theory of Climatic Change," *Tellus* 8 (1956): 140–54. H. N. Dingle, "The Carbon Dioxide Exchange between the North Atlantic Ocean and the Atmosphere," *Tellus* 6 (1954): 342.

53. Revelle and Suess, "Carbon Dioxide Exchange," 18–27.

54. Ibid., 26.

55. James R. Arnold and Ernest C. Anderson, "The Distribution of Carbon-14 in Nature," *Tellus* 9 (1957): 28–32; quote from 30. See also Weart, "Global Warming," 339–50.

56. Memo from Harry Wexler to Paul A. Humphrey, October 3, 1956, "Meeting with Dr. Roger Revelle," copy, International Geophysical Year 1955–1956, file 55, box 24, AC 6, Records 1890–1981, SIO Subject Files, Scripps Institution of Oceanography Archives. Harry Wexler to Jerry P. Eaton, June 10, 1957, file 56, in the same location. Eaton, the geophysicist in charge, was hopeful that measurements as sensitive as 0.01 percent of background could be made to detect the effluent of the volcano itself.

57. C. D. Keeling, "The Concentration and Isotopic Abundances of Carbon Dioxide in the Atmosphere," *Tellus* 12 (1960): 200–203.

58. Morgan and Morgan, *Roger*, 52.

59. Charles D. Keeling, "The Influence of Mauna Loa Observatory on the Development of Atmospheric CO_2 Research," in *Mauna Loa Observatory: A 20th Anniversary Report*, ed. John Miller, National Oceanic and Atmospheric Administration Special Report (Washington, D.C., 1978), 36–54; quote from 36.

60. I. Fung, G. Lambert, and L. Merlivat, "Preface, 4th CO_2 International Conference, Carqueiranne, France, 13–17 September 1993," *Tellus* 47B (1995): 1–3. Eric From and Charles D. Keeling, "Reassessment of Late 19th Century Atmospheric Carbon Dioxide Variations in the Air of Western Europe and the British Isles Based on an Unpublished Analysis of Contemporary Air Masses by G. S. Callendar," *Tellus* 38B (1986): 87–105.

61. Wallace and Smollar, "Roger Revelle, Founder of UCSD."

62. David M. Hart and David G. Victor, "Scientific Elites and the Making of US Policy for Climate Change Research, 1957–74," *Social Studies of Science* 23 (1993): 643–80. Hart and Victor employ a metaphor of entrepreneurial elites carving out a niche in climate research.

63. Callendar, "Temperature Fluctuations," 9.

64. Roger Revelle, "Introduction: The Scientific History of Carbon Dioxide," in *The Carbon Cycle and Atmospheric CO_2: Natural Variations Archean to Present*, ed. E. T. Sundquist and W. S. Broecker, Geophysical Monographs, vol. 32 (Washington, D.C.: American Geophysical Union, 1985), 1–4.

10. Global Cooling, Global Warming

1. Frederik Nebeker, "A History of Calculating Machines in Meteorology," in *Historical Essays on Meteorology, 1919–1995*, ed. James Rodger Fleming (Boston: American Meteorological Society, 1996), 157–178.

2. F. Kenneth Hare, [Changes of Climate], *Geogr. Rev.* 54 (1964): 455–57.

3. Syukuro Manabe and Richard T. Wetherald, "Thermal Equilibrium of the Atmosphere with a Given Distribution of Relative Humidity," *J. Atmos. Sci.* 24 (1967): 241–59; Manabe and Kirk Bryan, "Climate Calculations with a Combined Ocean-atmosphere Model," *J. Atmos. Sci.* 26 (1969): 786–89.

4. R. R. Rapp, "Climate Modification and National Security," Rand Paper P-4476 (October 1970), p. 8.

5. M. Weinstein and V. Suomi, "Analysis of Satellite Infrared Radiation Measurements on a Synoptic Scale," *Monthly Weather Rev.* 89 (1961): 419–28, cited in James F. W. Purdom and W. Paul Menzel, "Evolution of Satellite Observations in the United States and Their Use in Meteorology," in Fleming, *Historical Essays on Meteorology*, 99–155. See also Charles C. Bates, Thomas F. Glaskell, and Robert B. Rice, *Geophysics in the Affairs of Man* (New York: Pergamon Press, 1982), 133–42.

6. Francis Bello, "Climate: The Heat May Be Off," *Fortune*, August 1954, 108–11, 160, 162, 164; Betty Friedan, "The Coming Ice Age," *Harper's Magazine* 217 (September 1958): 39–45; Maurice Ewing and William L. Donn, "A Theory of Ice Ages," *Science* 123 (1956): 1061–66.

7. Samuel W. Matthews, "What's Happening to Our Climate?" *National Geographic* 150 (1976): 581–82.

8. U. S. Central Intelligence Agency (CIA), "A Study of Climatological Research as It Pertains to Intelligence Problems," (August 1974) and CIA, "Potential Implications of Trends in World Population, Food Production, and Climate," OPR-401 (August 1974), reprinted in *The Weather Conspiracy: The Coming of the New Ice Age* (New York: Ballantine Books, 1977), appendices 1 and 2. Spencer Weart did not discuss global cooling in his article "Global Warming, Cold War, and the Evolution of Research Plans," *Hist. Stud. Phys. Sci.* 27 (1997): 319–56.

9. George F. Will, "A Change in the Weather," *Washington Post*, January 24, 1975.

10. John von Neumann, "Can We Survive Technology?" *Fortune*, June 1955, 106–8, 151–52.

11. Lowell Ponte, *The Cooling* (Englewood Cliffs, N.J.: Prentice Hall, 1976), 177–231.

12. Ibid.

13. "Global Warming Has Begun, Expert Tells Senate," *New York Times*, June 24, 1988, 1.

14. *Climate Change 1992: The Supplementary Report to the IPCC Scientific Assessment*, ed. J. T. Houghton, B. A. Callander, and S. K. Varney (Cambridge: Cambridge University Press, 1992), 5; Intergovernmental Panel on Climate Change, Working Group 1, 1995, "Summary for Policy Makers: The Science of Climate Change," http: //www.unep.ch/ ipcc/wg1.html (December 5, 1996).

15. United Nations, Information Unit on Climate Change, "Are We Overlooking the Social and Political Implications of Climate Change?" http: //www.unep.ch/iucc/fs108.html (September 26, 1996).

16. David Keith and Hadi Dowlatabadi, "A Serious Look at Geoengineering," *EOS, Trans. Amer. Geophys. Union* 73 (1992): 289, 292–93.

17. Jerome Namias, "The Greenhouse Effect as a Symptom of Our Collective Angst," *Oceanus* 32 (Summer 1989): 66.

18. For example, "Managing Planet Earth," special theme issue of *Scientific American*, September 1989; and U. S. National Academy of Sciences, *Policy Implications of Greenhouse Warming* (Washington, D.C.: National Academy Press, 1991).

Bibliography

Archival and Manuscript Collections

American Philosophical Society Library. Archives, Manuscript Collections, and Manuscript Communications.

Bibliothèque nationale, Paris. Collection des papiers du mathématicién Fourier. MSS français, 22501–22529.

British Library, London. Department of Manuscripts. Alfred Russell Wallace Papers and Letters to James Croll.

Cambridge University Library. Department of Manuscripts and University Archives. Papers of Sir George Gabriel Stokes.

Carnegie Institution of Washington. Archives and Library. Ellsworth Huntington File.

National Register of Archives, London.

Royal Institution of Great Britain, London. John Tyndall Collection.

National Library of Scotland, Edinburgh. David Hume Correspondence and Papers.

Royal Society Library, London. Journal Book of the Royal Society, John F. W. Herschel Papers.

Scripps Institution of Oceanography Archives. Biographical Files, Charles D. Keeling, Roger Revelle. International Geophysical Year Files.

Smithsonian Institution Archives. Charles G. Abbot Papers, Records of the Smithsonian Astrophysical Observatory, Samuel P. Langley Papers.

167

University of Chicago. Department of Special Collections, Joseph Regenstein Library. Papers of Thomas Chrowder Chamberlin.

U. S. National Academy of Sciences (NAS) Archives. Division of Biology and Agriculture, Committee on the Atmosphere and Man, 1921–28.

U. S. National Archives and Records Administration (NARA). Naval Observatory Records. Naval Records Collection.

Yale University. Manuscripts and Archives, Sterling Memorial Library. Ellsworth Huntington Papers.

Reference Works and Bibliographies
(in chronological order)

Royal Society of London. *Catalogue of Scientific Papers.* Vols. 1–6, *1800–1863.* Vols. 7–8, *1864–1873.* London, 1867–77.

U. S. Army, Surgeon-General's Office. *List of Books and Articles on Climatology and Meteorology in the Library of the Surgeon-General's Office.* Washington, D. C., 1888.

U. S. Army Signal Office. *Bibliography of Meteorology.* 4 vols. Washington, D. C., 1889–91. Reissued as *International Bibliography of Meteorology: From the Beginning of Printing to 1889.* Ed. James Rodger Fleming and Roy E. Goodman, 4 vols. in 1. Upland, Pa.: Diane, 1994.

[Royal Society of London.] *International Catalogue of Scientific Literature.* sec. F. *Meteorology.* Vols. 1–14, *1901–1914.* New York: Johnson Reprint, 1968.

U. S. Department of Agriculture, Weather Bureau. *Brief List of Meteorological Text-books and Reference Books*, 2nd ed. Comp. C. Fitzhugh Talman. Washington, D. C., GPO, 1910.

Isis Cumulative Bibliography, A Bibliography of the History of Science Formed from Isis Critical Bibliographies . . . Vols. 1–6, *1913–65*, edited by Magda Whitrow. Vols. 1–2, *1966–75* and vol. 1, *1976–85*, edited by John Neu. London: Mansell, 1971–89.

World Weather Records Collected from Official Sources. Smithsonian Miscellaneous Collections. Vol. 79 (1927), from beginning of observations to 1930. Vol. 90 (1934), from 1921 to 1930. Vol. 105 (1947), from 1931 to 1940. Washington, D. C.: Smithsonian Institution.

Dictionnaire de biographie français. Paris: Letouzey et Ané, 1933– .

Tyndall, John. *A Record of the Scientific Work of John Tyndall, D.C.L., L.L.D., F.R.S. (1850–1888).* London: Chiswick, 1935.

A Bibliography of Scientific Papers on Climatic Variations. Comp. Henryk Arctowski. Mimeo. Lwów, International Geographical Union, Commission of Climatic Variations, 1938.

Lysgaard, Leo. *Recent Climatic Fluctuations.* Folia geographica Danica. Vol. 5. Copenhagen: H. Hagerup, 1949.

Darter, Lewis J., Jr., comp. *List of Climatological Records in the National Archives.* Washington, D. C.: NARA, 1942. Reprint, 1981.

Berry, F. A., Jr., E. Bollay, and Norman R. Beers, eds., *Handbook of Meteorology.* New York: McGraw-Hill, 1945.

Brooks, C. E. P. "Selective Annotated Bibliography on Climatic Changes." *Meteorological Abstracts and Bibliography* 1, no. 4 (1950): 446–75.

Shapley, Harlow, ed. *Climatic Change: Evidence, Causes, and Effects.* Cambridge, Mass.: Harvard University Press, 1953.

Havens, James M., ed. *An Annotated Bibliography of Meteorological Observations in the United States, 1731–1818.* Florida State University Department of Meteorology Technical Rept. No. 5. Tallahassee, Fla., 1956.

Bibliographic List of Recent Studies of Climatic Change by United States Citizens. Comp. J. Murray Mitchell, Jr. Washington, D. C.: U. S. Dept. of Commerce, Weather Bureau, 1961.

WMO Bibliography on Climatic Fluctuations. Geneva: World Meteorological Organization, 1961.

Dictionary of American Biography. 10 vols. Ed. Allen Johnson and Dumas Malone. New York: Scribner, 1964.

Dictionary of Scientific Biography. 16 vols. Ed. C. C. Gillispie. New York: Scribner, 1970–80.

Le Roy Ladurie, Emmanuel. *Times of Feast, Times of Famine: A History of Climate Since the Year 1000.* Trans. Barbara Bray. London: Allen and Unwin, 1972.

Friday, James R., Roy M. MacLeod, and Phillipa Shepherd. *John Tyndall: Natural Philosopher, 1820–1893: Catalog of Correspondence, Journals and Collected Papers.* London: Mansell, 1974.

Library of Congress, "Climatic Change." Comp. Constance Carter. *LC Science Tracer Bullet* TB-77-11. Washington, D. C., 1977.

Claxton, Robert H. *A Bibliography of Recent Works Regarding Climatic Variation and Its Effects in Historic Times.* Carrollton, Ga.: West Georgia College, 1981.

DeVorkin, David H. *The History of Modern Astronomy and Astrophysics: A Selected, Annotated Bibliography.* New York: Garland, 1982.

Brush, Stephen, and Helmut Landsberg. *The History of Geophysics and Meteorology: An Annotated Bibliography.* New York: Garland, 1985.

Catlett, Stephen J., ed. *A New Guide to the Collections in the Library of the American Philosophical Society.* Philadelphia: American Philosophical Society, 1987.

Morrisette, Peter M., ed. "A Selected Annotated Bibliography of Climate and Society Research." *National Oceanic and Atmospheric Administration Technical Report*, NCPO 002. Boulder, Colo.: National Climate Program Office, 1987.

Brush, Stephen G. *The History of Modern Science: A Guide to the Second Scientific Revolution, 1800–1950.* Ames, Iowa: Iowa State University Press, 1988.

Bibliography on Effects of Climatic Change and Related Topics. Mediterranean Action Plan, United Nations Environment Programme. MAP technical reports series, no. 29. Athens: UNEP, 1988, 1989.

Carbon Dioxide and Climate (Jan. 1970–Aug. 1989): Citations from the NTIS Bibliographic Database. Springfield, Va.: National Technical Information Service, 1989.

Fleming, James Rodger. *Guide to Historical Resources in the Atmospheric Sciences: Archives, Manuscripts, and Special Collections in the Washington, D.C. Area.* NCAR Technical Note 327+IA. Boulder, Colo.: National Center for Atmospheric Research, 1989. Revised Web

Edition, http://www.colby.edu/sci.tech/97guide/. Waterville, Me: Colby College, 1997.

Lockerby, Robert W. *Climatic Change and Global Warming: A Selected Bibliography.* Monticello, Ill.: Vance Bibliographies, 1989.

Maclean, Jayne T. *Global Warming and the Greenhouse Effect, January 1979–May 1989.* Beltsville, Md.: U. S. Dept. of Agriculture, National Agricultural Library, 1989.

Who's Who In Technology. 6th ed. Gale Research, 1989. Lexis/Nexis.

Baker, Alison J. *Australia and the Greenhouse Effect: A Bibliography.* Parkville, Victoria: Library and Information Studies, Institute of Education, University of Melbourne, 1990.

Doornkamp, John Charles. *Global Warming, Climate Change and Rising Sea-levels: A Bibliography.* Long Eaton: M1 Press, 1990.

Nordquist, Joan. *The Greenhouse Effect, A Bibliography.* Santa Cruz, Calif.: Reference and Research Services, 1990.

Olby, R. C., et al., eds. *Companion to the History of Modern Science.* London: Routledge, 1990.

Christensen, John O. *Greenhouse Effect and Public Policy: A Selective Bibliography of Recent References.* Monticello, Ill.: Vance Bibliographies, 1991.

Stanton, William. *American Scientific Exploration, 1803–1860.* Philadelphia: American Philosophical Society Library, 1991.

Handel, M. D., and J. S. Risbey. "An Annotated Bibliography on the Greenhouse Effect and Climate Change." *Climatic Change* 21, no. 2 (June 1, 1992): 97–255.

Oxford English Dictionary, CD Rom version 1.0b. New York: Oxford University Press, 1993.

American Men and Women of Science. New York: R. R. Bowker, 1995. Lexis/Nexis.

Good, Gregory A., ed. *Sciences of the Earth: An Encyclopdedia of Events, People, and Phenomena.* New York: Garland Press, 1998.

Primary Sources

Abbe, Cleveland. "Is Our Climate Changing?" *Forum* 6 (February 1889): 678–88.

Abbot, C. G., and F. E. Fowle. "Volcanoes and Climate." *Smithson. Misc. Collect.* 60 (1913): 29.

Adhémar, Joseph Alphonse. *Révolutions de la mer, deluges periodiques.* Paris, 1842.

Ahlmann, H. W. "The Present Climatic Fluctuation. " *Geogr. J.* 112, nos. 4–6 (October–December 1948): 165–95.

Angot, Alfred. "Premier catalogue des observations météorologiques faites en France depuis l'origine jusqu'en 1850." *Annales du Bureau Central Météorologique de France, 1895.* Vol. 1. *Mémoires* (Paris, 1897): 89–146.

Ångström, Knut. "Ueber die Bedeutung des Wasserdampfes und der Kohlensäure bei der Absorption der Erdatmosphäre." *Ann. Phys.* 4 (1900): 720–33.

Antill, Edward. "An Essay on the cultivation of the VINE, and the making and preserving of Wine, suited to the different Climates in North-America." *Trans. Amer. Philos. Soc.* 1 (1771): 117–97.

Arbuthnot, John. *An Essay Concerning the Effects of Air on Human Bodies.* London, 1733.

Archivo Meteorologico Centrale Italiano. Firenze, 1858. Reproduced in *Neudrucke von Schriften und Karten über Meteorologie und Erdmagnetismus,* edited by G. Hellmann. No. 7. Berlin, 1897. Pp. 9–17.

Arnold, James R., and Ernest C. Anderson. "The Distribution of Carbon-14 in Nature." *Tellus* 9 (1957): 28–32.

Arrhenius, Svante. *Lehrbuch der kosmichen Physik,* 2 vols. Leipzig: S. Hirzel, 1903.

Arrhenius, Svante. "On the Influence of Carbonic Acid in the Air upon the Temperature of the Ground." *Phil. Mag.* ser. 5, 41 (1896): 237–76.

Arrhenius, Svante. "Über die Wärmeabsorption durch Kohlensäure und ihre Einfluss auf die Temperatur der Erdoberfläche." *Ann. Physik* 4 (1901): 690–705.

Arrhenius, Svante. "Über den Einfluss des atmosphärische Kohlensäuregehalts auf die Temperatur der Erdoberfläche." *Bihang* 22, no. 1 (1896): 102ff.

Arrhenius, Svante. *Worlds in the Making: The Evolution of the Universe.* Trans. H. Borns. New York: Harper and brothers, 1908.

Becquerel, M. "Forests and Their Climatic Influence." *Smithson. Rept.* (1869): 394–416.

Blodget, Lorin. *Climatology of the United States.* Philadelphia, 1857.

Brooks, C. E. P. *Climate through the Ages: A Study of the Climatic Factors and Their Variations.* New York: R. V. Coleman, 1926.

Brooks, C. E. P. *The Evolution of Climate.* 2nd ed. New York: R. V. Coleman, 1925.

Callendar, G. S. "The Artificial Production of Carbon Dioxide and Its Influence on Temperature." *Quart. J. Roy. Meteorol. Soc.* 64 (1938): 223–40.

Callendar, G. S. "Can Carbon Dioxide Influence Climate?" *Weather* 4 (1949): 310–14.

Callendar, G. S. "Climatic Changes." *Weather* 12 (1957): 67ff.

Callendar, G. S. "The Composition of the Atmosphere through the Ages." *Meteorol. Mag.* 74 (1939): 33–39.

Callendar, G. S. "Infra-red Absorption by Carbon Dioxide, with Special Reference to Atmospheric Radiation." *Quart. J. Roy. Meteorol. Soc.* 67 (1941): 263–75.

Callendar, G. S. "On the Amount of Carbon Dioxide in the Atmosphere." *Tellus* 10 (1958): 243–48.

Callendar, G. S. "On the Present Climatic Fluctuation." *Meteorol. Mag.* 87 (1958): 204–07.

Callendar, G. S. "Temperature Fluctuations and Trends over the Earth." *Quart. J. Roy. Meteorol. Soc.* 87 (1961): 1–11.

Callendar, G. S. "Variations of the Amount of Carbon Dioxide in Different Air Currents. *Quart. J. Roy. Meteorol. Soc.* 66 (1940): 395–400.

Chamberlin, Thomas C. "A Group of Hypotheses Bearing on Climatic Changes." *J. Geol.* 5 (1897): 653–83.

Chamberlin, Thomas C. "An Attempt to Frame a Working Hypothesis of the Cause of Glacial Periods on an Atmospheric Basis." *J. Geol.* 7 (1899): 545–84, 667–85, 751–87.

Chamberlin, Thomas C. "The Method of Multiple Working Hypotheses." *J. Geol.* 5 (1897): 837–48.

Chamberlin, Thomas C. "Study of the Fundamental Problems of Geology." Carnegie Institution *Year Book*, no. 22 (1923): 324–34.

Chamberlin, Thomas C. *The Two Solar Families: The Sun's Children.* Chicago: University of Chicago Press, 1928.

Chamberlin, Thomas C., and Rollin D. Salisbury, *Geology.* Vol. 3. *Earth History.* 2nd ed. rev. New York: H. Holt, 1907.

Chardin, John. *Travels in Persia.* London: Argonaut Press, 1927.

Cleaveland, Parker. "Meteorological Observations made at Bowdoin College." *Mem. Amer. Acad. Arts Sci.* 3, pt. 1 (1809): 119–121.

Collin, Nicholas. "Observations Made at an Early Period on the Climate of the Country Along the River Delaware, Collected from the Records of the Swedish Colony." *Trans. Amer. Philos. Soc.* n.s. 1 (1818): 340–52.

Condorcet, Jean-Antoine-Nicolas de Caritat, marquis de. "Equisse d'un tableau historique . . ." (1795). In *Oeuvres completes de Condorcet,* vol. 8. Paris, 1804.

Cotte, Louis. *Traite de météorologie.* Paris, 1774.

Croll, James. *Climate and Time in their Geological Relations: A theory of secular changes of the earth's climate.* London, 1875.

Croll, James. "On the Physical Cause of the Change of Climate during Geological Epochs." *Phil. Mag.* 28 (1864): 121–37.

Currie, William. "An Enquiry into the Causes of the Insalubrity of Flat and Marshy Situations; And directions for preventing or correcting the effects thereof." *Trans. Amer. Philos. Soc.* 4 (1799): 127–42.

Cuvier, Georges, Baron. *Discours préliminaire [sur les révolutions de la surface du globe].* Paris, 1812.

Czerney, Franz von. *Die Veränderlichkeit des Klimas und ihre Ursachen.* Vienna, 1881.

Davis, William Morris. *Elementary Meteorology.* Boston, 1894.

Derham, William. "An Abstract of the Meterological Diaries." *Phil. Trans.* (1733–34): 101–05.

"Dichiarazione d'alcun Istrumenti per conoscer l'Alterazioni dell'Aria." *Saggi di naturali esperienze fatte nell'Accademia del Cimento.* Firenze, 1666.

Diderot, D., and J. D'Alembert, eds. *Encyclopdédie, ou Dictionnaire raisonné des sciences, des arts et des métiers.* Paris, 1779.

Dines, W. H. "The Heat Balance of the Atmosphere." *Quart. J. Roy. Meteorol. Soc.* 43 (1917): 151–58.

Dingle, H. N. "The Carbon Dioxide Exchange between the North Atlantic Ocean and the Atmosphere." *Tellus* 6 (1954): 342.

Dove, Heinrich Wilhelm. *Meteorologische Untersuchungen.* Berlin, 1837.

Drayson, Alfred W. *On the Cause, Date, and Duration of the Last Glacial Epoch of Geology, and the Probable Antiquity of Man.* London, 1873.

Du Bos, Abbé Jean-Baptiste. *Critical Reflections on Poetry, Painting and Music, with an Inquiry into the Rise and Progress of the Theatrical Entertainments of the Ancients.* 2 vols. Trans. Thomas Nugent. London, 1748.

Du Bos, Abbé Jean-Baptiste. *Réflexions critiques sur la poësie et sur la peinture.* 2 vols. Paris, 1719.

Dubois, Eugene. *The Climates of the Geological Past and their Relation to the Evolution of the Sun.* London, 1895.

Dunbar, William. "Meteorological Observations." *Trans. Amer. Philos. Soc.* 4 (1809): 48.

Ekholm, Nils. "On the Variations of the Climate of the Geological and Historical Past and Their Causes." *Quart. J. Roy. Meteorol. Soc.* 27 (1901): 61.

Ekholm, Nils. "Über Emission und Absorption der Wärme und deren Bedeutung für die Temperatur der Erdoberfläche." *Meteorol. Z.* 19 (1901): 1–26, 489–505.

Espiard de La Borde, François-Ignace. *Essais sur le génie et la caractère des nations.* 3 vols. Brussels, 1743.

Espy, James P. *Second Report on Meteorology to the Secretary of the Navy.* Washington, D. C., 1851.

Evelyn, John. *Silva, or, A Discourse of forest-trees and the propagation of timber in His Majesties dominions.* London, 1664.

Ewing, Maurice, and William L. Donn. "A Theory of Ice Ages." *Science* 123 (1956): 1061–66.

Faye, M. "Concordance des époques géologiques avec les époques cosmogoniques." *Compt. rend. acad, sci.* 100 (1895): 926–31.

Ferrel, William. "Note on the Influence of Forests upon Rainfall." *Amer. Meteorol. J.* 5 (1888–89): 433–35.

Ferrel, William. *Temperature of the Atmosphere and Earth's Surface.* Professional Papers of the Signal Service, no. 13. Washington, D. C., 1884.

Flint, Richard F., and Herbert G. Dorsey, Jr. "Iowan and Tazewell Drifts and the North American Ice-sheet." *Amer. J. Sci.* 243 (1945): 627–36.

Forry, Samuel. "Researches in Elucidation of the Distribution of Heat over the Globe, and especially of the Climatic Features peculiar to the Region of the United States." *Amer. J. Sci.* 47 (1844): 18–50, 221–41.

Fothergill, A. "Animadversions on the dangerous practice of sleeping on the damp ground and of exposure to the night air, particularly where the animal powers are diminished; illustrated on philosophical principles." *Mem. Amer. Acad. Arts Sci.* 2, pt. 1 (1793): 206.

Fourier, Jean-Baptiste Joseph. *The Analytical Theory of Heat.* Trans. Alexander Freeman. Cambridge, 1878.

Fourier, Jean-Baptiste Joseph. "Mémoire sur les températures du globe terrestre et des espaces planétaires." *Mém. Acad. Sci.* 7 (1827): 569–604.

Fourier, Jean-Baptiste Joseph. *Oeuvres de Fourier.* Vol. 2. Ed. Gaston Darboux. Paris, 1890.

Fourier, Jean-Baptiste Joseph. "Questions sur la théorie-physique de la chaleur rayonnante." *Ann. chim. phys.* (Paris) 6 (1817): 259–303.

Fourier, Jean-Baptiste Joseph. "Remarques générales sur les températures du globe terrestre et des espaces planétaires." *Ann. chim. phys.* (Paris) 2nd ser., 27 (1824): 136–67. Trans. Ebeneser Burgess. *Amer. J. Sci.* 32 (1837): 1–20.

Fourier, Jean-Baptiste Joseph. "Sur la propagation de la chaleur, présenté à l'Institut le 21 décembre 1807, avec notes présentées en 1808 et 1809." In Grattan-Guinness, *Joseph Fourier, 1768–1830*.

Fourier, Jean-Baptiste Joseph. "Sur la température des habitations et sur le mouvement varié de la chaleur dans les prismes rectangulaires." *Bull. Soc. Philomath.* (1818): 1–11. Reprinted in Joseph Fourier, *Oeuvres de Fourier*, ed. Gaston Darboux. Paris, 1890.

Fourier, Jean-Baptiste Joseph. *Théorie Analytique de la chaleur*. Paris, 1822.

Fourier, Jean-Baptiste Joseph. "Théorie de la chaleur" (Extrait). *Ann. chim. phys.* (Paris) 2nd ser., 3 (1816): 350–76.

Franklin, Benjamin. *The Papers of Benjamin Franklin*, 31 vols. Ed. Leonard W. Labaree, William B. Willcox, and Barbra B. Oberg. New Haven: Yale University Press, 1959–95.

Gregory, J. W. "Climatic Variations: Their Extent and Causes." *Smithson. Rept.* (1908): 339–54.

"Hadley Centre for Climate Prediction and Research, Historical temperature records," http://www.meto.gov.uk/sec5/CR_div/Tempertr/lsst_vals_nh.html (November 20, 1997).

Halley, Edmund. "Some Considerations About the Cause of the Universal Deluge." *Phil. Trans.* 33 (1724–35): 118–23.

Halley, Edmund. "Some Farther Thoughts Upon the Same Subject, Delivered on the 19th of the Same Month. By the Same." *Phil. Trans.* 33 (1724–35): 123–25.

Hariot, Thomas. A *Brief and True Report of the New Found Land of Virginia*. London, 1588. Reprint, New York: History Book Club, 1951.

Harmer, F. W. "Further Remark on the Meteorological Conditions of the Pleistocene Epoch." *Quart. J. Roy. Meteorol. Soc.* 51 (1925): 247–59.

Harmer, F. W. "The Influence of the Winds upon Climate during the Pleistocene Epoch: A Palaeometeorological Explanation of Some Geological Problems." *Quart. J. Geol. Soc. Lond.* 57 (1901): 405–78.

Hemmer, J. J. "Historia Societas Meteorologicae Palatinae." *Societatis Meteorologicae Palatinae Ephemerides*. Vol. 1, *1781* (1783): 1–54.

Hewatt, Alexander. *An Historical Account of the Rise and Progress of the Colonies of South Carolina and Georgia*. 2 vols. London, 1779.

Himpel, Kurt. "Die Klimate der geologischen Vorzeit." *Veröff. Astron. Ges. Urania.* no. 4. Weisbaden, 1937.

Himpel, Kurt. "Ein Beitrag zum Eiszeitproblem." *Z. Naturforsch.* 2a (1947): 419–27.

Hobbs, W. H. *The Glacial Anticyclones: The Poles of the Atmospheric Circulation*. New York: Macmillan, 1926.

Holm, Thomas Campanius. *Kort Beskrifning om Nya Sverige*. Stockholm, 1702.

Holyoke, Edward A. "An Estimate of the Excess of the Heat and Cold of the American Atmosphere beyond the European, in the same Parallel of Latitude; To which are added, some thoughts on the causes of this excess." *Mem. Amer. Acad. Arts Sci.* 2, pt. 1 (1793): 65–92.

Howard, Luke. *The Climate of London*. 2nd ed. London, 1820.

Hoyle, F., and R. A. Lyttleton. "The Effect of Interstellar Matter on Climatic Variation." *Proc. Camb. Philos. Soc.* 35 (1939): 405–15.

Hull, E. "Another Possible Cause of the Glacial Epoch." *Quart. J. Geol. Soc. Lond.* 53 (1897): 107–9; and *Victoria Inst. Trans.* (Lond.) 31 (1899): 141–57.

Humboldt, Alexander von. *Views of Nature: Or Contemplations on the Sublime Phenomena of Creation; with Scientific Illustrations.* Trans. E. C. Otté and Henry G. Bohn. London, 1850.

Hume, David. "Of the Populousness of Ancient Nations." In *Essays: Moral, Political, and Literary*, edited by T. H. Green and T. H. Grose. London, 1875.

Humphreys, W. J. *Physics of the Air.* Philadelphia: J. B. Lippincott, 1920.

Humphreys, W. J. "Volcanic Dust and Other Factors in the Production of Climatic Changes, and Their Possible Relation to Ice Ages." *J. Frankl. I.* 176 (1913): 131–72.

Huntington, Ellsworth. *Civilization and Climate.* New Haven: Yale University Press, 1915. 3rd ed., 1924.

Huntington, Ellsworth. *The Climatic Factor as Illustrated in Arid America.* With contributions by Charles Schuchert, Andrew E. Douglass, and Charles J. Kullmer. Carnegie Institution of Washington, pub. no. 192. Washington, D. C., 1914.

Huntington, Ellsworth. *Mainsprings of Civilization.* New York: Mentor, 1945.

Huntington, Ellsworth. *The Pulse of Asia: A Journey in Central Asia Illustrating the Geographic Basis of History.* Boston: Houghton Mifflin, 1907.

Huntington, Ellsworth, and Steven Sargent Visher. *Climatic Changes: Their Nature and Causes.* New Haven: Yale University Press, 1922.

Jefferson, Thomas. *Notes on the State of Virginia.* Paris, 1785. Reprint, Gloucester, Mass.: Peter Smith, 1976.

Jefferson, Thomas. *The Papers of Thomas Jefferson.* 26 vols. Ed. Julian Boyd, Charles T. Cullen, and John Catanzariti. Princeton: Princeton University Press, 1950–95.

Jefferson, Thomas. *The Writings of Thomas Jefferson.* 20 vols. Ed. Andrew A. Lipscomb and Albert Ellery Bergh. Washington, D. C.: Thomas Jefferson Memorial Association of the United States, 1904–7.

Jurin, James. "Invitatio ad Observationes Meteorologicas communi consilio instituendas." *Phil. Trans.* 32 (1723): 422–27.

Kanold, Johann, ed. *Sammlung von Natur- und Medicin-, wie auch hiezu gehörigen Kunst- und Literatur-Geschichten.* 1718–30.

Keeling, Charles D. "The Concentration and Isotopic Abundances of Carbon Dioxide in the Atmosphere." *Tellus* 12 (1960): 200–203.

Köppen, Wladimir, and Alfred Wegener. *Die klimate der geologischen vorzeit.* Berlin, 1924.

Kramer, C. "Carbon Dioxide in the Atmosphere in Relation to Climate." *Hemel en Dampkring* 48 (1950): 189–91.

Kreichgauer, Damian. *Die aquatorfrage in der geologie.* Steyl, 1902.

Lambert, J. H. "Exposé de quelques observations . . . por répandre du jour sur la métérologie." *Nouv. Mém. Acad. Roy. Sci. Belles-Let.* (Berlin) (1773): 60–65.

Langley, S. P. "The Bolometer." *Nature* (1881): 14–16.

Lasareff, P. "Sur une méthode permettant de démontrer la dépendance des courants océaniques des vents alizés et sur le rôle des courants océaniques dans le changement du climat aux époques géologiques." *Beitr. Geophysik* 21 (1929): 215–33.

Lavoisier, Antoine-Laurent. *Oeuvres de Lavoisier.* Vol. 3. *Correspondence.* Ed. R. Fric. Paris: Imprimerie Imperiale, 1964.

Lavoisier, Antoine-Laurent. "Règles pour Prédire le Changement de Temps." *Literary Magazine* (1790).

Loomis, Elias, and H. A. Newton."On the Mean Temperature, and On the Fluctuations of Temperature, at New Haven, Conn., Lat. 41° 18' N., Long. 72° 55' W. of Greenwich." *Trans. Conn. Acad. Arts Sci.* 1, pt. 1 (1866): 194–246.

Lyell, Sir Charles. *Principles of Geology.* London, 1830–33.

M'Sweeny, Joseph. "An Essay on the Climate of Ireland." *Trans. Roy. Irish Acad.* 17 (1837): 179–233.

MacSparran, James. *America Dissected, being a full and true account of all the American Colonies, shewing the intemperance of the climates, excessive heat and cold, and sudden violent changes of weather, terrible and mischievous thunder and lightning, bad and unwholesome air, destructive to human bodies, etc.* Dublin, 1753.

Malte-Brun, Conrad. *A System of Universal Geography.* 3 vols. Boston, 1834.

Mariotte, Edme. *Oeuvres de Mariotte.* 2 vols. in 1. Leiden, 1717.

Maritime Conference held at Brussels for devising an uniform system of meteorological observations at sea, August and September 1853. Brussels, 1853.

Mather, Cotton. *The Christian Philosopher.* London, 1721.

[Maury, Matthew Fontaine.] *On the Establishment of an Universal System of Meteorological Observations by Sea and Land.* Washington, D. C., 1851.

Maury, Matthew Fontaine. *The Physical Geography of the Sea and Its Meteorology.* Ed. John Leighly. Cambridge, Mass.: Belknap Press of Harvard University Press, 1963. Pp. ix–xxx.

Meigs, Josiah. "Geometric exemplification of temperature, winds, and weather for 1820 at Washington City." *Minutes Amer. Philos. Soc.* (October 19, 1821): 505.

Melloni, M. "Memoir on the Free Transmission of Radiant Heat through Different Solid and Liquid Bodies." Trans. Richard Taylor. *Scientific Memoirs* 1 (1837): 1–5.

Melloni, M. "Proposal of a New Nomenclature for the Science of Calorific Radiations." Trans. Richard Taylor. *Scientific Memoirs* 3 (1843): 527–36.

Meteorological Conference Proceedings. 12 vols. in 1. London, 1873–81.

Milankovitch, [Milanković] Milutin. *Kanon der Erdbestrahlung und seine Anwendung auf das Eiszeitenproblem.* Belgrade: Mihaila Curcica, 1941. Trans. *Canon of Insolation and the Ice-age Problem.* Jerusalem: Israel Program for Scientific Translations, 1969.

Milankovitch, [Milanković] Milutin. "Mathematische Klimalehre, un astronomische Theorie der Klimaschwankungen." In *Handbuch der Klimatologie*, edited by W. Köppen and R. Geiger. Vol. 1. Berlin: Gebruder Borntraeger, 1930. Pp. 1–176.

Milankovitch, [Milanković] Milutin. *Théorie mathématique des phéno-menes thermiques produits par la radiation solaire.* Paris: Gauthier-villars et Cie, 1920.

Montesquieu, Charles Louis de Secondat. *Correspondance de Montesquieu.* Ed. François Gebelin and André Morize. 2 vols. Paris: Imprimeries Gounouilhou, 1914.

Montesquieu, Charles Louis de Secondat. *The Spirit of Laws: A Compendium of the First English Edition.* Ed. D. W. Carrithers. Berkeley: University of California Press, 1977.

Montesquieu, Charles Louis de Secondat. *Persian Letters.* Trans. C. J. Betts. Baltimore: Penguin Books, 1973.

Myer, Albert James. *U. S. Army Signal Office Report* (1874).

National Research Council. *The Geography of Europe.* Ed. Ellsworth Huntington and Herbert E. Gregory. New Haven: Yale University Press, 1918.

New Edinburgh Encyclopedia, conducted by David Brewster, American ed. 30 vols. Philadelphia, 1808–24.

"Notice of a Meteorological Register for the years 1822, 1823, 1824 and 1825; from observations made by the Surgeons of the Army, at the Military Posts of the United States." *Amer. J. Sci.* 12 (1827): 149–54.

Pettersson, Otto. *Climatic Variations in Historic and Prehistoric Time.* Svenska Hydrografisk-Biologiska Kommissionens Skrifter, Haft 5. Berlin: Springer, 1914. Microfilm, Uppsala: Universitetsbiblioteket, 1967.

Pickering, Roger. "Scheme of a Diary of the Weather, together with draughts and descriptions of Machines subservient thereunto." *Phil. Trans.* 43 (May 3, 1744).

Plass, Gilbert N. "The Carbon Dioxide Theory of Climatic Change." *Tellus* 8 (1956): 140–54.

Plass, Gilbert N. "Effect of Carbon Dioxide Variations on Climate." *Amer. J. Phys.* 24 (1956): 387.

Pouillet, C. S. M. "Memoir on the Solar Heat, on the Radiating and Absorbing Powers of the Atmospheric Air, and on the Temperature of Space." Trans. Richard Taylor. *Scientific Memoirs* 4 (1846): 44–90.

Ramsay, David. *The History of South-Carolina: From its first settlement in 1670, to the year 1808.* Charleston, S. C., 1809.

Ramsay, M. "Orogenesis und Klima." *Ofver. Fin. Veten. Soc. Förhand.* 53 (1909–10): 1–48.

Ramsay, Wilhelm. *On Relations between Crustal Movements and Variations of Sea-level during the Late Quaternary Time, Especially in Fennoscandia.* Helsinki: Impremerie de l'état, 1924.

Raynal, Abbé Guillaume-Thomas François. *A Philosophical and Political History of the Settlements and Trade of the Europeans in the East and West Indies.* 8 vols. Trans. J. O. Justamond. London, 1783.

Revelle, Roger, and Hans E. Suess. "Carbon Dioxide Exchange between Atmosphere and Ocean and the Question of an Increase in Atmospheric CO_2 during the Past Decades." *Tellus* 9 (1957): 18–27.

Rush, Benjamin. "An Enquiry into the Cause of the Increase of Bilious and Intermitting Fevers in Pennsylvania, With Hints for Preventing Them." *Trans. Amer. Philos. Soc.* 2 (1786): 206–12.

Ruskin, John. "Remarks on the Present State of Meteorological Science." *Trans. Meteorol. Soc. Lond.* 1 (1839): 56–59.

Saussure, H. B. de. *Journal de Paris* no. 108 (1784): 475–78.

Saussure, H. B. de. *Voyages dans les Alpes, précédés d'un essai sur l'histoire naturelle des environs de Genève.* 4 vols. Neuchâtel-Geneva, 1779–96.

Schoepf, David. *The Climate and Diseases of America During the Revolution.* Trans. James Read Chadwick. Boston, 1875.

Schott, Charles A. "Tables and Results of the Precipitation, in Rain and Snow, in the United States and at Some Stations in Adjacent Parts of North America and in Central and South America." *Smithson. Contrib.* 18 (1872). Article 2.

Schott, Charles A. "Tables, Distribution, and Variations of the Atmospheric Temperature in the United States and Some Adjacent Parts of North America." *Smithson. Contrib.* 21 (1876). Article 5.

Simpson, G. C. "The Climate during the Pleistocene Period." *Proc. Roy. Soc. Edinb.* 50 (1930): 262–96.

Simpson, G. C. "Past Climates." *Manchester Lit. Philos. Soc. Mem.* 74, no. 1 (1929–30): 9–10.

Simpson, G. C. "Probable Causes of Changes of Climate and Their Limitations." *Proc. Linn. Soc. Lond.* pt. 2, 152 (1939–40): 190–219.

Simpson, G. C. "World Climate during the Quaternary Period." *Quart. J. Roy. Meteorol. Soc.* 60 (1934): 425–71.

Societas Meteorologicae Palatinae. *Ephemerides.* 12 vols. 1783–95.

Spitaler, Rudolph. *Das Klima des Eiszeitalters.* Prague: Selbstverlag, 1921.

Spitaler, Rudolph. "Die järlichen und periodischen Änderungen der Wärmverteilung auf der Erdoberfläche und die Eiszeiten." *Beitr. Geophysik* 8 (1907): 565–602.

Strachey, William. *The History of Travell into Virginia Britania.* Ed. Louis B. Wright and Virginia Freund. London: Printed for the Hakluyt Society, 1953.

Suess, Hans E. "Natural Radiocarbon and the Rate of Exchange of Carbon Dioxide between the Atmosphere and the Sea." *Proc. Conf. Nuclear Processes in Geologic Settings*, Williams Bay, Wisconsin, September 21–23, 1953. P. 52.

Tolman, C. R. "The Carbon Dioxide of the Ocean and Its Relations to the Carbon Dioxide of the Atmosphere." *J. Geol.* 7 (1899): 585–618.

Tyndall, John. "Action of Free Molecules on Radiant Heat, and its Conversion thereby into Sound." *Proc. Roy. Soc. Lond.* 216 (1881): 5.

Tyndall, John. *Contributions to Molecular Physics in the Domain of Radiant Heat.* London, 1872.

Tyndall, John. "Note on the Transmission of Heat Through Gaseous Bodies." *Proc. Roy. Inst. Gt. Br.* 10 (1859): 37.

Tyndall, John. "Notes for Lectures on Radiant Heat, c. 1855–1882." MS 3/D4, 1881. John Tyndall Collection, Royal Institution of Great Britain, London.

Tyndall, John. "On Radiation through the Earth's Atmosphere." *Proc. Roy. Inst. Gt. Br.* 4 (1851–66): 4–8.

Tyndall, John. "On Radiation through the Earth's Atmosphere." *Phil. Mag.* ser. 4, 25 (1862): 200–206.

Tyndall, John. "On the Absorption and Radiation of Heat by Gases and

Vapours, and on the Physical Connection of Radiation, Absorption, and Conduction." *Phil. Mag.* ser. 4, 22 (1861): 169–94, 273–85.

Tyndall, John. "On the Passage of Radiant Heat through Dry and Humid Air." *Phil. Mag.* ser. 4, 26 (1863): 44–54.

Tyndall, John. "On the Transmission of Heat of Different Qualities Through Gases of Different Kinds." *Proc. Roy. Inst. Gt. Br.* 3 (1858–62): 155–58.

U. S. Army Medical Department. *Meteorological Register for the Years 1822, 1823, 1824, and 1825 from Observations made by the Surgeons of the Army at the Military Posts of the United States.* Washington, D. C., 1826.

U. S. National Research Council. Committee on the Atmosphere and Man. "Causes of Geographical Variations in the Influenza Epidemic of 1918 in the Cities of the United States." Washington, D. C., 1923.

U. S. National Research Council. Committee on the Atmosphere and Man. "Weather and Health: A Study of Daily Mortality in New York City." Washington, D. C., 1930.

Vesselovski, Konstantin Stepanovich. *O Klimat Rossii.* St. Petersburg, 1857.

Volney, Constantin-François. *A View of the Soil and Climate of the United States of America.* Philadelphia, 1804.

Ward, Robert DeCourcey. "Climate and Man." *Science* n.s. 4 (1896): 749.

Webster, Noah. "On the Effects of Evergreens on Climate." *Trans. Soc. Promotion of Useful Arts* 1, pt. 4 (Albany, 1799): 51–52.

Webster, Noah. "On the Supposed Change in the Temperature of Winter." *Mem. Conn. Acad. Arts Sci.* 1, pt. 1 (1810): 216–60. Reprinted in Noah Webster, *A Collection of Papers on Political, Literary, and Moral Subjects.* New York, 1843.

Wegener, Alfred. *Die Entstehung der kontinente und ozeane.* Braunschweig: F. Vieweg, 1920.

Wells, William. *An Essay on Dew.* London, 1814.

Willett, H. C. "Temperature Trends of the Past Century." *Centennial Proc. Roy. Meteorol. Soc.* (1950): 195–211.

Williams, Samuel. *The Natural and Civil History of Vermont.* Walpole, N. H., 1794.

Williamson, Hugh. "An Attempt to Account for the Change of Climate, which has been Observed in the Middle Colonies in North-America." *Trans. Amer. Philos. Soc.* 1 (1771): 272–80.

Williamson, Hugh. *Observations on the Climate in Different Parts of America, Compared with the climate in corresponding parts of the other continent. To which are added remarks on the different complexions of the human race; with some account of the aborigines of America. Being an introductory discourse to the history of North-Carolina.* New York, 1811.

Willis, Bailey. "Isthmian Links." *Bull. Geol. Soc. Amer.* 43 (1932): 917–52.

Wilson, Job. "A Meteorological Synopsis, in connection with the prevailing diseases for sixteen years, as they occurred at Salisbury, Massachusetts." *Medical Repository* 22, n.s. 7 (1822): 409–13.

Wood, William. *New England's Prospect.* London, 1634.

Woodward, John. *An essay toward a natural history of the earth and ter-

restrial bodies, especially minerals, as also of the sea, rivers, and springs, with an account of the universal deluge, and of the effects that it had upon the earth. 1st ed. London, 1695; London: British Museum Photo Services, 1972.

Wright, George Frederick. *The Ice Age in North America and Its Bearings upon the Antiquity of Man. With an appendix on "The probable cause of glaciation," by Warren Upham.* New York, 1890.

Wright, Thomas. "On the Mode Most Easily and Effectually Practicable of Drying Up the Marshes of the Maritime Parts of North America." *Trans. Amer. Philos. Soc.* 4 (1799): 246.

Secondary Souces

Abarbanel, Albert, and Thorp McClusky. "Is the World Getting Warmer?" *Saturday Evening Post,* July 1, 1950, 22–23, 57, 60–63.

Abbe, Cleveland. "Biographical Memoir of Charles Anthony Schott." *Biog. Mem. Natl. Acad. Sci.* 8 (1915): 87–133.

Abbe, Cleveland. "Meteorology in Russia." *Monthly Weather Rev.* 27 (1899): 106.

Arrhenius, Gustaf O. S. "Svante Arrhenius' Contribution to Earth Science and Cosmology." In *Svante Arrhenius: till 100-årsminnet av hans födelse.* Uppsala: Almqvist and Wiksells, 1959. Pp. 65–81.

Ashley, Bernard. *Weather Men.* London: Allman, 1974.

Bach, Wilfrid. *Our Threatened Climate: Ways of Averting the CO_2 Problem through Rational Energy Use.* Trans. Jill Jäger. Dordrecht: D. Reidel, 1984.

Baron, W. R. "Historical Climate Records from the Northeastern United States, 1640 to 1900." In *Climate Since A.D. 1500,* edited by Raymond S. Bradley and Philip D. Jones. London: Routledge, 1992. Pp. 74–91.

Barr, E. S. "The Infrared Pioneers II." *Infrared Phys.* 2 (1962): 67–73.

Bates, Charles C., Thomas F. Glaskell, and Robert B. Rice. *Geophysics in the Affairs of Man.* New York: Pergamon Press, 1982.

Baxter, William J. *Today's Revolution in Weather!* New York: International Economic Research Bureau, 1953.

Bello, Francis. "Climate: The Heat May Be Off." *Fortune,* August 1954, 108–11, 160, 162, 164.

Berger, A. "Milankovitch Theory and Climate." *Rev. Geophys.* 26 (1988): 624–57.

Berner, Robert A. "A. G. Högbom and the Development of the Concept of the Geochemical Carbon Cycle." *Amer. J. Sci.* 295 (1995): 491–95.

Bohren, Craig F. *Clouds in a Glass of Beer: Simple Experiments in Atmospheric Physics.* New York: Wiley, 1987.

Bradley, Raymond S., and Philip D. Jones, eds. *Climate Since A.D. 1500.* London: Routledge, 1992.

Brooks, C. E. P. *Climate through the Ages: A Study of the Climatic Factors and Their Variations.* 2nd ed., rev. New York: McGraw-Hill, 1949.

Brooks, C. E. P. "Geological and Historical Aspects of Climatic Change." In *Compendium of Meterology,* edited by Thomas F. Malone. Boston: American Meterological Society, 1951. Pp. 1004–18.

Brooks, C. E. P. "Present Position of Theories of Climatic Change." *Meteorol. Mag.* (June 1955): 204–6.

Bruinenberg, Arent. *Een numerieke methode voor de bepaling van temperatursveranderingen door straling in de vrije atmosfeer.* 's-Gravenhage, 1946.

Brunt, David. "A Hundred Years of Meteorology, 1851–1951." *Adv. Sci.* 8 (1951): 114–24.

Brunt, David. "The Centenary of the Meteorological Office: Retrospect and Prospect." *Sci. Prog.* 44 (1956): 193–207.

Brush, Stephen G. *Fruitful Encounters: The Origin of the Solar System and of the Moon from Chamberlin to Apollo.* New York: Cambridge University Press, 1996.

Buch, Kurt. "Carbon Dioxide Content as an Indicator of Meteorological Condition of the Air." *Geophysica* 3 (1948): 63–79.

Bull, G. A. "Short History of the Meteorological Office." *Meteorol. Mag.* 83 (1955): 163–67.

Burton, Jim. "Robert Fitzroy and the Early History of the Meteorological Office." *Brit. J. Hist. Sci.* 19 (1986): 147–76.

Cappel, Albert. "Societas Meteorologica Palatina (1780–1795)." *Annalen der Meteorologie* n.s. 16 (1980): 10–27, 255–61.

Cassidy, David C. "Meteorology in Mannheim: The Palatine Meteorological Society, 1780–1795." *Sudhoffs Archiv: Zeitschrift für Wissenschaftsgeschichte* 69 (1985): 8–25.

Ce qu'est la météorologie française. Paris: Bureau central météorologique de France, 1952.

Champlin, Peggy. *Raphael Pumpelly: Gentleman Geologist of the Gilded Age.* Tuscaloosa: University of Alabama Press, 1994.

Changes of Climate: Proceedings of the Rome Symposium organized by UNESCO and the World Meteorological Organization. UNESCO Arid Zone Research no. 20. Paris, 1963.

Chappell, John E., Jr. *Huntington and His Critics: The Influence of Climate on Civilization.* Ph.D. diss., University of Kansas, 1968.

Chinard, Gilbert. "Eighteenth Century Theories on America as a Human Habitat." *Proc. Amer. Philos. Soc.* 91 (1947): 27–57.

Clawer, F. *Catalog der Meteorologischen Beobachtungen im Russichen Reich Zusammengestelt.* In *Repertorium für Meteorologie,* edited by H. Wild, vol. 2. St. Petersburg, 1872.

Climate Change 1992: The supplementary report to the IPCC scientific assessment. Ed. J. T. Houghton, B. A. Callander, and S. K. Varney. Cambridge: Cambridge University Press, 1992.

Columbus, Ferdinand. *The Life of the Admiral Christopher Columbus by His Son Ferdinand.* Trans. B. Keen. New Brunswick, N.J.: Rutgers University Press, 1959.

Corless, Richard. "A Brief History of the Royal Meteorological Society." *Weather* 5 (1950): 78–83.

Crawford, Elisabeth. *Arrhenius: From Ionic Theory to the Greenhouse Effect.* Canton, Mass.: Science History Publications, 1996.

Crawford, Elisabeth. "Not Warm but Cold: The Genesis of Arrhenius's 1896 Work on the Greenhouse Effect." Paper presented at American Geophysical Union, Baltimore, spring, 1996.

Cronon, William. *Changes in the Land: Indians, Colonists, and the Ecology of New England*. New York: Hill and Wang, 1983.

Davis, John L. "Weather Forecasting and the Development of Meteorological Theory at the Paris Observatory, 1853–1878." *Ann. Sci.* 41 (1984): 359–82.

Dedieu, Abbé. *Montesquieu et la tradition politique anglaise en France*. Paris: J. Gabalda, 1909.

Dodds, Muriel. *Les récites des voyages, sources de l'Esprit des Lois de Montesquieu*. Paris: H. Champion, 1929.

Doublet, E. "La météorologie en France et en Allemagne." *Revue philomathique de Bordeaux et du Sud Ouest* 14 (1911): 213–32, 250–67; 15 (1912): 103–28, 169–86.

Dutton, John A. "The Challenges of Global Change." In *Science, Technology, and the Environment: Multidisciplinary Perspectives*, edited by James Rodger Fleming and Henry A. Gemery. Akron, Ohio: University of Akron Press, 1994. Pp. 53–111.

Echeverria, Durand. *Mirage in the West: A History of the French Image of American Society to 1815*. Princeton: Princeton University Press, 1957.

Eisenstadt, Peter. "The Weather and Weather Forecasting in Colonial America." Ph.D. diss., New York University, 1990.

Elsasser, Walter M. *Heat Transfer by Infrared Radiation in the Atmosphere*. Harvard University and Blue Hill Meteorological Observatory, Milton, Mass. *Harvard Meteorol. Stud.* no. 6 (1942).

Elsasser, Walter M., and Margaret F. Culbertson. *Atmospheric Radiation Tables*. Boston: American Meteorological Society. *Meteorol. Monogr.* 4 (1960).

Eve, Arthur Stewart, and Clarence Hamilton Cressey. *The Life and Work of John Tyndall*. London: Macmillan, 1945.

Fantechi, R., and A. Ghazi, eds. *Carbon Dioxide and Other Greenhouse Gases: Climatic and Associated Impacts*. Dordrecht: Kluwer Academic, 1987.

Fassig, Oliver L. "A Sketch of the Progress of Meteorology in Maryland and Delaware." *Maryland Weather Service* 1 (1899): 333–34.

Fassig, O. L., ed. *Report of the International Meteorological Congress held at Chicago, Ill., August 21–24, 1893, under the auspices of the congress auxiliary of the World's Columbian Exposition*. U. S. Dept. of Agriculture, *Bull. U. S. Weather Bureau* 11. Washington, D. C., 1894, 1896.

Feldman, Theodore Sherman. "The History of Meteorology, 1750–1800: A Case Study in the Quantification of Experimental Physics." Ph.D. diss., University of California, Berkeley, 1983.

Fleagle, Robert G. *Global Environmental Change: Interactions of science, policy, and politics in the United States*. Westport, Conn.: Praeger, 1994.

Fleming, James Rodger. "Charles Lyell and Climatic Change: Speculation and Certainty." In *Lyell: The Past is the Key to the Present*, edited by D. J. Blundell and A. C. Scott. London: Geological Society, 1998.

Fleming, James Rodger. "Cloud Wars: Weather Modification and the U. S. Military, 1947–1977." Unpublished manuscript.

Fleming, James Rodger. *Meteorology in America, 1800–1870.* Baltimore: Johns Hopkins University Press, 1990.

Fleming, James Rodger. "T. C. Chamberlin and H_2O Climate Feedbacks: A Voice from the Past." *EOS, Trans. Amer. Geophys. Union* 73 (1992): 505, 509.

Fleming, James Rodger, ed. *Historical Essays on Meteorology, 1919–1995.* Boston: American Meteorological Society, 1996.

Fleming, James Rodger, and Henry A. Gemery, eds. *Science, Technology, and the Environment: Multidisciplinary Perspectives.* Akron, Ohio: University of Akron Press, 1994.

Fletcher, Frank T. H. "Climate and Law: Influence of Montesquieu on British Writers." *Geography* 19 (1934): 29–36.

Fletcher, J. O. "Climatic Change and Ice Extent on the Sea." Rand Paper P-3831, April 1968.

Fournol, E. *Bodin prédécesseur de Montesquieu.* Paris, 1896.

Friedan, Betty. "The Coming Ice Age." *Harper's Magazine* 217 (September 1958): 39–45.

Frisinger, H. H. *The History of Meteorology to 1800.* New York: Science History Publications, 1977.

From, Eric, and Charles D. Keeling. "Reassessment of late 19th Century Atmospheric Carbon Dioxide Variations in the Air of Western Europe and the British Isles Based on an Unpublished Analysis of Contemporary Air Masses by G. S. Callendar." *Tellus* 38 B (1986): 87–105.

Fung, I., G. Lambert, and L. Merlivat. "Preface, 4th CO_2 International Conference, Carqueiranne, France, 13–17 September 1993." *Tellus* 47 B (1995): 1–3.

Gates, Warren E. "The Spread of Ibn Khaldûn's Ideas on Climate and Culture." *Journal of the History of Ideas* 28 (1967): 415–22.

Gillispie, Charles C. *Science and Polity in France at the End of the Old Regime.* Princeton: Princeton University Press, 1980.

Glacken, Clarence J. *Traces on the Rhodian Shore: Nature and Culture in Western Thought from Ancient Times to the End of the Eighteenth Century.* Berkeley: University of California Press, 1967.

"Global Warming Has Begun, Expert Tells Senate." *New York Times,* June 24, 1988, 1.

Goldberg, L. "The Absorption Spectrum of the Atmosphere." In *The Earth as a Planet,* edited by G. P. Kuiper. Chicago: University of Chicago Press, 1954. Pp. 434ff.

Grant, John. *Natural and Political Observations . . . Upon the Bills of Mortality.* London, 1662.

Grattan-Guinness, I., with J. Ravitz. *Joseph Fourier, 1768–1830: A Survey of His Life and Work, Based on a Critical Edition of His Monograph on the Propagation of Heat Presented to the Institute of France in 1807.* Cambridge, Mass.: MIT Press, 1972.

Handel, M. D., and J. S. Risbey. "An Annotated Bibliography on the Greenhouse Effect and Climate Change." *Climatic Change* 21, no. 2 (1992): 97–255.

Hare, F. Kenneth. [Changes of Climate]. *Geogr. Rev.* 54 (1964): 455–57.

Hart, David M., and David G. Victor. "Scientific Elites and the Making of

US Policy for Climate Change Research, 1957–74." *Social Studies of Science* 23 (1993): 643–80.

Hellmann, Gustav. "Die Ältesten instrumentellen meteorologischen Beobachtungen in Deutchland." *Beitr. Gesch. Meteorol.* bd. 1, nr. 2. Berlin, 1914. Pp. 103–7.

Hellmann, Gustav. "Die Entwicklung der meteorologischen Beobachtungen in Deutchland von der ersten Anfängen bis zur Einrichtung staatlicher Beobachtungsnetze." *Abh. Preuss. Akad. Wiss. Phys.- math. Kl.*, no. 1. Berlin, 1926.

Hellmann, Gustav. "Die Vorläuffer der Societas Meteorologica Palatina." *Beitr. Gesch. Meteorol.* bd. 1, nr. 5. Berlin, 1914. Pp. 139–47.

Hellmann, Gustav. *Geschichte des Königlich Preussischen Meteorologischen Instituts von seiner Gründing im Jahre 1847 bis zu seiner Reorganisation im Jahre 1885.* Berlin, 1887.

Hellmann, Gustav. "Katalogen der Schriften und Erfindungen." *Repertorium der Deutchen Meteorologie* (1883): 1–744.

Hellmann, Gustav. *Neudrucke von Schriften und Karten über Meteorologie und Erdmagnetismus.* No. 7. Berlin, 1897.

Hellmann, Gustav. "Umriss einer Geschichte der meteorologischen Beobachtungen in Deutchland." *Repertorium der Deutchen Meteorologie* (1883): 884–86.

Henry, Alfred J. "Early Individual Observers in the United States." *Bull. U. S. Weather Bureau* 11 (1893): 291–302.

Herivel, John. *Joseph Fourier: The Man and the Physicist.* Oxford: Clarendon Press, 1975.

Hunt, Gary E., Robert Kandel, and Ann T. Mecherikunnel. "A History of Pre-satellite Investigations of the Earth's Radiation Budget." *Rev. Geophys.* 24 (1986): 351–56.

Imbrie, John, and Katherine Palmer Imbrie. *Ice Ages: Solving the Mystery.* Short Hills, N.J.: Enslow Publishers, 1979.

Intergovernmental Panel on Climate Change. Working Group 1, 1995. "Summary for Policy Makers: The Science of Climate Change." http://www.unep.ch/ipcc/wg1.html (December 5. 1996).

Jacobson, Harold K., and Martin F. Price. *A Framework for Research on the Human Dimensions of Global Environmental Change.* Paris: UNESCO, 1991.

Jones, M. D. H., and A. Henderson-Sellers. "History of the Greenhouse Effect." *Prog. Phys. Geog.* 14, no. 1 (1990): 5.

Jones, Philip D., Raymond S. Bradley, and Jean Jouzel, eds. *Climatic Variations and Forcing Mechanisms of the Last 2000 Years.* Berlin: Springer, 1996.

Kauffman, George B. "Svante August Arrhenius, Swedish Pioneer in Physical Chemistry." *J. Chem. Ed.* 65 (1988): 437–38.

Keeling, Charles D. "The Influence of Mauna Loa Observatory on the Development of Atmospheric CO_2 Research." In *Mauna Loa Observatory: A 20th Anniversary Report*, edited by John Miller. National Oceanic and Atmospheric Administration Special Report. Washington, D. C., 1978. Pp. 36–54.

Keith, David and Hadi Dowlatabadi. "A Serious Look at Geoengineering." *EOS, Trans. Amer. Geophys. Union* 73 (1992): 289, 292–93.

Kellogg, William W. "Mankind's Impact on Climate: The Evolution of an Awareness." *Climatic Change* 10 (1987): 113–136.

Keston, David A. "Joseph Fourier—Politician and Scientist." http://www.astro.gla.ac.uk/~davidk/fourier.htm (October 29, 1996).

Khrgian, Alexsandr Khristoforovich. "The History of Meteorology in Russia." *Actes du VIIIᵉ Congrès International d'Histoire des Sciences.* Vinci, Italy: Gruppo italiano di storia delle scienze, 1958.

Khrgian, Alexsandr Khristoforovich. *Meteorology: A Historical Survey.* 2nd ed. Vol. 1. Trans. Ron Hardin. Jerusalem: Israel Program for Scientific Translations, 1970.

Kington, J. A. "A Late Eighteenth-Century Source of Meteorological Data." *Weather* 25 (1970): 169–75.

Koller, Armin Hajman. *The Abbé du Bos: His Advocacy of the Theory of Climate, a Precursor of Johann Gottfried Herder.* Champaign, Ill.: Garrard Press, 1937.

Kupperman, Karen Ordahl. "The Puzzle of the American Climate in the Early Colonial Period." *Amer. Hist. Rev.* 87 (1982): 1262–89.

Kutzbach, J. E. "Steps in the Evolution of Climatology: From Descriptive to Analytic." In *Historical Essays on Meteorology, 1919–1995*, edited by James Rodger Fleming. Boston: American Meteorological Society, 1996. Pp. 353–77.

Kutzler, Charles R. "Can Forests Bring Rain to the Plains?" *Forest History* 15, no. 3 (October, 1971): 14–21.

Ladurie, Emmanuel Le Roy. *Times of Feast, Times of Famine: A History of Climate since the Year 1000.* Trans. Barbara Bray. Garden City, N.Y.: Doubleday, 1971.

Lamb, H. H. *Climate, History and the Modern World.* 2nd ed. London: Routledge, 1995.

Landsberg, H. E. "Early Stages of Climatology in the United States." *Bull. Amer. Meteorol. Soc.* 45 (1964): 270.

Latour, Bruno. "Visualization and Cognition: Thinking with Eyes and Hands." *Knowledge and Society: Studies in the Sociology of Culture Past and Present* 6 (1986): 22–23.

Lewis, R. P. W. "The Founding of the Meteorological Office, 1854–55." *Meteorol. Mag.* 110 (1981): 221–27.

Lombard, Alfred. *L'Abbé Du Bos: Un initiateur de la pensée moderne (1670–1742).* Paris: Hachette, 1913. Geneva: Slatkine Reprints, 1969.

Lopez, Barry. *Of Wolves and Men.* New York: Scribner's, 1978.

Ludlum, David M. *Early American Hurricanes, 1492–1870.* Boston: American Meteorological Society, 1963.

Ludlum, David M. *Early American Winters, 1604–1820*, and *1821–1870.* 2 vols. Boston: American Meteorological Society, 1966, 1968.

Ludlum, David M. "Thomas Jefferson and the American Climate." *Bull. Amer. Meteorol. Soc.* 47 (1966): 974–75.

Manabe, Syukuro, and Kirk Bryan. "Climate Calculations with a Combined Ocean-atmosphere Model." *J. Atmos. Sci.* 26 (1969): 786–89.

Manabe, Syukuro, and Richard T. Wetherald. "Thermal Equilibrium of the Atmosphere with a Given Distribution of Relative Humidity." *J. Atmos. Sci.* 24 (1967): 241–59.

"Managing Planet Earth." *Scientific American* September, 1989.

Manley, Gordon. "The Revival of Climatic Determinism." *Geogr. Rev.* 48 (1958): 98–105.

Manley, Gordon. "Some Recent Contributions to the Study of Climatic Change." *Quart. J. Roy. Meteorol. Soc.* 70 (1944): 197–219.

Martin, Geoffrey J. *Ellsworth Huntington: His Life and Thought.* Hamden, Conn.: Archon Books, 1973.

Martin, Paul Edmund. "Infrared Absorption Spectrum of Carbon Dioxide." *Phys. Rev.* 41 (1932): 291–303.

Marx, Leo, "The Environment and the 'Two Cultures' Divide." In *Science, Technology, and the Environment: Multidisciplinary Perspectives*, edited by James Rodger Fleming and Henry A. Gemery. Akron, Ohio: University of Akron Press. Pp. 3–21.

Matthews, Samuel W. "What's Happening to Our Climate?" *National Geographic* 150 (1976): 576–615.

"Meteorological Office, 1855–1955." *Nature* 175 (1955): 963–65.

"Meteorological Office Centenary, 1855–1955." *Meteorol. Mag.* 84 (1955): 161–98.

Middleton, W. E. Knowles. *A History of the Thermometer and Its Use in Meteorology.* Baltimore: Johns Hopkins Press, 1966.

Middleton, W. E. Knowles. *The History of the Barometer.* Baltimore: Johns Hopkins Press, 1964.

Middleton, W. E. Knowles. *Invention of the Meteorological Instruments.* Baltimore: Johns Hopkins Press, 1969.

Milutin Milanković, 1879–1958. Katlenburg-Lindau, FRG: European Geophysical Society, 1995.

Morel, Auguste. *Etude sur l'abbé Dubos.* Paris, 1850.

Morgan, Judith, and Neil Morgan. *Roger: A Biography of Roger Revelle.* San Diego: University of California, San Diego–Scripps Institution of Oceanography, 1996.

"Mr. G. S. Callendar." Obituary notice. *Quart. J. Roy. Meteorol. Soc.* 91 (1965): 112.

Mudge, F. B. "The Development of the 'Greenhouse' Theory of Global Climate Change from Victorian Times." *Weather* 52 (1997): 13–17.

Mumford, Lewis. *Technics and Civilization.* London: Routledge, 1934.

Namias, Jerome. "The Greenhouse Effect as a Symptom of Our Collective Angst." *Oceanus* 32 (Summer 1989): 65–67.

Nebeker, Frederik. "A History of Calculating Machines in Meteorology." In *Historical Essays on Meteorology, 1919–1995*, edited by James Rodger Fleming. Boston: American Meteorological Society, 1996. Pp. 157–78.

Nolan, Martin F. "Taking Time to Toast 1991—Additions to Roll Call of the Great Beyond." *Boston Globe*, January 1, 1992, 1. Lexis/Nexis.

Oppenheimer, Michael, and Robert H. Boyle. *Dead Heat: The Race Against the Greenhouse Effect.* New York: Basic Books, 1990.

Panofsky, Hans A. "Theories of Climate Change." *Weatherwise* 9 (1956): 183–87, 204.

Ponte, Lowell. *The Cooling.* Englewood Cliffs, N.J.: Prentice-Hall, 1976.

Purdom, James F. W., and W. Paul Menzel. "Evolution of Satellite Observations in the United States and Their Use in Meteorology." In

Historical Essays on Meteorology, 1919–1995, edited by James Rodger Fleming. Boston: American Meteorological Society, 1996. Pp. 99–155.

Ramanathan, V. "The Greenhouse Theory of Climate Change: A Test by Inadvertent Global Experiment." *Science* 240 (1988): 293–99.

Ramanathan, V. "The Radiative and Climatic Consequences of the Changing Atmospheric Composition of Trace Gases." In *The Changing Atmosphere*, edited by F. S. Rowland and I. S. A. Isaksen. New York: Wiley, 1988.

Rapp, R. R. "Climate Modification and National Security." Rand Paper P-4476, October 1970.

Revelle, Roger. "Introduction: The Scientific History of Carbon Dioxide." In *The Carbon Cycle and Atmospheric CO₂: Natural Variations Archean to Present*, edited by E. T. Sundquist and W. S. Broecker. Geophysical Monographs, vol. 32. Washington, D. C.: American Geophysical Union, 1985. Pp. 1–4.

Rigg, J. B. "Climatic Determinism." *Weather* 16 (1961): 255–60, 298–303, 327–33.

"Roger Revelle, Oceanographer and Population Expert; at 82." *Boston Globe*, July 17, 1991. Lexis/Nexis.

Rolén, Mats, and Bo Heurling, eds., *Environmental Change: A Challenge for Social Science and the Humanities*. Stockholm: Norstedts, 1994.

Rotberg, Robert I., and Theodore K. Rabb, eds. *Climate and History: Studies in Interdisciplinary History*. Princeton: Princeton University Press, 1981.

Rowlands, Ian H. *The Politics of Global Atmospheric Change*. Manchester: Manchester University Press, 1995.

Russell, Richard Joel. "Climatic Change through the Ages." In U. S. Dept. of Agriculture. *Climate and Man: Yearbook of Agriculture 1941*. House Doc. 27, 77th Cong., 1st sess. (Washington, D. C., 1941): 67–97.

Schultz, Susan F. "Thomas C. Chamberlin: An Intellectual Biography of a Geologist and Educator." Ph.D. diss., University of Wisconsin, Madison, 1976.

Schwarzbach, Martin. *Alfred Wegener: The Father of Continental Drift*. Trans. Carla Love. Madison, Wisc.: Science Tech, 1986.

Seilkopf, Heinrich. "Zur Geschichte der meteorologischen Arbeit an der Deutchen Seewarte, Hamburg." *Annalen der Meteorologie* 3 (1950): 53–56.

Sellers, William D. *Physical Climatology*. Chicago: University of Chicago Press, 1965.

Shackleton, Robert. "The Evolution of Montesquieu's Theory of Climate." *Rev. intl. philos.* 9 (1955): 317–29.

Simpson, G. C. "Some Studies in Terrestrial Radiation." *Mem. Roy. Meteorol. Soc.* 2 (1928): 69–95.

Smyth, J. Henry, Jr., ed. *The Amazing Benjamin Franklin*. New York: Frederick A. Stokes, 1929.

Sprat, Thomas. *History of the Royal Society*. London, 1667. Reprint, edited by J. I. Cope and H. W. Jones. St. Louis: Washington University Press, 1958.

Stanton, William. *American Scientific Exploration, 1803–1860*. Philadelphia: American Philosophical Society Library, 1991.

Stehr, Nico. "Trust and Climate." Typescript paper prepared for the fourteenth International Congress of Biometeorology, Ljubljana, Slovenia, September 1996.

Sullivan, Walter. "Roger Revelle, 82, Early Theorist In Global Warming and Geology." *New York Times*, July 17, 1991, B-5. Lexis/Nexis.

Symons, George J. "The First Daily Weather Map." *Meteorol. Mag.* 32 (1897): 133–35.

Symons, George J. "History of English Meteorological Societies, 1823 to 1880." *Quart. J. Roy. Meteorol. Soc.* 7 (1881): 65–98.

Tarozzi, Gino, ed. *Leopoldo Nobili e la cultura scientifica del suo tempo.* Bologna: Nuova Alfa Editoriale, 1985.

Thompson, Kenneth. "Forests and Climate Change in America: Some Early Views." *Climatic Change* 3 (1980): 47–64.

Tichomirov, E. I. "Instructions for Russian Meteorological Stations of the 18th Century." (In Russian, English summary.) *Proc. Central Geophys. Obs.* (1932): 3–12.

Tooley, Marian J. "Bodin and the Mediaeval Theory of Climate." *Speculum* 28 (1953): 64–83.

Torrini, Maurizio. *Scienziati a Napoli, 1830–1845* . Naples: CUEN, 1989.

Traumüller, Friedrich. *Die Mannheimer meteorologische Gesellschaft (1780–1795): Ein Beitrag zur Geschichte der Meteorologie.* Leipzig, 1885.

Tuan, Yi-fu. *Landscapes of Fear*. New York: Pantheon Books, 1979.

Tverskoi, Pavel Nikolaevich. *Razvitie Meteorologii v U.S.S.R.* [Development of meteorology in the U. S.S.R.] Leningrad, 1949.

U. S. Central Intelligence Agency. "A Study of Climatological Research as It Pertains to Intelligence Problems." August 1974. In *The Weather Conspiracy: The Coming of the New Ice Age*, edited by the Impact Team. New York: Ballantine Books, 1977. Appendix 1.

U. S. Central Intelligence Agency. "Potential Implications of Trends in World Population, Food Production, and Climate." OPR-401. August 1974. In *The Weather Conspiracy: The Coming of the New Ice Age*, edited by the Impact Team. New York: Ballantine Books, 1977. Appendix 2.

U. S. House of Representatives. Committee on Appropriations. *National Science Foundation—International Geophysical Year*. Washington, D. C., 1956.

U. S. National Academy of Sciences. *Policy Implications of Greenhouse Warming*. Washington, D. C.: National Academy Press, 1991.

United Nations. Information Unit on Climate Change. "Are We Overlooking the Social and Political Implications of Climate Change?" http://www.unep.ch/iucc/fs108.html (September 26, 1996).

United Nations. "World Requirements of Energy, 1975–2000." *International Conference on Peaceful Uses of Atomic Energy*. Vol. 1. Geneva, 1955.

Uppenbrink, Julia. "Arrhenius and Global Warming." *Science* 272 (1996): 1122.

von Neumann, John. "Can We Survive Technology?" *Fortune*, June 1955, 106–8, 151–52.

Wallace, Amy, and David Smollar. "Roger Revelle, Founder of UCSD, is Dead at 82." *Los Angeles Times*, San Diego County edition, July 16, 1991. Lexis/Nexis.

Walter, Emil J. "Technische Bedingungen in der historichen Entwicklung der Meteorologie." *Gesnerus* 9 (1952): 55–66.

Watson-Watt, Robert. "The Evolution of Meteorological Institutions in the United Kingdom." *Quart. J. Roy. Meteorol. Soc.* 76 (1950): 115–24.

Weart, Spencer. "The Discovery of the Risk of Global Warming." *Physics Today* (January 1997): 34–40.

Weart, Spencer. "From the Nuclear Frying Pan into the Global Fire." *Bull. Atom. Sci.* (June 1992): 19–27.

Weart, Spencer. "Global Warming, Cold War, and the Evolution of Research Plans." *Hist. Stud. Phys. Sci.* (1997): 319–56.

"Weather Weapon: New Race with the Reds." *Newsweek,* January 13, 1958, 54.

Weber, Louis Russell. "The Infrared Absorption Spectrum of Water Vapor beyond 10μ." Ph.D. diss., University of Michigan, 1932.

Weinstein, M., and V. Suomi. "Analysis of Satellite Infrared Radiation Measurements on a Synoptic Scale. *Monthly Weather Rev.* 89 (1961): 419–28.

Wigley, T. M. L., M. J. Ingram, and G. Farmer, eds. *Climate and History: Studies in Past Climates and Their Impact on Man.* Cambridge: Cambridge University Press, 1981.

Will, George F. "A Change in the Weather." *Washington Post*, January 24, 1975.

Williams, Frances Leigh. *Matthew Fontaine Maury: Scientist of the Sea.* New Brunswick, N.J.: Rutgers University Press, 1963.

Williams, Michael. *Americans and Their Forests.* New York: Cambridge University Press, 1989.

Woeikof, Alexander. "Meteorology in Russia." *Smithson. Rept.* (1872): 267–98.

Wolf, Abraham. *A History of Science, Technology, and Philosophy in the Eighteenth Century.* New York: Macmillan, 1939.

Index